The Science of
Adhesive Joints

THE SCIENCE OF
ADHESIVE JOINTS

J. J. Bikerman

HORIZONS INCORPORATED
CLEVELAND, OHIO

SECOND EDITION

1968

ACADEMIC PRESS   New York and London

ACADEMIC PRESS INC.
111 Fifth Avenue, New York, New York 10003

United Kingdom Edition published by
ACADEMIC PRESS INC. (LONDON) LTD.
Berkeley Square House, London W.1

LIBRARY OF CONGRESS CATALOG CARD NUMBER: 68-18658

PRINTED IN THE UNITED STATES OF AMERICA

Preface to the Second Edition

The personal experience of the author and the measurements described by other scientists since 1960 confirm the concepts on which the first edition of this monograph (1961) is based; consequently, no changes were called for in the philosophy of the book. However, several lacunae in the theory have been filled and many new experiments reported. This caused a marked increase in the book's volume, but it is hoped that it is still small enough to encourage reading.

Several adhesion specialists in Russia sent me papers and books almost unobtainable in U. S. A.; it is a pleasure to thank them here.

January, 1968   J. J. BIKERMAN
Cleveland, Ohio

v

Preface to the First Edition

Some sciences were born and bred in laboratories; consequently, their development was almost logical and their advance consisted in adding new, more than in rejecting old, concepts and observations. The science of radioactivity is a suitable example of this class.

The science of adhesive joints belongs to the opposite type. The art of making adhesive bonds is older than are physics and chemistry, and a large number of disconnected ideas, rules, and traditions has been accumulated by the many generations familiar with adhesives. In such an instance, the first task of a monograph writer is to remove the chaff and to expose the grains. This was attempted in the present volume.

The (presumably) most fundamental alternative to be decided can be explained by referring to the well-known field of medicine. There are diseases which are caused by the *presence* of unwanted organisms (these are the infectious diseases), and there are diseases produced by the *absence* of wanted ingredients (these are the deficiency diseases occurring when the vitamin intake is insufficient). If an adhesive joint is weak, is weakness present or is strength absent? The tradition leaned toward the latter opinion; it was believed that the breaking stress of an adhesive joint was small when the molecular forces between the adherend and the adhesive were not strong enough. We now prefer the former alternative; when a joint is weak and breaks apparently in adhesion, a weak boundary layer is likely to be present. It is hoped that attentive readers of this book will be converted to our creed.

The word Science is included in the title of this book to avoid misleading potential users into expecting ready-made formulations for producing adhesives or adhesive joints. I believe, and experience confirms this belief, that the new science of adhesive joints is eminently practical; but it has to be intelligently applied to bring practical results. The last chapter of the book is intended to indicate how such an application should be attempted. Neither this nor any other chapter contains recommended adhesive compositions or recommended designs of the bond.

I took the liberty of inventing a new word; *adhint* as an abbreviation for *adhesive joint*. This portmanteau word is explained in the text and also listed in the subject index, and I hope that not many readers will be puzzled or annoyed by it.

The book was written when the author's laboratory was supported by grants from Lord Manufacturing Company of Erie, Pennsylvania; Allied Chemical Corporation of New York, N. Y.; Owens-Corning Fiberglas Corporation of Ashton, Rhode Island; and the National Science Foundation. I am deeply grateful to all these organizations.

The help given to me by Professors A. G. H. Dietz and F. J. McGarry of M.I.T. was invaluable.

November, 1960   J. J. BIKERMAN

Contents

Preface v

Chapter I/ **Solid Surfaces** 1

WHY ADHESIVES ARE NEEDED 1
TRANSITION LAYERS RATHER THAN SURFACES 3
SURFACE ROUGHNESS 3
NUMERICAL DATA ON SURFACE ROUGHNESS 15
SURFACE POROSITY 16
VARIABILITY ALONG THE SURFACE 17
VARIABILITY ACROSS THE SURFACE 18
GAS ADSORPTION 22
ADSORPTION FROM SOLUTIONS 26
REFERENCES 27

Chapter II/ **Adhesive and Other Joints** 29

FASTENING DEVICES 29
SOLID-TO-SOLID ADHESION 30
CLASSIFICATION OF ADHINTS 34
HOOKING ADHINTS 35
REFERENCES 42

Chapter III/ Formation of Adhints 43

CLEANING OF THE ADHEREND SURFACES 43
WETTING 49
MEASUREMENT OF CONTACT ANGLES 54
HYSTERESIS OF WETTING 59
RATE OF WETTING. REMOVAL OF AIR 63
REFERENCES 89

Chapter IV/ Tack 91

TEXT 91
REFERENCES 118

Chapter V/ Setting 120

WEAKNESS CAUSED BY SETTING 128
FLAWS IN THE BULK OF THE ADHESIVE 133
TIME OF SET 135
REFERENCES 136

Chapter VI/ Final Strength of Adhints 137

IMPROBABILITY OF TRUE ADHESIONAL FAILURES 137
OLDER THEORIES 150
THE BREAKING STRESS 153
REFERENCES 162

Chapter VII/ Improper Adhints 164

WEAK BOUNDARY LAYERS 164
REFERENCES 189

Chapter VIII/ Stresses in Proper Adhints 192

FROZEN STRESSES 192
BUTT JOINTS 204

BLOCK JOINTS 213
LAP JOINTS 215
PEELING 242
WORK OF FRACTURE 258
REFERENCES 261

Chapter IX/ Experimental Strength of Adhints 264

ADHINTS OF DIFFERENT TYPES 265
STRENGTH AND DIMENSIONS OF AN ADHINT 273
ADHESIVES IN BULK AND *In Situ* 289
STRENGTH OF ADHINTS AND OF ADHESIVES 293
EFFECT OF THE ADHESIVE COMPOSITION 299
RATE OF LOADING AND OF RUPTURE 303
EFFECT OF TEMPERATURE 309
EFFECT OF ENVIRONMENT 313
REFERENCES 316

Chapter X/ Tests 319

TEXT 319
REFERENCES 328

Chapter XI/ Summary for the Practical Man 330

TEXT 330

Author Index 337
Subject Index 345

The Science of
Adhesive Joints

CHAPTER I / **SOLID SURFACES**

Why Adhesives Are Needed

§1   If a solid, such as a glass rod, is broken and the newly formed ends are brought together, the initial solid is not restored. We are so used to this common phenomenon that we do not pause to think it over, but it is striking and its explanation explains also why adhesives are used at all.[1]

The irrevocability of rupture is remarkable because the interatomic and intermolecular forces known to us are conservative forces, that is, their magnitude does not depend on the past history of the system. In the intact glass rod the atoms attracted each other so strongly that a considerable force was required to separate them. Consequently, after the two fragments were brought together into the initial position, an equal force ought to be needed when a second rupture is attempted. In reality, of course, the mutual attraction of the two fragments is almost zero. The discrepancy is due to two reasons, namely, surface roughness and weak boundary layers.

The rupture surfaces are rough. Because of the insufficient steadiness of our hands and tools it would be impossible to fit every hill of one surface exactly in the corresponding valley on the opposite surface, even if such a correspondence existed. However, as practically every solid exhibits some plasticity before it breaks, or stresses in it are relieved during fracture, a hill torn out of surface B and now a part of surface A has a shape different from that of the valley remaining in surface B; thus no perfect fit would be achieved even by an absolutely precise guide.

This was well shown,[2] for instance, by cleaving lithium fluoride crystals, placing the two fragments one on the other under a load,

1

and heating at 820–830°. Air pockets remained along the interface. Even when the splitting was incomplete, that is the two halves were never shifted relative to each other, no air-free boundary could be achieved although the melting point of LiF is only 40–50° above the heating range used. The authors conclude: ". . . evidently, the two surfaces of the cleavage crack are not related to each other as a medal and its impression, i.e., do not represent exactly anti-equal patterns. During the splitting some areas give rise to powders, and this effect hinders complete contact between the crack surfaces."

When a solid is broken in any medium except an extraordinarily good vacuum, the two fracture surfaces very rapidly become covered with adsorbed molecules. In atmospheric air, water is the main substance "physically" adsorbed (see §12). In addition, air which we inhale contains numerous particles larger than a molecule; they also settle on every freshly exposed surface. Thus on the fracture surfaces, contrary to the testimony of the unaided eye, no atoms of the glass are exposed. When these surfaces are mutually pressed, there is no glass-to-glass contact. Moist air is present everywhere between the two glass bodies, and the thickness of the air film varies from point to point on the surface; at some spots the two adsorbed layers are in contact and only a few (perhaps only two) foreign molecules keep the solids apart, while at other points the clearance between the solids may be a million times as great.

As the adsorbed layers on the surfaces A and B and the air remaining between them have a mechanical strength negligible in comparison with the strength of glass, a zone of weakness is present between the two fragments after the recombination; and, when tensile stress is applied to them, rupture takes place in this zone. This is the first example of weak boundary layers in this monograph; many others will follow.

An adhesive has to counteract the effects of surface roughness and boundary layers. It has to fill the valleys and to remove surface impurities. If it does this, a continous contact between the solids (often called *adherends*) and the adhesive is established, and the new three-layer solid (consisting of adherend–adhesive–adherend) has a notable strength.

Transition Layers Rather Than Surfaces

§2   Properties of solid surfaces influence a host of important phenomena and ought to be generally known. As, however, experience
shows that the nature of solid surfaces is very often misunderstood
and that this misunderstanding is an obstinate obstacle to approving
a logical concept of *adhints* (= adhesive joints, abbreviated), a
condensed review of solid surfaces must be given here.

At a zero-order approximation, solid surfaces are geometrical
planes (having no thickness) separating two homogeneous phases.
This approximation is unsatisfactory for any but the crudest experiments. In reality, transition layers rather than surfaces exist on
every solid. Figure 1 schematically represents a cross section of a
typical transition layer. The top part is air. The density and composition of the gas phase a few angstroms from the solid are affected
by the solid; this effect belongs to adsorption, and adsorbed gas is
denoted by dots in the graph. Often, some molecules penetrate into
the solid lattice and may be said to be dissolved in it; they are shown
as dots among the dashes.

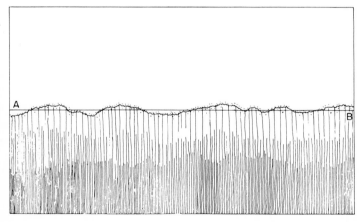

FIG. 1. Cross section of a typical solid surface. The solid is shaded, and grada-
tion of shading indicates gradual change of properties on nearing the interface with
air (white). The dots are adsorbed molecules.

The bottom part of the figure is the solid. The densely shaded lowest portion of it has the properties of the material in bulk. The graded shading toward the interface is intended to convey the idea that the change in the properties of the solid from the middle to the interface is gradual.

If the hills on the surface were rased and used to fill the valleys, the interface would have been a plane, shown in the figure by the straight line *AB*. This plane usually is referred to as the *main plane* or the *mean surface*.

Surface Roughness

§**3**.   If the geometrical surface represented by line *AB* in Fig. 1 is curved, the true surface is said to have waviness in addition to roughness. If the former surface is plane, the latter is only rough.

Surface roughness (also known as *rugosity*) can be expressed in many different forms. An exaggerated profile of the surface, exemplified by Fig. 2, is a striking representation. The curves of Fig. 2 were obtained by dragging a thin needle (also called a stylus), whose tip was a hemisphere of 13 μ ($= 0.0013$ cm) radius, over metal surfaces and magnifying the displacements of the needle. The instruments used for these tests are called profilometers, surface analyzers, and so on. The magnification in the direction of the main plane is much smaller (for instance, in the ratio 1:13000 in the figure) than in the perpendicular direction, thus simulating nonexistent sharp peaks on the surface; since, however, the magnifications are known, the actual outline can be deduced from the curves, and this actual profile often resembles that shown in Fig. 1.

If an area A of the solid has been explored by a tracer needle, the vertical distance (that is, perpendicular to the main plane) between the highest peak and the deepest valley over this area is h_{max}. Naturally the value of h_{max} increases with A. The height of the tallest peak above the main plane often is not very different from $0.5h_{max}$. If the height of the true surface above the main plane has been determined for n points and was found to be h_1, h_2, $\cdots$ h_n, then

$$(1/n)\,(h_1 + h_2 + \cdots h_n) = h_{av}$$

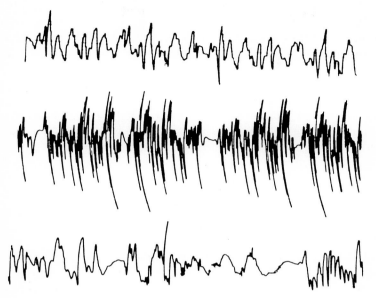

FIG. 2. Stylus curves of two metal surfaces; vertical magnification about 40,000; horizontal magnification about 3.3. Upper curve: stainless steel No. 302, Finish No. 4. Middle curve: nickel, nominal roughness 3 μin. Lower curve: same nickel surface examined in a perpendicular direction.

is the average height of elevations. The average depth of valleys also is equal to h_{av}. The root-mean-square deviation from the main plane is directly given by some instruments on the market; it is

$$h_{rms} = [(1/n)(h_1^2 + h_2^2 + \cdots h_n^2)]^{1/2}$$

and the values of h are determined along both hills and valleys. For a profile which can be represented as a sum of sinusoids, $h_{rms} = 1.11\, h_{av}$.

§4   If the length of the boundary line as shown in Fig. 1 is z times the length of the straight line AB, then the actual area of the interface (assumed to be isotropic) is z^2 times the geometrical area. The measurement of true surface areas has been performed on powdered or porous solids more often than on bars, plates, etc. However, a few methods are available also for measuring z^2 of adherends.

If, for instance, a piece of metal M is immersed in a solution containing a radioactive isotope of M (in the form of ions), and the activity of the metal is determined from time to time, it is found that this activity rapidly rises in the first few seconds or minutes of contact but later remains almost stationary. The amount rapidly taken up is equal to that amount of M which is present so near to the solution that it can react with the liquid without intervening slow diffusion processes. Suppose that this amount is m grams for 1 cm² of the geometrical surface. If the volume of 1 gm of the metal is v_0 cm³/gm, the volume exchanged is mv_0 cm³. When spread in a film one atom thick, this volume would cover $mv_0^{2/3}N^{1/3}$ cm², if N is the number of atoms in the gram (i.e., Avogadro number/atomic weight). If the penetration of radioactive atoms into the metal lattice (see §2) and similar complications are disregarded, then $z^2 = mv_0^{2/3}N^{1/3}$.

Another method requires electrochemical equipment. According to the accepted theory of the electric double layer at a metal–solution boundary, the capacity of this layer is independent of the nature of the metal and is determined above all by the nature of the solution and by the difference between the actual potential ψ of the metal and its zero-charge potential ψ_0 in the same solution. Thus, if the capacity of a mercury–solution interface is measured and found to be C_0 microfarads per square centimeter at a definite $\psi - \psi_0$, and then, in an identical solution and at the identical value of $\psi - \psi_0$, the capacity of a solid electrode proves to be C_1 microfarads for 1 cm² of the geometrical surface (or of the main plane, §2), then the true area of the solid is approximately C_1/C_0 times its geometrical area, as liquid mercury has a smooth surface. One of the methods of finding C_0 and C_1 employs very weak direct currents. The electrode (either of mercury or a solid) is cathodically polarized with a current density of, say, 10^{-6} A for cm² of the geometrical surface. This current brings, in t sec, $10^{-6}t$ coulomb of charge to each square centimeter of the surface. The potential of the metal against a reference electrode is measured during this charge. Let $\psi_2 - \psi_1$ be the change in this potential caused by the approach of $10^{-6}t$ coulomb. If both $\psi_2 - \psi_1$ and ½ $(\psi_2 - \psi_1) - \psi_0$ are made identical for the solid and the liquid electrode, then $z^2 = t_1/t_0$, if t_1 is the duration of charging for the solid metal, and t_0 is that for mercury. The main difficulty of the method resides in the necessity to avoid any passage of current across the metal–solution boundary; thus, the solution should not contain easily dischargeable metal ions, oxygen, and so on.

The method of calculating z^2, based on the adsorption of gases or solutes is referred to in §§12 and 13.

§5   A value almost identical with h_{av} is found by determining the thickness of the "stagnant" layer of liquid on a rough surface. The experiment consists in moistening the surface (e.g., of a plate) with an excess of a nonvolatile liquid, suspending the plate vertically so that its bottom edge touches a bibulous pad (filter paper or unglazed porcelain), and weighing the plate with the remaining liquid from time to time. It is found that the liquid drains down as if a layer of it, H_0 cm thick, did not participate in the motion. This H_0 in the author's experiments[3] was nearly equal to the h_{rms}, as illustrated in Table I.

TABLE I

THICKNESS OF "STAGNANT" LAYER (H_0) AND HEIGHT OF ELEVATIONS (h_{rms}) ON STAINLESS STEEL SURFACES. VACUUM OIL

	H_0 (μ)	h_{rms} (μ)
Surface finish No. 1	2.9 −3.6	3.15−3.83
No. 2D small	0.84−1.1	0.91−0.94
No. 2D large	0.52	0.28
No. 2B small	0.22−0.54	0.17−0.33
No. 2B large	0.26	0.12

Instead of weighing the plate plus liquid, the thickness of the liquid film can be determined optically.[4]

When a drop of molten asphalt was spread over a granite plate, permitted to solidify, and then scraped off with a razor blade, the average thickness (by weighing) of the asphalt which could not be removed was 1.9 h_{rms} on a polished surface, and 2.4 h_{rms} on a rough surface.[5] Presumably, this thickness was equal or closely related to the h_{max} of the plates.

A similar and much older procedure also permits an estimate of h_{max}. An optical flat, that is a glass disc whose plane faces are flat within about $\pm 0.1 \, \mu$, is pressed against a flat but rough solid surface on which beforehand a droplet of an oil has been deposited. The droplet is squashed and now occupies an area A; the outline of this area usually is visible to the unaided eye. If the volume of the droplet is v, the h_{max} of the solid is approximately equal to $2v/A$. This is explained by Fig. 3. The optical flat (near the top of the figure) rests on a few hills of the solid surface (A and B are shown). If the main plane is represented by the dotted line, it is clear that $0.5h_{max}$ is the distance between this plane and the optical flat. On the other hand, the volume occupied by the liquid is $0.5Ah_{max}$ because the volume of hills rising above the main plane is approximately compensated by the volume of the valleys below this plane.

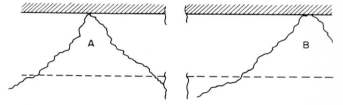

FIG 3. Contact of a very smooth and a very rough surface.

Another value related to h_{max} is determined with gas leakage instruments. Figure 4 demonstrates the principle of these instruments. A metal or glass tube A with a well-polished end surface is placed on the rough surface B, and air (or another gas) is forced along the tube. Since there are air passages between the hills on B, air escapes along the surface of B, and from the rate of this escape at a given overpressure in the tube the average clearance between A and B and thus the height of the few highest hills on B can be computed. When the smooth surface was of a hard steel and had h_{av} of 4 to 5×10^{-6} cm and the rough surface was of copper having h_{av} varying between 2×10^{-5} and 10^{-4} cm, the volume leaking out in unit time was[6] proportional to the square of the latter h_{av}.

Friction phenomena afford valuable information on surface roughness.

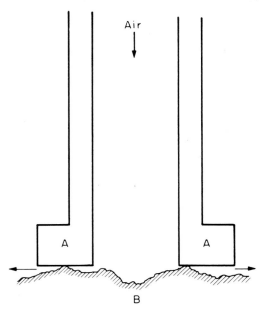

FIG. 4. A pneumatic roughness meter. The rate of flow of air depends on the height of hills on the test surface B.

As long as "the law of friction" (Leonardo da Vinci, Amontons, Coulomb) is valid for sliding, that is as long as frictional force F is independent of the area of contact and proportional to the normal load F_n, the coefficient of friction μ ($= F/F_n$) is equal to the tangent of the "effective slope" which cannot be significantly different from the average slope of a few tallest hills on the rubbing surfaces. The most frequent values of μ are confined to the region 0.1 to 0.5. Since 0.1 is approximately equal to tan 6° and 0.5 to tan 27°, this means that the most common hills on usual surfaces have slopes between 6° and 27°, which well accords with the data supplied, for instance, by tracer instruments (§3).

The conventional coefficient of rolling friction (contrary to the coefficient of sliding friction, which is a pure number) is a length; it is defined as $\chi = Fr/F_n$, r being the radius of the rolling sphere. For small values of F_n and rough surfaces, this coefficient is approximately equal to twice the distance between hills so tall that the sphere can rest on them. The approximate height h of these hills is given by the equation $h = \chi^2/2r$. This h should be nearer to h_{max} than to h_{av}.

When a liquid drop slides along a tilted plate which is poorly wetted by the liquid, the ratio $F_n \sin \alpha/w$ is independent of the drop dimensions. F_n is the weight of the drop, w is its width during the sliding, and α is the tilt at which sliding proceeds without deceleration or acceleration. This ratio is greater the greater the rugosity of the plate.[7] Its physical meaning is the force driving the drop along the plate, per unit width of the drop. A quantitative correlation between it and a geometrical parameter of surface roughness (such as h_{max} or h_{rms}) has not been established yet. See also §28.

§**6**   The importance of waviness for adhesive joints is commented on in §45. There exists a stylus-type instrument[8] which determines both waviness and rugosity in one operation, but usually estimation of waviness is based on optical measurements. An optical flat is placed on the surface of an adherend. If, after a slight wringing, the whole adherend–glass interface acquires one color, the adherend is as flat as the glass plate. Usually, however, the interface will exhibit one or a few sets of interference fringes. The clearance between the glass and the adherend increases (for normal incidence) by half the wavelength (that is approximately 0.25 μ in daylight) from one to the next fringe. Suppose, for instance, that only one set of fringes is visible and that it forms concentric rings around the middle of the adherend surface. If n is the number of the rings, we may conclude that the air gap between the two solids is about $0.25n$ μ thicker (or, rarely, thinner) at the edge than in the center; in other words, the adherend is curved so that its highest point is $0.25n$ μ higher than the lowest. If the surface is convex toward the air, the interference fringes move out (or the concentric rings become greater) if the two solids are more strongly pressed together.

Optical methods often are used for determination or estimation of roughness also.

Interferometric procedures give results most easily correlated with the geometry of the surface. Let an optical flat be placed on the adherend whose main plane also is perfectly flat (§2). Then the glass disc rests on a few (at least three) tallest hills, and the thickness of the air gap at any point depends on the height of the hills and the depth of the valleys which face each other at this point; see Fig. 5. Consequently the interference fringes will have an irregular pattern, and from this pattern the distribution of protuberances and depressions on the two surfaces can be derived. A better vertical resolution is achieved by multiple interferometry,[9] and a better horizontal resolution is attained in microinterferometers.[10] The first of these improvements permits one to notice and measure the height of lower hills and the depth of more shallow valleys, while the second renders possible the recording of sharper peaks, more narrow ridges, finer cracks, and similar features whose extension along the main plane is too small for the naked eye.

FIG. 5. Clearance between two solids.

The reflectivity of a surface is well suited for a qualitative estimate of its roughness. If it does not reflect light as a mirror does, we may be sure that it has many irregularities exceeding the wavelength of the light used, that is, its h_{av} must be at least 0.5 μ. If the surface does have a mirror finish, it still can have (and usually has) hills and valleys of this and greater dimensions, but they are not easily visible because of the high intensity of the light reflected in the specular fashion.

Quantitative information on the rugosity of an isotropic surface can be obtained by using an integrating sphere. Its mode of action

is illustrated in Fig. 6. The sample (S) is placed in a hollow spherical vessel whose internal surface is covered with a white material
(magnesia) which reflects the light in a diffuse manner. When, as at
the left, the sample surface is perpendicular to the light beam, the
specularly reflected light escapes through the hole in the sphere and
the photocell PC registers only the scattered light. Let R_s be its
intensity. Next, as at the right, the sample is tilted so that also the
specularly reflected light is spread over the whole internal surface
and thus reaches the photocell. This now registers an intensity R_t,
where t stands for total. Both theoretically and experimentally,[11]
the ratio R_s/R_t is, within a range, proportional to the ratio $(h_{rms}/\lambda)^2$,
λ being the wavelength of the light used.

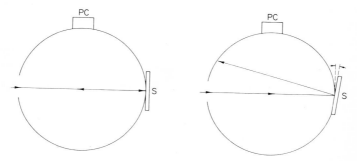

FIG. 6. Determination of roughness with an integrating sphere.

The information gathered is more specific if the intensity of the
reflected light is measured as a function of the angle of reflection.
If a parallel beam of light (see Fig. 7) falls on a surface containing
facets inclined at different angles to the main plane, the reflected
light is divergent instead of being parallel, and from the intensity
of the radiation reflected, for instance, parallel to direction BC the
area covered with facets parallel to MN can be calculated. If the
intensity of the beam parallel to EF (that is, reflected from NO
which is parallel to the main plane) is n times that of the beam
parallel to BC, then the area of the surfaces parallel to MN is $1/n$th
that of the surfaces parallel to the main plane. Each of these facets

must be large compared with the wavelength employed. Analogous calculations have been made also for surfaces covered with circular buttons or depressions[12]; the latter type is obtained, for instance, by sandblasting.

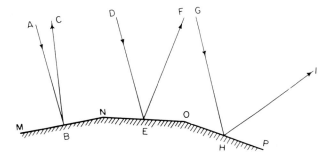

FIG. 7. Reflection of light from a rough surface.

An easy and often excellent method of estimating surface roughness is simply looking at it in a microscope, especially when the surface is obliquely illuminated. Irregularities as small as 1 μ in the shortest dimension often can be noticed. There are special microscopes on the market which permit one to see two surfaces (a test object and a standard plate) next to each other and thus to decide whether their rugosities are or are not similar.

FIG. 8. Replica method of estimating surface roughness.

Absorption of electrons is often resorted to for the determination of the topography of a solid surface in a slightly devious way. In Fig. 8 the shaded part represents the object of study, which may be denoted by letter S. It is coated with another material (a "replica") which, according to the circumstances, may be a thermo-plastic polymer, or silica, or something else. This material should have the property of filling all depressions on the solid and of giving a very smooth surface at the opposite side of the coating (that is, *AB* should be as straight as possible). Then the coating film is removed from the solid; this can be achieved by stripping or, when permissible, by dissolving S away. Finally, the coating is placed in an electron microscope. The electrons cross it normally to the main plane of the film. Evidently, fewer electrons will be absorbed by the film along path b than along path a, and from the number of electrons emerging at any point the film thickness at this point can be estimated. This number is given by the degree of blackening of a photographic plate placed in the path of the emerging electrons. In turn, the film thickness is, ideally, the depth of valleys on the original solid surface plus a constant, or a constant minus the height of hills.

The method is based on several assumptions. The replica is supposed to achieve a perfect contact over the whole surface of S and to be removed from the sample without any deformation. According to the views advocated in this book (§56), this combination is almost impossible. If a molecular contact has been achieved between two solids, these cannot be cleanly separated from each other by any mechanical means. Thus, if the replica is easily stripped off, in all probability there always was a zone of air, moisture, etc., between it and S. If no weak boundary layer (§1) was present between S and the replica, either the latter or the former must be broken during the peeling. In neither case is the profile of the film a mirror image of that of S.

If S is dissolved away, this difficulty is absent. However, the profile of the replica after separation is still likely to be different from that before because (a) stresses present in the film before are free to alter the shape of the surface hills as soon as these cease to be confined by the valleys of S, and (b) the solvent used for S may swell or otherwise deform the replica. These effects may be small and of no importance as long as the height of the hills is ascertained within, say, 100 Å, but they ought to be considered whenever a better precision is attempted.

Numerical Data on Surface Roughness

§7   Each surface has its own values of h_{av}, h_{max}, z^2, and so on, just as every object has its own mass. However, a range of probable roughness parameters can be given for each type of surface finish, especially on metals. Table II reproduces the typical values of h_{av} as found by a Committee of the American Society of Mechanical Engineers.[13]

TABLE II

AVERAGE HEIGHT OF HILLS PRODUCED BY VARIOUS TREATMENTS

	h_{av}	
	Microns	Microinches
Lapped or polished	0.02 − 0.25	1 − 10
Honed	0.10 − 0.50	4 − 20
Cold drawn or extruded	0.25 − 4	10 − 160
Die cast	0.40 − 4	16 − 160
Ground	0.50 − 2.5	20 − 100
Drilled	2.5 − 5	100 − 200
Turned, shaped, milled, bored	3 − 6	120 − 240

Stainless steel is usually sold in six "standard" finishes. Their h_{rms} may be expected to be 3–4 μ for finish No. 1, 0.3–1 μ for 2D (D is for dull), 0.1–0.4 μ for 2B (B is for bright), 0.04–0.05 μ for No. 4 in the direction of the grooves, 0.1 μ for No. 6 in the direction of the grooves, and 0.02–0.03 μ for No. 7, which has a mirror polish.

Roughness comparison specimens of the American Standards Association[14] represent 26 types and degrees of rugosity. Thus, honed, lapped, or polished specimens have h_{av} of 0.05, 0.10, and 0.20 μ; specimens ground with the periphery of the wheel and with the flat side of the wheel range from 0.10 to 1.60 μ; shaped or turned, from 0.8 to 12.7 μ; and side-milled, end-milled, profiled, and milled with the periphery of the cutter, from 1.6 to 12.7 μ. They are visually or tactually (i.e., by touch) compared with the surfaces under test.

Surface Porosity

§8   All solid surfaces are rough and many are, in addition, porous.
A surface may be porous because the whole solid is porous; this
is the case of wood, paper, textiles, leather, and so on. Or the
porosity may be confined to a surface layer only, while the bulk
of the solid is dense. Perhaps the best studied example of the second type is anodized aluminum.

Aluminum surfaces are anodically oxidized in a suitable electrolyte to produce relatively thick oxide films because such films im-
part an enhanced chemical and mechanical resistance to the material and also because they can be dyed. The film thickness may
be less than 1μ or exceed 10μ[15]; at any rate it is of a micro-
scopical rather than of a molecular dimension.

The porosity of the film can be determined, for instance, from its
density; if this is ρ and if ρ_0 is the density of perfect oxide crystals,
the relative pore volume is $(\rho_0 - \rho)/\rho_0$, that is, 1 cm^3 of the coating
contains $(\rho_0 - \rho)/\rho_0$ cm^3 of air. The dimensions and the number of
the pores can be found from electron micrographs of the films or
their replicas.[16] The relative pore volume of coatings of industrial
importance may be anything between 0.1 and 0.5, depending on the
aluminum alloy treated and the treating procedure. The pore diameter often ranges between 0.01 and 0.05 μ, which means that the
cross section of an average pore is near 4×10^{-12} cm^2. If the relative pore volume is 0.2 and the pores extend through the whole
depth of the film, then $0.2/(4 \times 10^{-12}) = 5 \times 10^{10}$ pores must be
present on each square centimeter of the surface.

The oxide layers, which form on metals in air and therefore
are present on almost all metal surfaces kept under atmospheric
conditions usually are thinner and less porous than the films on
anodized aluminum, but some porosity generally may be expected.
When oxide crystals grow, the growth, as always, starts from discrete nuclei and gives rise to separate crystals; and it would not
often happen that all these crystals would join each other without
any interstices.

Metal coatings, such as of tin on blackplate (iron), also are
porous, as a rule. The frequency of pores reaching almost to the
iron surface is tested by chemical means in industrial laboratories

and usually is quite small, but pores which do not traverse (almost) the whole thickness of the tin layer are not recorded in these tests and may be more numerous than those detected.

Glass which was in contact with our humid atmosphere for any length of time has a porous surface. Moisture condenses on the glass and leaches out the alkali present near the surface. Thus, a skeleton consisting chiefly of silica remains, and the space initially occupied by Na_2O, K_2O, and so on now is available to air. This process can be followed, for instance, by measuring the refractive index of the glass surface before and after exposure to air.

Variability Along the Surface

§9 Several kinds of this variability exist. If we follow any line along a surface, we shall meet a hill, then a valley, then another hill, and so forth; this is geometrical variability. Sometimes it is directed; e.g., the surface is covered with more or less distinct, more or less parallel grooves, and the variability across the grooves is greater than along these. Grooves produced by machining a metal can be seen at a small magnification, but much finer anisotrophy can be detected by means of condensation phenomena. If a solid is rubbed with another and then breathed upon, water droplets may be preferentially oriented along the rubbing direction so that the "breath figure" obtained will reveal this direction. Or a dye solution is permitted to evaporate on the rubbed surface; the dye crystals thus formed may be oriented along the direction of the strokes, in which case the surface will look different along, and perpendicularly to, this direction. The natural anisotrophy of wood surfaces and the difference between warp and weft in fabrics are too well known to be discussed in detail; for wood see, e.g., reference 17.

All metals used in daily life are polycrystalline, and the orientation of the crystals in space, as a rule, is approximately random. Therefore, when a cut is made across a piece of metal, different crystals are cut at different angles to their crystallographic axes. Thus the area exposed differs in its crystallographic orientation from one to another spot. Since the work function (that is, work required to remove an electron from the metal) depends on this orientation, the electric properties of a metal surface vary from point to point. Apparently, also chemical reactivity depends on orientation and, consequently, is not identical for different surface regions.

Many common metals are alloys containing more than one phase, that is, they contain two or more types of crystals, each type having a chemical composition different from that of the others. When a part made from such an alloy is cut, different phases are exposed in different regions of the surface. The electric potential difference between these phases is the main cause of corrosion of alloys. Its importance for the strength of adhints is mentioned in §121.

The variability caused by impurities should not be forgotten. The amount of finger grease transferred to a metal handle or a glass pane is sufficient for the detectives to reconstruct the fingerprint. It is also sufficient to affect the "breath figures" or many other thin deposits on the contaminated surface.

Variability Across the Surface

§10   As a rule, the chemical composition of a solid surface is different from that of the bulk, and the transition between the two compositions is gradual.

Metals have been extensively studied in this respect. Starting from the gas phase and proceeding toward the interior of a piece of metal, we meet first adsorbed gases and vapors, then dust and dirt partly embedded in (usually) an oil film, then a more or less porous layer of oxides, sulfides, and so on, then metal greatly distorted by the act of cutting (that is, by producing the surface), and finally metal having the bulk properties of the material.

The gas and water adsorption is touched upon in §§11 and 12. To make clear the importance of dust, it is sufficient to reproduce here some data on the number of aerosol particles (i.e., of suspended grains and droplets) in 1 cm^3 of air, assuming 1 mg to be equivalent to 5×10^7 particles: in a dust storm or cloudburst, 10^5 to 5×10^5; in a cotton mill, up to 10^3; and in city air, 5 to 50.

The difficulty of removing the last traces of oil which was once put on a solid is well illustrated in Table I, §5, which shows that an oil layer about as thick as h_{av} of the surface is not readily removed in the gravitational field.

A panel of stainless steel which had been washed first with toluene or acetone and then with water, was slightly rubbed with potassium bromide powder. When the powder was pressed into a disk, and the disk subjected to an infrared analysis, the spectrum was that of a phthalate ester.[18] Apparently, the phthalate was used in the finishing of the panel and remained in its surface layer for an indefinite time. Then it was occluded by the powder and detected in it.

Analogous observations[19] were made on an aluminum sheet which was supposed to be "ready for painting." The infrared spectrum of the material obtained from its surface by abrading with potassium bromide, alumina, and glass fibers contained strong lines belonging to $-CH_2-$, CH_3-, $-COO-$, and so on. See also §20.

Oxide layers on metal surfaces are mentioned, e.g., in §8. In dry air, the oxide on aluminum is from 10 to 30 Å thick[20] but is sufficient practically to preclude any further oxidation. In the presence of moisture, the protective film is thicker (e.g., over 100 Å), continues to grow slowly for years, and consists of two more or less clearly defined strata; the one next to metal is thin (usually, 10 to 20 Å), amorphous, and free of hydrate water, while the other (next to the air) is thicker, porous, and contains crystalline hydrates such as bayerite $Al_2O_3 \cdot 3 H_2O$.

When a tantalum film was sputtered on a barium fluoride crystal (apparently rinsed with 2-propanol) and then anodically oxidized in a bath containing ethylene glycol, the tantalum oxide surface showed infrared absorption bands characteristic for the CH group and which did not disappear after heating to 200° in a moderate vacuum (of about 1 barye).[21]

The protective oxide coating on zinc may have a thickness of, for instance, 4×10^{-7} cm. Also the germanium oxide film on the surface of germanium transistors usually is from 10^{-7} to 5×10^{-7} cm thick, and the whole action of transistors depends on this film.

The existence of modified metal near the surface is proved, for instance, by metallographic examination of sections perpendicular to the original surface. Another method is based on the measurement of "microhardness," that is of the stress required to produce a small, definite indentation in the surface. It is found that this stress varies when the depth of indentation increases; consequently, the true hardness of the material must vary with the distance from the surface. Usually, surface layers, because of machining and similar treatments, are harder than the underlying metal. Figure 9 is an example of this behavior.[22] The abscissa of the graph represents the force on the indenter; when this force increases, the depth of indentation also increases. The ordinate is the stress needed for a definite indentation. The ordinates are smaller at greater forces; this means that microhardness is smaller at greater depths. The upper curve refers to a mechanically polished single crystal of aluminum and the lower curve to the same crystal after electropolishing. Electropolishing removes the distorted external layers; therefore, the variation of microhardness with depth is less pronounced for the lower than for the upper curve.

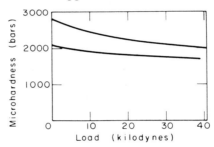

FIG. 9. Dependence of hardness on depth. Abscissa: load (kilodynes). Ordinate: stress (bars), needed for a standard indentation. Upper curve: mechanically polished aluminum. Lower curve: electropolished aluminum. Data of reference 22.

The change in the preferred orientation of metal crystals (grains) on moving from the surface into the bulk of a cold-rolled strip or foil can be determined from the dependence of the reflection of X rays on the angle of incidence. In one example (aluminum foil[20]), the X-ray patterns were compared for (a) the original surface, (b) after dissolving a layer 45 μ thick, and (c) after dissolving a layer 160 μ thick. The patterns (a) and (b) were similar to each other and different from pattern (c); thus, cold-rolling caused a distortion in the crystal orientation for a depth between 50 and 150 μ.

The removal of the distorted material by electropolishing often is chemically selective; if the metal, as usual, contains various ingredients, their rate of dissolution will not be identical, the surface will lose more of the active than of the less active component, and, after treatment, will contain a higher relative amount of the latter. Thus, when cartridge brass is electropolished under nonideal conditions, sometimes red spots of copper are visible on its surface.

Surface layers produced by corrosion of glass are mentioned in §8. Their existence is well shown by measurements of surface conductance. When a glass cylinder is placed between two metal electrodes and alternating current is sent from one to the other metal disk, the major part of the current proceeds in the thin layer along the surface of the glass. The thickness of this film can be estimated from optical measurements (§8); let it be δ cm. The measured resistance Ω of the cylinder, from Ohm's law, is $\Omega = l/2\pi r\delta\kappa$, l being the distance between the electrodes, r the radius of the cylinder, and κ the conductivity of the material of the surface film. This κ was on quartz nearly equal to that of a saturated solution of quartz in water, and on glass it was equal to the conductivity of a dilute sodium hydroxide solution. The thickness δ was, for instance, 5×10^{-7} cm.[23]

Surface conductance is valuable also for studying semiconductor surfaces. If, for instance, a material conducts electricity because it contains an excess of electrons, and gas molecules which readily accept electrons are adsorbed on its surface, then adsorbed particles become negative ions and these ions electrostatically repel free electrons in the lattice with the result that there is a deficiency of electrons immediately adjacent to the adsorbed layer and a corresponding change in surface conductivity.

In §4 a method for estimating the surface area of a solid was mentioned, based on the observation that most exterior atoms (or ions) react with the surroundings more rapidly than those less accessible. More elaborate measurements demonstrate that the isotope exchange between a gas and a solid alters its rate rather gradually when the depth of the solid affected increases. Thus,[24] when gaseous chlorine was admitted to a vessel containing sodium chloride crystals tagged with ^{36}Cl, the transfer of radioactivity into the gas phase continued, albeit at a low rate, also when all the surface ions must have been exchanged.

Gas Adsorption

§11   Adsorption of foreign atoms and molecules by solids is important for understanding adhesion because, when adhints are made, an intimate contact between two different kinds of atoms (of the adherend and the adhesive) is desired, and one of the two components is solid, while adsorption is the best studied facet of just this phenomenon of making contact between a solid and another substance. Since adhesives are applied as liquids rather than as gases, adsorption of liquids would be a more fitting effect to consider, but gas adsorption is fundamentally similar to that of liquids and is easier to comprehend. It is briefly surveyed in this and the following section, while §13 deals with the interaction between liquids and solid surfaces.

When a gas is admitted in an evacuated space containing a solid or liquid body M, or when a gas stream is forced through a powder or a liquid, a part of the gas is seen to "disappear." Experimentally this means that, when so much gas is introduced that its final pressure should be p_0, the actual pressure is p_1 and $p_1 < p_0$; analogously, if v_0 cm³ of gas was present before bubbling, only v_1 cm³ is recovered after it, and $v_1 < v_0$. In the instance of a liquid we say that $v_0 - v_1$ cm³ was absorbed in, or dissolved by, the liquid. In the instance of a solid we say that volume $v_0 - v_1$ was adsorbed.

For a time, the mechanisms of absorption and adsorption were believed to be entirely different. At present, it seems best to consider both phenomena from one point of view. A uniform condensed body M of mass m would, in equilibrium, dissolve, say, x gm of gas at the (final) pressure p_1. The equilibrium is relatively easily attained as long as M is a liquid of moderate viscosity. In this instance, convection and diffusion in a reasonable time would distribute the gas molecules, which of course enter first the surface layer, over the whole volume of the liquid. However, there is no convection in a solid and the rate of diffusion usually is only a small frac-

tion of that in a liquid. Consequently the gas, in the short time
allowed for laboratory experiments, cannot penetrate far from the
surface, and only that fraction of the solid volume takes part in
dissolving the gas which, as mentioned in §§8 and 10, is porous
or distorted.

A typical gas adsorption experiment starts with degassing the
solid (i.e., the *adsorbent*) at a high temperature; then the adsorbent is permitted to cool to the chosen temperature, and gas is
brought in contact with it. The pretreatment is necessary if adsorption uncomplicated by desorption is the object of study. An un-
heated adsorbent contains gases and vapors originating from its
previous environment; thus a solid previously kept in air has moisture, oxygen, and other constituents of the atmosphere present in
its surface layer. When such a solid is introduced in a vessel filled
with, say, krypton, this gas has to displace some adsorbed molecules of H_2O, O_2, etc., before it can be adsorbed; thus, adsorption
of Kr depends on desorption of other gases.

Solid adherends are not heated and degassed before the application of an adhesive, but the fact that adsorbents are, is instructive;
it demonstrates the tenacity with which adsorbed atoms and molecules cling to the solid phase. When an adhesive is applied, it must
cause desorption of pre-adsorbed compounds from the surface; this
step is discussed in §22.

§12   When it is asked, which of the two gases G_1 and G_2 is likely to be
adsorbed by M in a greater amount, the answer depends on both
chemical and physical factors. If G_1 can, and G_2 cannot, chemically
react with M, then adsorption of G_1 is likely to be the greater one;
thus oxygen is more avidly taken up by active carbons than nitrogen is. If neither of the gases has a "chemical affinity" to M, then
either the reduced temperature T/T_c or the relative pressure p_1/p_s
is deciding. As in §11, p_1 is the gas pressure around the adsorbent
at equilibrium, T is the absolute temperature of the experiment, T_c
the absolute critical temperature of the gas, and p_s is saturation
pressure at temperature T. Ratio T/T_c is more useful when T is
greater than T_c, and p_1/p_s is more useful when $T < T_c$. The amount
adsorbed usually is greater when T/T_c is smaller and p_1/p_s is greater.

For instance, at atmospheric pressure at 35°, the adsorbed amount x/m of carbon dioxide as a rule will be found to exceed that of methane because the critical temperatures for these substances are 304.2° and 191.0°K, thus making the ratio T/T_c equal to 1.01 and 1.61, respectively. At 20°C, x/m of carbon dioxide generally will be smaller than that of n-butane (both at atmospheric pressure) because under these conditions p_1/p_s is approximately 0.49 for butane and 0.018 for CO_2.

All ingredients of customary adhesives are far below their critical points during application and their saturation pressures p_s at the application temperature generally are very small; thus, as long as no chemical reaction intervenes, adhesives may be expected to be adsorbed preferentially to the main ingredients of our atmosphere (nitrogen, oxygen, noble gases, carbon dioxide, and, less safely, water).

The behavior outlined in the two preceding paragraphs is altered when wetting effects interfere. At small values of p_1/p_s, for instance, less than 0.3, the adsorbed amount is greater when the vapor belongs to a liquid which wets the adsorbent. This is readily noticed when the relative adsorbed amount, that is, the amount x taken up at a small p_1/p_s divided by the amount x_s adsorbed at p_s, rather than x itself, is considered. If x/x_s is plotted as a function of p_1/p_s, the curve for a substance which wets the adsorbent usually lies higher than the curve for a poorly wetting compound. This is true, for instance, for the adsorption of benzene (well wetting) and water (poorly wetting) by commercial active carbons. The importance of wetting in the application of adhesives is discussed in §§22 to 29.

At large values of p_1/p_s, say at $p_1/p_s > 0.9$, the amount adsorbed is approximately determined by the rule that the *liquid volume* taken up is independent of the liquid. An illustration of this rule is presented in Fig. 10, based on one of the earliest confirmations of this rule.[25] Its abscissa is p_1/p_s at 15°, and its ordinate shows the liquid volumes (that is, mass x divided by the density of the liquid at 15°) adsorbed by 1 gm of solid silica gel; the volumes are expressed in cubic centimeters. It is seen that the adsorbed volumes are different for benzene and water as long as p_1/p_s is less than 0.8 but are almost identical at $p_1/p_s > 0.8$. The explanation for this behavior is that at high relative vapor pressures the pores of the adsorbent are filled with the liquid, and the volume taken up is simply the volume of the pores. Thus, 1 gm of the silica gel studied by Anderson contained 0.56 cm³ of pores. It was mentioned in §1 that one of the main tasks to be accomplished by an adhesive is to fill the valleys on the surface of the adherent; Fig. 10 teaches us that this state can be reached even if the filling substance is a vapor.

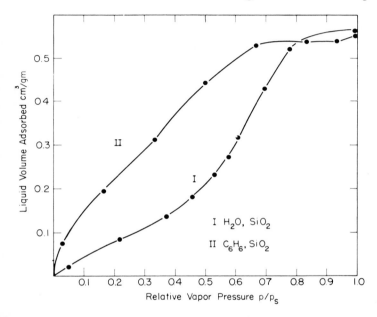

FIG. 10. Adsorption isotherms of water vapor (lower curve) and benzene vapor (upper curve) on dry silica gel at 15°. Abscissa: relative vapor pressure. Ordinate: liquid volume, in cubic centimeters, adsorbed by 1 gm of gel. Data of reference 25.

At small values of p_1/p_s, the quantity adsorbed often is proportional to the area of the adsorbent, and this area can be calculated from the adsorption isotherm. Adsorption isotherms are curves of x/m versus p_1/p_s, as in Fig. 10, or versus p_1. For instance, if N_1 is the number of nitrogen molecules taken up by 1 gm of a solid at −195.8°C and 63 mbars (=47 mm Hg) or at −183.0° and 323 mbars, then the surface area of this gram (i.e., the specific surface area of the solid) is $15\,N_1$ square angstroms.

Adsorption from Solutions

§13   The majority of industrial adhesives in the moment of application are solutions, and adsorption undoubtedly occurs when these solutions are brought in contact with solid surfaces.

When an adsorbent is introduced in a solution containing y_0 gm solute for each $1 - y_0$ grams of solvent, the concentration of the liquid changes and its final composition may be expressed as y grams of solute for each $1 - y$ grams of solvent. Thus, apparently, $y_0 - y$ grams of solute was adsorbed from each gram of solution. This, however, is only an apparent adsorption because it is not known how much of the solvent was taken up when the solute was adsorbed. To make the relation clearer, let us denote the true adsorbed amounts, from 1 gm of solution, as x_1 and x_2 for solute and solvent, respectively. Then, $1 - x_1 - x_2$ gm of liquid remains, and $y = (y_0 - x_1)/(1 - x_1 - x_2)$. Solving for x_1 we obtain

$$x_1 = \frac{y_0 - y - yx_2}{1 - y} .$$

As long as x_2 is unknown, no value can be given for x_1. Only if there is a reason to believe that x_2 is negligible and if $y \ll 1$, is it permitted to set $x_1 = y_0 - y$.

Experimentally, the apparent adsorption $(y_0 - y)/m$ from dilute solutions is approximately as large as the vapor adsorption x/m at large p_1/p_s values, if the solute has a much higher critical temperature, or a much higher melting point, or a much greater molecular weight than the solvent has. It is natural to believe that in these instances $x_2 \ll x_1$ and the apparent adsorption is nearly equal to the true one. Thus, if the adhesive contains a polymer mixed with low-molecular-weight liquids, we may expect the polymer to be adsorbed preferentially to the other components. However, chemical effects may upset this rule (see §12).

The surface area of the adsorbent can be calculated from x_1 in a manner analogous to that outlined in §12.

This is more easily achieved when the solid is present as a fine powder rather than a plate or a bar, but determination of z^2 of relatively flat surfaces also has been attempted (§4). For instance,[26] plates of glass or of cold-rolled steel were equilibrated with solutions of acetic or stearic acid in cyclohexane. The acids contained a radioactive carbon (^{14}C) in their carboxyl groups; consequently, the amount truly adsorbed could have been measured directly by radiation, if it were possible to separate the acid adsorbed from that present in the liquid clinging to the solid. The solid was dry-blotted before measuring the radiation but, presumably, another blotting procedure would have given a different result. The amount of radioactive acid detected on abraded glass was, e.g., 2 and 8 times that on polished glass for, respectively, stearic acid and acetic acid. Abrasion must have increased the surface area but probably also made removal by blotting more diffcult (see §5); and the relative importance of these two effects is not known.

Additional information on the topics covered in §§2 to 13 can be found, for instance, in reference[27.]

REFERENCES

1. Bikerman, J. J., *Chem. Age (London)* **47,** 186 (1942).
2. Mokievskii, V. A., Smirnova, Z. A., and Afanas'ev, I. I., *Kristallografiya* **7,** 768 (1962).
3. Bikerman, J. J., *J. Colloid Sci.* **11,** 299 (1956).
4. Muller, R. H., *J. Electrochem. Soc.* **113,** 943 (1966); J. J. Bikerman, *ibid.* **114,** 651 (1967).
5. Bikerman, J. J., *J. Mater.* **1,** 34 (1966).
6. Armand, G., Lapujoulade, J., and Paigne, J., *Vacuum* **14,** 53 (1964).
7. Bikerman, J. J., *J. Colloid Sci.* **5,** 349 (1950).
8. Hull, H. H., *Proc. 8th Tech. Meeting Tech. Assoc. Graphic Arts, 1956* A, p. 53 (1956).
9. Koehler, W. F., and White, W. C., *J. Opt. Soc. Am.* **45,** 1011 (1955).
10. Sugg, R. E., *Chem. Eng.* **61,** No. 3, 216 (1954).
11. Froment, M., and Lestrade, J. C., *Electrochim. Acta* **11,** 21 (1966).
12. Blet, G., *Publ. Sci. Tech. Min. Air (France)* No. **241** (1950).
13. American Standards Assoc. B 46.1. Am. Soc. Mech. Engineers, New York, 1955.

14. "ASME Handbook, Metal Engineering Design," 2nd ed., p. 599. McGraw-Hill, New York, 1965.
15. Spooner, R. C., *J. Electrochem. Soc.* **102,** 156 (1955).
16. Keller, F., Hunter, M. S., and Robinson, D. L., *J. Electrochem. Soc.* **100,** 411 (1953).
17. Nearn, W. T., *Offic. Dig., Federation Soc. Paint Technol.* **37,** 720 (1965).
18. Johnson, W. T. M., *Offic. Dig., Federation Soc. Paint Technol.* **33,** 1489 (1961).
19. Bullett, T. R., and Prosser, J. L., *Trans. Inst. Metal Finishing* **41,** 112 (1964).
20. Altenpohl, D., "Aluminium und Aluminiumlegierungen," pp. 843 and 392. Springer, Berlin, 1965.
21. Vratny, F., *J. Electrochem. Soc.* **112,** 289 (1965).
22. Popilov, L. Ya., and Zaitseva, L. P., "Electropolishing and Electroetching of Metallographic Sections," p. 63. GNTI Literature Iron and Noniron Metallurgy, Moscow, 1955.
23. Kuznetsov, A. Ya., *Zh. Fiz. Khim.* **27,** 657 (1953).
24. Harrison, L. G., Morrison, J. A., and Rose, G. S., *in* "Surface Activity" (J. H. Schulman, ed.), Vol. 2, p. 287. Academic Press, New York, 1957.
25. Anderson, J. S., *Z. Physik. Chem.* **88,** 191 (1914).
26. Adams, R. J., Weisbecker, H. L., and McDonald, W. J., *J. Electrochem. Soc.* **111,** 774 (1964).
27. Bikerman, J. J., "Surface Chemistry," 2nd ed., Academic Press, New York, 1958.

CHAPTER II / **ADHESIVE**
AND
OTHER JOINTS

Fastening Devices

§14   The function of an adhesive is to fasten two solids together. Fastening can be achieved by many other devices, and it seems advisable to make clear the difference between them and real adhints.

As one extreme, purely mechanical methods of joining may be mentioned, such as riveting, nailing, sewing, hooking, and knitting. At the other extreme, welding would be found. Adhints differ from the first group in so far as — contrary to rivets, sewing thread, etc. — the adhesive is more or less liquid during at least the formation of the adhint. They differ from welded joints since the adhesive is chemically different from the adherends and no part of the adherends is in the molten state at any stage of the adhint existence. In the so-called cold-welding, also known as solid-to-solid adhesion or dry adhesion or cold adhesion, no adhesive is used and the adherends are never liquid although they may be in the plastic range.

A nail driven into wood is fastened to the latter not by any molecular adhesion but by the pressure exerted by the wood on the nail; the nail pushes the wood around it away thus causing compression of the wood, and the compressed wood in its turn presses on the nail. Obviously, no removal of weak boundary layers (§1) is needed for this type of joining. Riveting, knitting, etc., are as easy to understand as nailing.

Solid-to-Solid Adhesion

§15   The term "solid-to-solid adhesion" is applied to at least four different phenomena.

1. When two platinum wires were for a long time heated (for outgassing) in the best vacuum obtainable in 1936, permitted to cool, and slightly pressed against each other, a measurable force was needed to break them apart.[1]

Similar experiments have been performed several times since, and with similar results. Adherence of two solids in a high vacuum attracts particular attention in this decennium as vehicles travelling in the interplanetary space or near the surface of the Moon are surrounded by a medium which may be even less dense than the laboratory vacua, and every solid encountered by the vehicle may adhere to it. Thus, as the Moon's surface presumably consists of silicates, adherence of orthoclase and some other silicate minerals to each other was determined[2] at a pressure of about 10^{-7} baryes (1 mm Hg is equal to 1333 baryes). When a mineral was cleaved in air, the two fragments kept for a time in the above vacuum, pressed together in it by a load L, and finally separated (in it) by a tensile force F, the ratio of F to L was of the order of 10^{-5}. Markedly higher values of F/L were obtained when also the cleavage was performed in a good vacuum, but their precise measurement did not succeed. As in Holm's experiments,[1] admission of nitrogen to the vacuum chamber had little effect on F, but admission of air greatly lowered the adherence.

In these instances, true atomic contact between the two wires or crystals is very probable. The gas concentration in the vessel is so small that, e.g., platinum atoms are exposed on the two surfaces and, when wires A and B are pressed together, some of the atoms of A come so near to the atoms of B (their number being determined by surface roughness) that attractive forces between them reach a measurable intensity. In short, weak boundary layers (§1) are partially removed by profound evacuation.

2. A second type of solid-to-solid adhesion presumably differs from ordinary nailing or the adherence between a fork and a piece of meat only insofar as the number of nail-like protuberances on the

surface is great and these are too small to be discerned by the unaided eye.

When a pin of hard metal is pressed into a soft metal, an effort is required to raise the "plunger" again. Indium has frequently been used as the soft "pin cushion," and the initial pressure (see L, above, was, for instance,[3] 4×10^4 baryes (or 0.6 psi). The ratio of F/L was raised by vapor degreasing, heating in a vacuum, and so on, and lowered by contaminating the interface between a hard metal (or glass) and indium with detergents; this observation may be summarized simply by saying that lubricants lowered the friction between the nails and the plates into which they were driven.

3. In a third type, two solids are not only pressed one against the other but also wrung together or suffer another mutual tangential displacement. The degree of joining achieved in this operation may be illustrated by the following examples. When two optically flat glass surfaces were worked into a "contact" at which the average clearance between them was about 1.5×10^{-5} cm, a force of nearly 10^5 dynes/cm^2 was required to shear the joint.[4] When two metal bars were similarly wrung together under a pressure of, for instance, 10^8 dynes/cm^2, an approximately equal tensile stress was needed to break them apart.[5] Ratios of F/L greater than 1 were obtained, e.g., when the basis face of a metal pipe was rotated under pressure against the basis face of a solid metal cylinder.[6] When the rod and the pipe were of an identical alloy, there was some tendency for F/L to be greater for softer metals. In one instance, F/L was greater for a very pure metal (99.999% copper) than for a less pure sample (99.98%) but the cause of this observation is not known.

The adherence of the third type sometimes is applied in industry. A gold wire squashed and spread over the quartz surface can be used as a suspension for a quartz crystal. The ancient art of gilding copper and other metals by mechanical means at temperatures far below the melting point of gold also should be mentioned here.

The mechanism of this effect apparently has never been investigated. The following explanations are advanced as the most probable guesses in the present state of our knowledge (see also reference 7). Figure 11 may serve for both the second and the third type. If, for instance, an eminence (A) is forced into a depression (B) on the opposite surface (see Fig. 11), the walls of B are elastically pushed apart and then exert a lateral pressure on A; this is the mechanism of a snap fastener. If no preformed depression is present, A can act as a nail. The function of wringing is to increase the probability of these processes. If the two solids are pressed together without any tangential motion, an eminence which may have a diameter of about $1\ \mu$ and, consequently, an area of about 10^{-8} cm^2, will be in contact with only 10^{-8} cm^2 of the other surface, and on this minute area the surface of B may offer no suitable indentation for a snap and no weak spot for a nail. If the tangential motion was such that each protuberance traveled 1 cm, it was in contact with 10^{-4} cm^2 of the surface of B; hence, the probability of meeting a suitable contour was much greater. In some instances, the interpenetration of A and B is such that we may speak of "plastic mixing"; mixing which took place on wringing together a copper and an aluminum rod can be seen in the photomicrographs of reference 8.

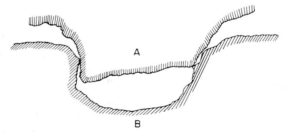

FIG. 11. Mechanical attachment of the snap-fastener type.

If separation is achieved by a shearing motion, the force needed for it presumably is analogous to the force needed to spread butter over bread or to maintain uniform sliding of a drop along an inclined plane (see §§5 and 28). When a liquid drop (or a chunk of butter) moves along a solid surface, those parts of it above the surface hills can — in favorable circumstances — maintain a steady motion parallel to the surface; but those parts of the liquid which must meander between the hills cannot keep pace with the higher layers and remain behind as a wet track left by the drop. As long as viscosity (or consistency) is small, the tension $F_n \sin \alpha/w$ of §5 is determined by the surface tension of the liquid in the wake of the drop; when the drop slides along dx cm, the liquid–air interface behind it increases by $kw\ dx$ cm², k being the ratio of the combined widths of the wet tracks to the width of the drop.

The adherence observed when two metal strips are rolled or otherwise deformed together is, presumably, analogous to that caused by wringing. Tangential flows occur in both instances. When the central part of two aluminum foils was pressed together by a copper plate, the area under the center of the plunger became, after the compression, 1.8–3.2 times as great as before. The mixing after such a treatment may be on a finer scale than after wringing, especially when the rolling is performed at an elevated temperature. Thus, when sheets of steel and of titanium were hot-rolled together, the Fe–Ti eutectic could be detected along the interface.[9] Between the same pair of metals, a stratified diffusion band was visible after deformation.[10]

4. The solid-to-solid adhesion of the fourth type greatly depends on the rate of separation and, consequently, is discussed together with tack (§37).

§16   Adhesion of coatings deposited from vapor obviously does not belong to the solid-to-solid adhesion but is discussed here because no more suitable environment seems to be available. Coatings of this kind are produced on an industrial scale; metallized plastics are probably the most familiar example. They are deposited in a vacuum, but the residual gas pressure is, perhaps, 100,000 times as high as that necessary to achieve the molecular adhesion outlined in §15.1. Thus, no molecular attraction would be expected. Nevertheless, the coatings are coherent and often adhere well to the substrate.

The scientific literature dealing with these coatings is very meager (see §76). In the author's laboratory, electropolished brass plates were kept in the vapor of molten selenium until the Se deposits were, say, 5 to 100 μ thick. The adherence was estimated by gluing a flexible tape or a wooden rod to the coating and peeling the former or applying tensile stress to the latter. In all instances, rupture occurred so near the brass that the brass surface appeared, at a small magnification, untouched. In all probability, there was a weak boundary layer (of air, of oil from the diffusion pump, etc.) between the substrate and selenium. The coating tended to contract (§76) and its tensile strength was far below that of solid selenium. Apparently, the vapor cooled in contact with brass so rapidly that selenium atoms had no time to reach the equilibrium positions corresponding to any of the solid modifications of the element.

Classification of Adhints

§17   If the definition of adhints given in §14 is accepted, i.e., the systems of §§15 and 16 are excluded, at least three kinds of adhesive joints still remain, namely *hooking, proper,* and *improper* adhints.

As its name implies, in a hooking adhint the adhesive, after solidification, acts as a multiple hook. Usually, removal of weak boundary layers is not needed to achieve strong bonds of this type: a dirty lab coat hangs on a hook just as securely as a clean one. When there is no significant interpenetration of adherend and adhesive, the adhints are either proper or improper. In the former, the boundary layers are absent or are so strong that rupture occurs elsewhere, and in the latter, separation proceeds in a weak boundary layer.

When an adhint is described as consisting of two adherends and the adhesive, the description may be more or less accurate from the chemical viewpoint but it usually conveys a wrong idea of the structure of the system. In hooking adhints, five layers, rather than three, ought to be recognized, namely unchanged adherend–adherend intermixed with the adhesive–unchanged adhesive–adhesive intermixed with the second adherend–unchanged second adherend. Five layers are present also in all improper joints; first adherend–first boundary layer–adhesive film–second boundary layer–second adherend. If the two adherends are identical, their boundary layers also are likely to be identical (see, however, §§33 and 53) and there are only three different strata, namely, the two adherends, the two boundary layers, and the adhesive film (also known as *glue line*). In exceptional instances, boundary layers are absent, but the adhints of this kind belong, for instance, to high-vacuum physics rather than to any industry utilizing adhesives.

It is interesting to note that hooking and proper adhints usually are not broken at all. If, for instance, a leather strip is glued to a shoe heel, the strip and the heel are never separated; the whole shoe is discarded and destroyed when it ceases to be usable. An identical observation applies to the combinations postal stamp–adhesive–envelope, couch leg–adhesive–couch, and so on. In many airplanes aluminum panels are glued rather than riveted to each other, and the hulls of many boats consist of glass fibers connected to each other by a polymer adhesive; and both airplanes and boats are disposed of without breaking the adhesive bonds. On the other hand, improper joints often fail when the rest of the assembly is still perfectly sound. Thus, control and research laboratories have to deal with them. Customers, fortunately, deal mainly with hooking and proper adhints.

The history of an adhint usually comprises three periods. During the first the adhesive is applied, during the second it sets, and during the third its properties remain constant or almost constant; Chapters III and IV treat the first stage, Chapter V is concerned with the second, and Chapters VI to X deal with the third. The necessity of three stages is clear from the discussion, §1, of the function of an adhesive. It must be applied liquid to displace weak boundary layers and to fill the depressions; this is period No. 1. The majority of the adhesives are expected to be strong and, consequently, must be solid all their "working life"; this is period No. 3. Period No. 2 is the transition from No. 1 to No. 3.

The so-called *pressure-sensitive* adhesives (for which also a better name, namely *permanently tacky,* is used) set so slowly that the third period is not observed in their use. Adhesive tapes, insulating tapes, and similar goods contain such adhesives. The mechanism of their action is outlined in Chapter IV.

Hooking Adhints

§18   Hooking adhints usually are obtained with adherends which are (at least in the surface layer) fibrous, porous, or exceptionally rough. Paper, paperboard, and fabrics certainly, and wood and leather presumably, are among these adherends, provided that no coat (of varnish, paint, etc.) hinders penetration of the adhesive into the pores. This list of adherends includes most common materials which are so often subjected to gluing operations that hooking adhints are made probably more frequently than any other type. Nevertheless, only a few attempts have been made to study them in a scientific manner. Results which are specific for hooking joints are reported in this chapter while effects which, fundamentally, would be observed also in other adhints are mentioned later where the effects are discussed.

Figure 12 shows the "hooks." It is schematic because photographs of the cross section of a coated paper or a paper–adhesive–paper joint usually are not very clear and also lose some resolution in reproduction. White areas represent paper fibers cut by a microtome, and the patterned fields are meant to be adhesive intrusions. Usually, the two components can be distinguished in polarized light more easily than in unpolarized light because cellulose fibers are birefringent and the adhesive hooks, isotropic. It is clear from Fig. 12 and many photographs on which it is based that the intermixing is so intimate that no mechanical separation of the two ingredients is feasible.

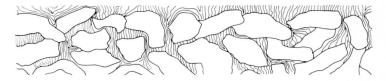

FIG. 12. The surface layer of paper (white) into which an adhesive (shaded) has penetrated.

Similar conclusions have been arrived at much earlier, e.g., in reference 11, and photographs of phenol–formaldehyde adhesives (§50) which penetrated into Douglas fir surface layer, may be seen in reference 12. When wood is cut (or sawed through) the thick-walled summerwood usually splits between two cells, i.e., in the cell wall, so that only a few lumens are accessible. Nevertheless, the adhesive fills the hollows of the exterior cells. This occurs more easily with springwood as many of its thin-walled cells become open to the outside when a cut is made. Apparently, the adhesive is occluded also in the cells walls. When an adhint is broken, wood cells are visible on both rupture surfaces (see §56).

Whoever is interested in the contrary opinion, according to which wood–adhesive–wood adhints are not of the hooking type, may be referred to references 13 and 14.

§**19**   Two problems specific for hooking adhints have been investigated recently. In order to achieve interlocking, seen in Fig. 12, the adhesive must wet the fibers. This condition would not be necessary if the pores were much wider; then the adhesive could flow into the pores because of gravitation or a difference in hydrostatic pressure. Wetting is discussed in §§22 to 28 as it is essential for other adhint types also. The problem of this section is how deeply the adhesive must penetrate into the fiber mat to achieve the maximum strength possible in the given system.

The answer[15] is relatively simple for filter paper. A strip of this was pressed into a pool of molten adhesive (a copolymer of vinyl acetate and dibutyl maleate) spread on an aluminum ribbon, the sandwich was permitted to cool, and then the paper and the foil were peeled apart. The tension Γ necessary for peeling increased with the thickness τ of the adhesive layer as long as this was below 10–20 μ but was nearly independent of τ at greater thicknesses. Tension here means force needed for stripping divided by the width of the strip; the dimension of Γ is gm/sec², identical with that of surface tension (see §32). When a layer, 10 to 20 μ thick, of the adhesive melt was imbibed by the paper, the depth z of penetration was greater than 10 to 20 μ. In the simplest instance, the melt fills the voids present between the paper fibers. The volume of voids, φ, in the paper studied was 0.66, meaning that 1 cm³ of paper contained 0.34 cm³ of fibers and 0.66 cm³ of air. Thus z ($=\tau/\varphi$) was $\tau/0.66$, i.e., penetration equal to 15 to 30 μ was sufficient to render the peeling tension as high as it could be. As the most common fiber diameter in the paper was 9 ± 1 μ, it is clear that only two or three fibers, nearest to the surface, have to be "hooked" to attain the maximum strength. This is the state shown in Fig. 12.

The situation is more intricate in paperboard (boxboard) because this material, as a rule, is stratified; one or both of the exterior layers (which may be, for instance, 70 or 100 μ thick) is (are) stronger than the interior ply. This causes a striking difference in Γ between adhints of the geometry of Fig. 13(a) and those of Fig. 13(b); the Γ of the former was, for instance, three times as great as the Γ of the latter. In Fig. 13(a) the foil is shown to be glued to a piece of board far from the edge. The stresses produced by the peeling force act on the strong ply only, and the rupture (crack) starts in this ply. In Fig. 13(b) the foil is glued to the edge of the board. When it is pulled down, the whole right-hand face of the board is strained and a crack is initiated in the weakest layer. Hence, in these systems, less force is needed for peeling.

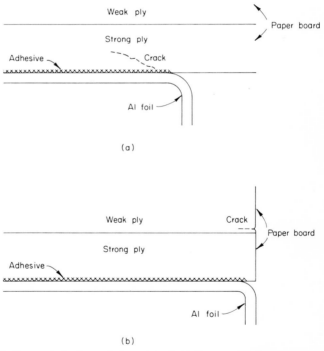

FIG. 13. Rupture of a layered paper board. (a) Force applied to a strong ply. (b) Force applied to a weak ply.

The observations reported in the preceding paragraph are one of the many examples in this book of the fact that the geometry of an adhint, the texture of the adherends, and other macroscopical and mechanical factors must be known and understood to account for the experimental strength of a joint; no abstract discussion of van der Waals forces, polarity, and so on, would be of any help (see §60).

The second of the problems referred to in the beginning of this section is how rapidly the necessary penetration of the adhesive into the paper is achieved; in gluing paper and boxboard the speed of production usually is more important than the final strength of the adhint, (§55), as the adherends themselves are not strong.

Two similar devices are available for studying the rate of imbibition. In the older,[16] paper wound on a rotating drum slightly rubs against the open end of a slit (1.5×0.02 cm) filled with a liquid. The volume of the liquid occluded at different rates of rotation is determined, and it is thus possible to calculate the time of contact (between the liquid and the paper) required to achieve the penetration of, say, 30 μ.

The newer device is simpler.[17] A more or less cubical container (about 4 cm edge) with a flat and smooth rim is partly filled with a liquid, placed bottom up on a strip of paper, and pulled along the strip at a constant velocity. The amount M taken up by 1 cm² of the paper along the middle part of the trajectory is weighed. The depth z of penetration is $M/\rho\varphi$, if ρ is the density of the liquid; and this depth was reached in time $t = bt_1/l$, b being the inside dimension of the cube (doctor cup) and t_1 the time taken by the latter to cover the length l. (If the cup is not a cube, b is the inside dimension in the travel direction.) As soon as, for a given combination of liquid and paper, the relation between z and t is found by experiment, it is possible by interpolation to determine that t at which z has the desired value (e.g., 30 μ).

Difficulties were experienced when the method was applied to real adhesives. If, for instance, a dextrin solution is employed, it first fills the voids but voids reappear when water evaporates; consequently, the maximum depth of penetration is greater than $M/\rho\varphi$ but not the whole thickness $M/\rho\varphi$ is embedded in dextrin.

It is not known how much of the adherence of rubber to tire cord and of polymer matrix to reinforcing glass yarn is of the hooking type. Apparently, at least some of the adhesion of enamel to iron is caused by mechanical interlocking. Figure 14 is a 1330-fold enlargement[18] of a section of the interface between polished iron and a "normally fired groundcoat" enamel and clearly shows interpenetration. The iron spots in the upper phase are not separate grains but rather cross sections of dendrites which somewhere else are connected with the main body of iron.

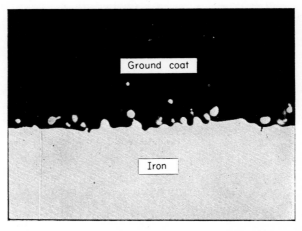

FIG. 14. Interface between ingot iron and a normally fired ground-coat enamel containing 0.8% by weight Co_3O_4. The iron surface was polished before coating. Unetched. Magnification 1330×. From reference 18.

Figure 15 illustrates[19] a connection between the degree of interpenetration and the breaking stress of the adhint. Thin molybdenum films were deposited on two different ceramics at 1700°, 1600°, and 1500° (reading from top to bottom). Then they were brazed to a handle, and the strength of the systems solder–molybdenum–ceramics was determined. The results are marked on the photographs. The left-hand ceramics which gave rise to a pronounced mixing produced stronger adhints than the other, whose boundary with the metal remained relatively smooth.

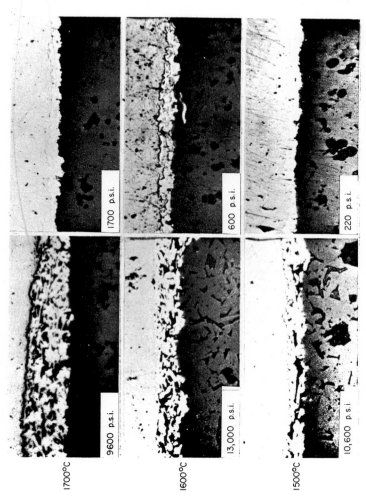

FIG. 15. Photomicrographs of molybdenum-ceramics seals. Magnification 500×.
From reference 19.

REFERENCES

1. Holm, R., and Kirschstein, B., *Wiss. Veroeffentl. Siemens-Werken* **15,** I, 122 (1936); **18,** II, 73 (1939).
2. Ryan, J. A., *J. Geophys. Res.* **71,** 4413 (1966).
3. Krieger, G. L., and Wilson, G. J., *Mater. Res. & Std.* **5,** 341 (1965).
4. Macaulay, J. M., *Nature* **138,** 587 (1936).
5. Anderson, O. L., *J. Appl. Phys.* **30,** 593 (1959).
6. Sikorski, M. E., *J. Basic Eng.* **85,** 279 (1963).
7. Bikerman, J. J., *in* "Fundamental Phenomena in the Materials Sciences" (L. H. Bonis and H. H. Hausner, eds.), Vol. 2, p. 165. Plenum Press, New York, 1966.
8. Anderson, O. L., *Bell Lab. Record* **35,** 441 (1957).
9. Dolzhenkov, F. E., and Krivonosov, Yu. I., *Tsvetn. Metal.* **37,** No. 6, 63 (1964); *Chem. Abstr.* **61,** 8004 (1965).
10. Pavlov, I. M., and Brinza, V. N., *Protsessy Prokatki, Mosk. Inst. Stali i Splavov 40, Moscow, Sb.* 1962, 160; *Chem. Abstr.* **59,** 11031 (1963).
11. Clark, G. L., *Colloid Symp. Monograph* **4,** 145 (1926).
12. Nearn, W. T., *Offic. Dig., Federation Soc. Paint Technol.* **37,** 720 (1965).
13. Marian, J. E., and Stumbo, D. A., *Holzforschung* **16,** 134 (1962); *Chem. Abstr.* **58,** 5875 (1963).
14. Bosworth, P., *Adhesives Age* **6,** No. 11, 22 (1963).
15. Bikerman, J. J., and Whitney, W., *Tappi* **46,** 420 (1963).
16. Sweerman, A. J. W., *Tappi* **44,** No. 7, 172A (1961).
17. Bikerman, J. J., and Whitney, W., *Tappi* **46,** 689 (1963).
18. Moore, D. G., Pitts, J. W., Richmond, J. C., and Harrison, W. N., *J. Am. Ceram. Soc.* **37,** 1 (1954).
19. Cole, S. S., and Sommer, G., *J. Am. Ceram. Soc.* **44,** 265 (1961).

Chapter III | FORMATION OF ADHINTS

Cleaning of the Adherend Surfaces

§**20**   Except for many hooking adhints (§17), preparation of an adhesive joint usually starts with cleaning the adherends. The aim of this operation is to remove from the surfaces all weak materials which would give rise to weak boundary layers of the third class (§70). All gases, every liquid, every powder, and every solid of a lesser mechanical strength than the adherend and the adhesive should be eliminated, if possible. As a rule, the task would be relatively easy if the composition and the location of the impurities were known. Unfortunately, the chemistry and the texture of surface layers depend on the history of each sample at least as much as on the nature of its bulk. Thus, if a panel of metal A and a panel of metal B each was oiled (to retard corrosion) with the same oil, the two surface layers would be identical (or almost identical), however different the two metals may be (see §10).

The above references to the location of impurities and the texture of surface layers may be made clearer by an example. Oxide films are present on the surface of almost all metals in air. If such a metal is deformed (e.g., in a rolling mill), the oxide may be forced under the metal surface, as in the "solid-to-solid" adhesion (§15.3), and thus protected from dissolution in a subsequent chemical cleaning operation.

As the aim of pretreatment is to obtain a strong rather than a pure surface layer, some "impurities" may with impunity be left on the adherend, while the material to be removed may include the substance of the bulk solid. Thus, aluminum oxide on aluminum metal

43

(§8) obviously is, chemically, a contaminant, but there is no need to eliminate it as long as organic adhesives are employed because apparently no polymer is capable of rupturing the natural alumina film (see §71) or its interface stratum with the metal. On the other hand, aluminum powder on an aluminum surface is not a foreign matter in the chemical sense, but—analogously to the lithium fluoride dust of §1—it must be disposed of before a strong adhint can be formed.

When the experimenter takes, say, a copper plate in his hand, he may be sure that the surface layer of the plate is not copper metal, but a more detailed knowledge of this layer is not available unless he knows all the heat treatments which the specimen was subjected to, all the lubricants, corrosion inhibitors, etc., smeared on the plate, and so on. As this knowledge is practically never available, empirical methods have been devised to produce "adhesionable" specimens from those manufactured in a more or less traditional manner. Descriptions of these methods exist in many languages, e.g., references 1 and 2. It is worth pointing out that a book[1] of 216 pages is called for to report cleaning procedures recommended for just one metal.

Such reports obviously are very useful but their value is more technological than scientific. If, for instance, a radically new process of manufacturing steel plate is introduced, the present cleaning methods may prove ineffective. At present, the usual contaminations on metals may be sifted into three groups: inorganic impurities (oxides, sulfides, sulfates from the pickling, etc.), organic impurities (lubricating oils and so on), and particulate impurities (dust, filings, etc.); and each of these groups may be altered when the metal-forming procedure changes.

Since no scientific foundation exists for the recommended cleaning treatments, they are not systematically described in this book. However, a few examples are given to demonstrate the difficulties unavoidable when action must be based on ignorance.

In the literature, statements similar to the following quotation[3] are frequently encountered: "It is easiest to attach rubber to steel, brass, cast iron, and aluminum alloys. It is difficult to make it adhere to stainless steel, bronzes, and magnesium alloys, and particularly difficult to tin-containing bronzes." An analogous generalization[4] is that mechanical methods of cleaning (abrasion, sandblasting, etc.) appear to be the best for carbon steel while titanium, stainless steel, and aluminum respond better to chemical methods. The rivalry between mechanical and chemical cleaning processes enjoys wide attention. One specialist[3] advocates degreasing and sandblasting for all metals (to be attached to rubber) and stresses the importance of roughening the metal surfaces, while, in an almost simultaneous publication, a second authority[5] insists on a mirror finish of metal adherends, warns against sandblasting to which grit blasting is preferred, and recommends chemical pickling of aluminum, magnesium, zinc, and brass. Chemical treatment, without any mechanical abrasion, is considered to be sufficient also by another expert.[6]

Some instances of the effect exerted by cleaning operations on the breaking strength of adhints may be adduced here (see also reference 7). First, steel. Table III reproduces some values found[8] for the breaking stress of butt joints (§79) "steel–an epoxy adhesive –alkyd paint–steel–the epoxy adhesive–steel"; the percentages in the third column mean the number of adhints (per 100) in which separation seemed to occur along the paint–steel interface.

TABLE III
BREAKING STRESS AND SURFACE TREATMENT — STEEL

Pretreatment	Breaking stress (bars)	Improper joints, (%)
Solvent washing	155	100
Solvent wash, abrasion, solvent wash	208	100
Solvent wash, abrasion, solvent wash, extraction with hot butanone	260	20
Solvent wash, abrasion, solvent wash, extraction with hot petroleum ether	255	25

The breaking stress[9] of lap joints "steel–an industrial adhesive–steel" was 233 bars when the adherends were degreased in liquid trichloroethylene, 237 bars after degreasing and an attack with acids and a borax solution, and 277 bars after grit blasting, so that the gain achieved by a more drastic treatment was only moderate.

According to reference 10, the adherence (how measured?) of an enamel to steel was identical for (a) steel degreased by heat, pickled in sulfuric acid and washed, and (b) steel heated in mixtures of nitrogen, hydrogen, carbon monoxide, etc., at 700° and 900°. The strength of butt joints of steel–polycaprolactam (Nylon 6)–steel was raised from below 400 to almost 600 bars by a prior sandblasting of the steel members.[11]

Some data for aluminum[12] are listed in Table IV. They are for

TABLE IV
BREAKING STRESS AND SURFACE TREATMENT—ALUMINUM

Pretreatment	Breaking stress (bars)
"As received"	31
Vapor degreasing, abrasion with Al wool	102
Vapor degreasing, aqueous alkali, chromic acid, distilled water (with or without grit blast)	193–214

single lap joints (§82) and a "catalyzed resin" as the adhesive. Relative humidity, RH, of the atmosphere, in which the ingredients of the adhint were kept separately and in which the adhint formation was performed, strongly influenced the breaking stress. When RH was 50% throughout, the stress was, for instance, 182 bars; when the metal only was kept at 92%, it was lowered to 109 bars; and it was only 63 bars when the metal, the resin, and the catalyst were all stored at 92% RH. The breaking stress[9] of lap joints "aluminum–an industrial adhesive–aluminum" was more sensitive to the cleaning procedure than that of the analogous steel adhints. It was 269 bars after degreasing in trichloroethylene; 342 bars after degreasing, washing in NaOH and HNO_3, and pickling in chromic acid; and 362 bars after degreasing, washing, pickling, and immersion in an alcoholic solution of dicyandiamide.

Lap joints of copper and brass glued together with an epoxy adhesive had a breaking stress of 245 bars whether the metals were previously blasted with sand of various particle sizes or briefly immersed in chromic acid.[13] Much more interesting observations were made by Stuart.[14] α-Brass (Cu 70, Zn 30 wt %) is widely used whenever metal–rubber adhints are made (see also §72). When this brass is electropolished in strong phosphoric acid, combined with a rubber mix, and the assembly is cured, rubber can easily be peeled off, and its surface (which was in contact with the brass) is covered with a metal sulfide film, thick enough to show interference colors. Slight rubbing of the electropolished metal with the finest emery paper renders it so receptive to rubber that peeling tension of, e.g., 1230 kilodynes/cm (or 70 lb/in.) was needed to break the adhint. When then about 50 to 100 Å of the brass surface was dissolved away in a persulfate solution, the metal again lost its ability to bond rubber.

The old established methods of abrasion and pickling have recently been supplemented by corona discharge,[15, 16] by ionic bombardment in a vacuum, and so on.

§21   When an attempt is made to detect the rationale of the data of §20, the first thing to remember is that the above methods, with perhaps the one exception of high-vacuum ionic bombardment, do not achieve any cleaning in the strict sense of the word. If a metal is pickled and rinsed, for instance, its surface after drying is covered with an oxide or a salt. Abrasion leaves abrasive powder (and binder, if any) in the surface layer, as was several times discovered and rediscovered.[17, 18] Thus, successful pretreatment of an adherend, as a rule, means substituting a strong for a weak boundary layer.

When, after cleaning, the boundary layer on a metal is stronger than the adhesive—which condition is usually satisfied when the adhesive is an organic polymer—then the rupture occurs in the polymer film, and the breaking stress is determined to a large degree by the properties of this film (see Chapter VIII); in brief, the adhint is of the proper type. Perhaps this state of cleanness was achieved in those tests of §20 in which the breaking stress appeared almost independent of the cleaning method; indeed, if all weak materials are removed, the behavior of the resulting system often (but see §35) would be expected to show no effect of the procedure employed.

In those instances in which the average breaking stress increases after each additional cleaning operation and, especially, when (see Table III) the percentage of improper breaks simultaneously decreases, it is clear that a gradual removal of the weak impurities is taking place. This statement still does not satisfy an inquiring mind. Is it necessary to administer so many medicines one after the other? Perhaps, a way will be found to eliminate the contaminants by fewer, and more selective, operations. It is probable, for instance, that the useful result of immersion in chromic acid (which is advocated even for a metal as active as magnesium) is simply destruction of the organic "dirt" but it is clear that corrosion of the metal (which is not desirable at all) occurs at the same time.

When an adhint of "electropolished metal–metal sulfide–rubber" easily breaks near the metal–sulfide interface while an analogous system with a slightly abraded metal (i.e., with a disordered surface layer?) is strong, a reason must be sought for formation of a weak boundary layer in the first instance, and its absence in the second. In §72 the observation is reported that, at the interface of copper and brass, zinc from the latter may diffuse into copper more rapidly than copper diffuses into brass and that voids may thus form between the two phases; perhaps an analogous diffusion effect occurs in oriented crystals when their one face reacts with sulfur, while the diffusion in random grains is, on the average, less rapid.

General statements that one solid (A) is easier to glue than another (B) may mean that displacement of detrimental surface impurities from A has been sufficiently standardized while no satisfactory procedure for an analogous cleaning of B has been found as yet; or their meaning may be that a weak boundary layer of the 6th class (§72) forms in an interaction between B and the adhesive while A does not react with the adhesive in this manner. Stress concentration effects of Chapter VIII are less likely to be decisive in this instance.

The contradictions between the test results of different investigators may be due partly to the difference between the contaminants on the specimens used and partly to the ambiguity of the terms describing the cleaning operations and the subsequent determination of adhint strength. For instance, sandblasting may be expected to result in different effects according to whether the sand was or was not heated to destroy organic impurities. Also the roughening achieved by sandblasting may or may not be important according to the amount of the adhesive used. Suppose, for instance, that the experimenter standardizes this amount so as to have an adhesive film of the average thickness of 20 μ. If the h_{max} (§3) of the adherends is, say, 5 μ, the clearance would be filled with the adhesive and a proper joint may result, but if h_{max} is raised to 100 μ by sandblasting, a "starved" joint containing many voids will be obtained. On the other hand, if the adhesive amount is not standardized and the experimenter uses ten times as much glue on the rough as on the smooth surface, the effect of roughness may appear negligible.

Analogous remarks can be made in reference to the other procedures. Thus, if heating in water was the last treatment accorded to an aluminum part, the breaking stress of an adhint will depend on how well water was removed before the application of the adhesive, on the purity of the water used, and so on.

Removal of weak boundary layers of better known composition is discussed in the rest of this, and in Chapter VII.

Wetting

§**22**   As the vast majority of adhints are made in air, air is probably the most common substance of weak boundary layers. To displace air from the surface of a solid, the liquid adhesive must wet the latter. The degree of wetting is quantitatively expressed in terms of contact angle. Contact angle is the angle (in the liquid) between the air–liquid and the liquid–solid interface. In Fig. 16, showing a drop on a horizontal plane, it is acute, and in Fig. 17, showing a meniscus in a capillary, it is obtuse. The letter θ generally is used to denote contact angle. If the solid is flat, that is encloses an angle of 180°, the angle occupied by the gas space is $180 - \theta°$.

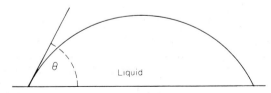

FIG. 16. A drop on a horizontal plane; θ is the contact angle.

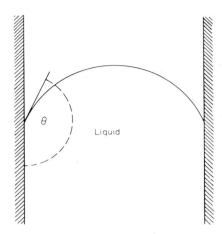

FIG. 17. Meniscus in a capillary; θ is the contact angle.

The value of θ, as would be expected, depends on the composition of the three phases in contact but is affected also by surface roughness (§3) and by the pre-history of the system. Because of these complications it is impossible to assign a definite value to the contact angle when the chemical nature of the solid, the liquid, and the gas is known. In this respect contact angles unfortunately differ from any other properties of three-phase systems, such as the vapor pressure of a solution in equilibrium with the excess solid. In §§24 and 25 the main methods of measuring θ are described, but it should always be remembered that the values obtained may not be characteristic of the chemical system studied; and additional investigation is needed to judge how near they are to the theoretical value which would be observed on a perfectly smooth solid surface in the absence of time effects [of which the hysteresis of wetting (§27) is the most important]. This theoretical value usually is denoted by the term *equilibrium contact angle, θ_e.*

It appears almost obvious that equilibrium contact angles should be determined by the molecular forces in and between the three phases in contact (rather than, for instance, by gravitation or the profile of the solid body). According to Thomas Young (1805), θ_e depends on the three boundary tensions, that is, one along the vapor

–liquid, one along the vapor–solid, and the third along the liquid –solid interface (see §60). Young dispensed with any justification for his hypothesis, and the later attempts to buttress the latter were shown to be futile.[19] It was also proved[19] that the surface tension of the liquid raised a ridge in the solid (if it was very soft) along the three-phase line so that, at least for soft solids whose modulus of elasticity is below, say, 10^{10} baryes (or 140,000 psi), the macroscopic mechanical properties of the solid also must be taken into consideration.

Simultaneously with Young, P. S. Laplace derived an equation for the relation between θ_e and the molecular attractions acting on a liquid molecule situated at the three-phase line; the resultant of the two attractions (toward the liquid and toward the solid) must be perpendicular to the liquid–vapor surface. A weakness in his derivation was pointed out[20]; and at any rate the equation is not definite enough.

The most recent attempt, in its simplest form,[20] may be reproduced here. If L is the energy of a molecule whose "sphere of molecular action" is wholly in the liquid, V is the analogous magnitude in the vapor, and S would be its energy in the solid environment, then the energy of a molecule at the three-phase line is $[\theta_e L + (\pi - \theta_e)V + \pi S]/2\pi$ because the liquid occupies $\theta_e/2\pi$ of the volume of the sphere, the vapor takes $(\pi - \theta_e)/2\pi$, and the solid, one-half the sphere (Fig. 18). The energy of an identical molecule in the vapor–liquid interface far from the wall obviously is $0.5L + 0.5V$. To avoid any tendency of molecules to move along the interface, that is in order to have an equilibrium, the two energies should be equal. Thus the relation $\theta_e/\pi = (L-S)/(L-V)$ is obtained. As V usually is much smaller than L, the approximation

$$\theta_e = \frac{\pi (L-S)}{L} \tag{1}$$

may be used. L may be identified with γA, γ being the surface tension of the liquid and A the area of the vapor–liquid interface occupied by one molecule. The magnitude S, in principle, can be calculated.

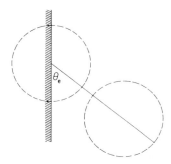

FIG. 18. Contact angle θ_e at the boundary between a solid (shaded), a liquid (below the inclined line), and a gas (above this line). Far from the solid, the sphere of molecular action (dashes) is equally divided by the gas–liquid interface. At the three-phase line, the gas occupies a volume proportional to $\pi - \theta_e$; the liquid, to θ_e; and the solid, to π.

§23   As long as these calculations have not been performed, only two empirical rules are available for predicting, very crudely, the values of a contact angle in a given system. Provided the gas is our common air,

(a) the θ_e is smaller the smaller the surface tension γ of the liquid, as long as the solid is not modified by the contact with the latter; and

(b) when the solid swells in, or otherwise mixes with, the liquid, θ_e is smaller than would be expected from the value of γ.

To (a): A statement by Laplace can be understood as a claim for the product $\gamma(1 + \cos \theta_e)$ to be a constant characteristic for each solid and independent of the liquid. Young simultaneously formulated an identical hypothesis and, in addition, identified the above product with twice the surface tension of the solid. Apparently, there is some justification for Laplace's belief. The equilibrium contact angle was, as far as it was feasible, measured for three liquids and two solids, and the average value (for both solids) of the quantity $\gamma(1 + \cos \theta_e)$ was 85 gm/sec² for water, 71 for glycerol, and 84 for benzyl benzoate.[21] The three values do not differ much from each other, although the surface tensions of the three liquids cover a wide range: 73, 64, and 43 gm/sec². The solids were aluminum and polyethylene, and the measurements were performed at 21° and 50% relative humidity.

To (b): The expression $\gamma(1 + \cos\theta_e)$, if it is constant at all, obviously can be constant only as long as the solid remains constant, that is, is not altered by the contact with the liquid. The increase of this product (and the corresponding decrease of angle θ_e) caused by miscibility of liquid and solid can be shown by many examples. The contact angles along the boundary of air, water, and copper usually are not far from 80°, i.e., $\cos\theta$ is approximately 0.17 and $\gamma(1 + \cos\theta)$ is near 84 gm/sec². As the surface tension of mercury at room temperature is about 510 gm/sec², the value of 84 for copper would predict $\cos\theta$ at the air–mercury–copper boundary to be -0.835, i.e., θ to be 146°. In reality, this contact angle is zero because copper forms an amalgam with mercury, and the latter wets the amalgam perfectly. From $\theta = 0$ for the air–mercury–copper system, it could be concluded that $\gamma(1 + \cos\theta)$ was $\geqslant 1020$ rather than equal to 84 gm/sec².

Analogous effects are quite common. Suppose that a polymer is not attacked by liquid A but swells in liquid B, surface tension being identical for the two liquids; contact angle θ will be smaller for the air–B–polymer than for the air–A–polymer system.

The effect of the composition of the gas phase on θ is large but presumably is more often indirect than direct; gas composition affects θ because it alters the composition of the solid–gas interface. Consider, for instance, water vapor in air. This vapor is readily adsorbed by all common solid surfaces, as follows from §12; there exists no other important component of the atmosphere whose p_1/p_s is as high as the p_1/p_s of water. When the relative humidity changes between 0% and 100%, the composition of the solid surface changes between 100% solid and almost 100% water. It is clear that contact angle should change accordingly. Figure 19, based on the data of Bartell and Bristol,[23] illustrates this change. Its abscissa is the relative humidity of air, and its ordinate, the contact angle (probably not very different from the equilibrium contact angle) at the air–*sym*-tetrabromoethane–quartz boundary.

Although this ought to be clear from the foregoing discussion, it may be emphasized here that the value of the contact angle is not a reliable measure of molecular attraction between the solid and the liquid; this point seems to be sometimes overlooked. Contact angle depends on all three phases in contact and can give information

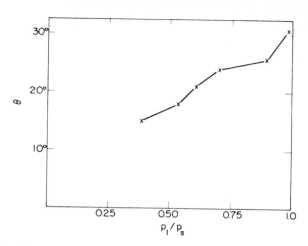

FIG. 19. Effect of relative humidity on contact angle in the system air, acetylene tetrabromide, and quartz. Abscissa: relative humidity. Ordinate: contact angle. Data of reference 23.

only on the *relative* strength of the attractions between solid and liquid on one hand and solid and gas on the other hand; the greater the first attraction compared with the second, the smaller the contact angle (in the liquid!). However, the solid–liquid attraction can still be very strong even if the contact angle is large. That θ depends on all three phases in contact is particularly clear when the system consists of two liquids and one solid, when, for instance, the contact angle in a water drop sitting on a glass plate submerged in benzene is measured.

Measurement of Contact Angles

§**24**   There are four main methods of measuring contact angles.

1. A sessile drop, such as illustrated in Fig. 16, is observed directly, or photographed, or its image is projected on a screen. For direct observation, a low-power microscope whose eyepiece is provided with a filament is convenient. First the filament is set so as to coincide with the visible base line of the drop, and then it is

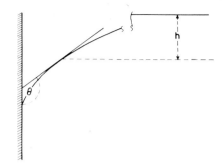

FIG. 20. Meniscus along a vertical wall.

turned to lie along the tangent to the drop at its base. The angle through which the filament must be rotated is the contact angle. On a photograph or a projected image contact angle is measured, e.g., with a protractor.

The method is very simple and easy but does not give exact results because the tangent rapidly changes along the vertical cross section of the drop and it is difficult to make sure that the tangent measured indeed belongs to the lowest point of this cross section. The change of tangent at a point with the height of this point is not easily calculated for a round drop but can be expressed by a simple equation if the meniscus along a flat vertical wall is observed. In this instance,

$$1 - \sin \theta = \frac{g \rho h^2}{2 \gamma} ,$$

g being acceleration due to gravity, ρ the density of the liquid minus that of air, and h the vertical distance between the horizontal expanse of the liquid surface and the three-phase line (in which gas, liquid, and solid meet). For water in air at room temperature, γ is approximately 72 gm/sec^2 and $g\rho/2\gamma$ is about 6.8 cm^{-2}. Thus, for example, for $\theta = 150°$ as in Fig. 20, that is for $1 - \sin \theta = 0.50$, the depth $h = 0.271$ cm. If the tangent is observed 0.02 cm above the true three-phase line (see Fig. 20), then $h = 0.251$ cm, $h^2 = 0.0630$ cm^2, $1 - \sin \theta = 0.428$, and $\theta = 145°$. It is usually believed that the angle θ measured by this method is correct within $\pm 1°$ or $\pm 2°$.

2. The method of level surface is a little less simple and has a

higher precision; it requires a large volume of liquid and thus is more suitable for water than for less common substances. Its principle is shown in Fig. 21. Plate 1 is partly immersed in the liquid (2). It is rotated about the horizontal axis 3 until the liquid surface is flat all the way to the solid plate. Angle θ is then read on the protractor scale 4. As a rule, visual inspection is sufficient to determine whether the liquid is or is not flat at the three-phase line; if necessary, a narrow beam of light is directed on this line and the presence of any curved meniscus is detected from the shape of the reflected beam.

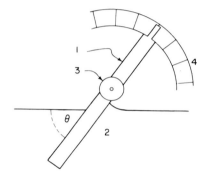

FIG. 21. The level-surface method of measuring contact angle.

A horizontal cylinder can be used instead of a tilted plate, especially when the contact angle is less or not much greater than 90°. Figure 22 represents a vertical view of the setup. The cylinder (1) can be raised or lowered with a screw (2), and its height is adjusted so that the liquid (3) is flat right to the solid surface. The angle can be calculated, for instance, from the displacement of the screw. If the area of the liquid surface is much greater than πr^2, r being the radius of the cylinder, then the distance l, by which the screw is moved from the point at which the cylinder just touches the liquid to the position in which the surface is level, is $l = r(1 + \cos \theta)$.

§25   3. Contact angle θ can be calculated from the dimensions of a sessile drop. The computation would be quite simple if the drops were parts of a sphere. For part-spherical drops, the height would be equal to $r(1 - \cos \theta)$, the volume equal to $(\pi/3)r^3(1 - \cos \theta)^2 (2 + \cos \theta)$, and the diameter of the base $2r \sin \theta$. Thus, any two of these quantities would be sufficient to calculate both angle θ and r, i.e., the radius of the sphere whose segment the droplet is. As determination of the height is not easy because the bottom of the drop may be obscured by the waviness of the solid surface (see §24), it is easier to use volume v and base diameter Δ. The ratio used is

$$\frac{\Delta^3}{v} = \frac{24 \sin^3 \theta}{\pi(2 - 3 \cos \theta + \cos^3 \theta)} \tag{2}$$

and a table for computing θ from the experimental values of Δ^3/v is available.[24]

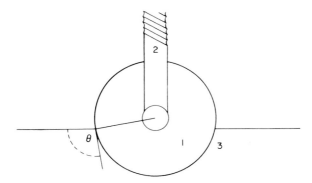

FIG. 22. The lying-cylinder method of measuring contact angle.

The drops, however, are not segments of a sphere as they are distorted by gravitation. Tables accounting for this distortion exist (see, for instance, reference 25) but sometimes it is easier to measure Δ^3/v for several drops of different volumes and to extrapolate the ratio to $v = 0$. The extrapolated ratio satisfies Eq. (2).

The main source of error in this determination is revealing. It is generally found that diameter Δ is not constant along the circumference of the drop, however carefully the drop has been deposited;

different diameters of the base may easily differ from each other by
several percent. The mean value of all measured diameters is set in
Eq. (2) to calculate θ but the calculated angle obviously also is an
average; as solid surfaces are not uniform, the real contact angle
along, say, 1 μ of the three-phase boundary is a little different from
that along the next micron.

4. The method of capillary pull often is convenient. A thin solid
plate is vertically suspended at one end of a balance beam or a
calibrated spring. Let the weight of the plate in air be W_0. When a
dish containing liquid is placed under the plate so that the lower
edge of the latter is immersed, a weight W_1 will be found necessary
to counterbalance the downward force on the plate. This force is
a sum of three components:

$$W_1 = W_0 - B + L\gamma \cos \theta.$$

The bouyancy B decreases the apparent weight of the plate and the
capillary force (equal to the weight of the liquid meniscus lifted or
depressed at the solid) $L\gamma \cos \theta$ augments it when θ is $< 90°$ and
diminishes it when θ is $> 90°$. L is the perimeter of the horizontal
cross section of the plate.

The bouyancy term B is not easy to determine with precision. It is
$B = abh\rho g$, if a is the width, b the thickness of the plate, h the
depth of its immersion in the liquid, g acceleration due to gravity,
and ρ the density of the liquid minus density of air. The value of h is
the quantity which eludes a simple measurement. To make the
error in W_1, caused by the inexact knowledge of B, as small as
possible, the plate immersion h is made small and the plate is selected as thin as feasible. It is clear that the ratio of B to $L\gamma \cos \theta$
is proportional to ab/L, that is to $ab/2(a + b)$, and thus tends to zero
when b tends to zero. When a foil 0.0025 cm ($=0.001$ in.) thick is
used in a 10-cm width, γ is 72 gm/sec² (as for water), $\cos \theta = 0.5$
and $h = 0.05$ cm, then $B = 1.25$ gm cm/sec² and $\gamma L \cos \theta = 720$
gm cm/sec². Thus, even a considerable error in B will not markedly
affect the calculated value of $\cos \theta$ in this instance.

§26   The great sensitivity of contact angles to the cleanness of the
solid has already been referred to (§23). To emphasize the warning,

it may be mentioned that deposition of 5×10^{-8} gm of a triphenyl-methane dye ("Night Blue") on 1 cm² of glass raised θ at the air–water–glass boundary[26] from 0° to 35° and deposition of 0.00015 mg of octylamine on 1 cm² of platinum made the platinum surface identical with octylamine surface as far as wetting was concerned.[27]

As stated in §23, the contact angle on a given solid often is smaller the smaller the surface tension γ of the liquid. But γ is very easily lowered (not raised) by impurities. Hence, if liquid in a particular test contains traces of surface-active materials, it may wet the solid adherend while, in a duplicate test, only imperfect wetting may be realized because the liquid was more thoroughly purified.

If the chemical compositions of solid and liquid are identical in the two tests, the duplicate experiment still may give a different result as long as surface roughness of the adherend is not kept constant. The effect of rugosity on contact angle is easily understood when it is realized that each groove on the surface acts similarly to a capillary tube in which liquid rises above or descends below the main level of the liquid outside. If the real equilibrium angle is > 90°, the liquid in the groove will contract, and at θ_e < 90° it will spread, compared to a drop on an absolutely smooth solid. The effect of this unequal spreading is particularly transparent in the methods of §25. When θ is < 90°, the measured Δ is greater, and at θ > 90°, Δ is smaller than on a smooth surface. Consequently, θ calculated from Eq. (2) would be too small in the first and too great in the second instance. Thus, even if rugosity has no effect on the real θ (that is θ on submicroscopical scale), it renders the calculated angles smaller when they are small and greater when they are great. The effect of roughness on the weight of meniscus, in method No. 4, is of the same kind. The amount of liquid hanging on a rough vertical slide is greater or smaller than on a smooth slide according to whether θ_e is smaller or greater than 90°; thus rugosity again exaggerates the difference between acute and obtuse contact angles.

Hysteresis of Wetting

§**27**   Some difficulties encountered when measuring contact angles were outlined in the preceding sections but hysteresis of wetting is probably an even greater obstacle to obtaining reliable values for θ. This hysteresis is observed in all four procedures described in §§24 and 25. If a drop is placed on a horizontal plate, the contact angle is determined either directly or from the drop dimensions, and then a small droplet is added to the initial drop, it is found that the three-phase line does not shift, that is the drop becomes taller and the contact angle greater; see a and b in Fig. 23. When more liquid is added, the drop continues to increase in volume but not in the area of the base until the contact angle reaches a more or less definite value called "the maximum advancing contact angle"; then the drop spreads with a jerk and the new contact angle is similar to that of the initial drop. If, instead of adding liquid to the drop, liquid is gradually removed from it, drop a gets flatter (see drop c) until "the minimum receding contact angle" is reached, when the drop suddenly contracts.

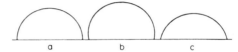

FIG. 23. Hysteresis of wetting. The base of the drop does not change when volume increases from a to b or decreases from a to c. From reference 28.

In the level-surface method, the contact angle is smaller when the slide, in rotating, emerges from the liquid, and greater when the liquid invades the slide surface.

In the fourth method, capillary pull initially is greater the further the vertical foil is lifted; see Fig. 24, in which the continuous line represents the meniscus before, and the dotted line the meniscus after, the foil was lifted by distance h. When the foil is further raised, the pull eventually reaches its highest value corresponding to the minimum receding angle, and remains constant on further withdrawal. If the foil is gradually immersed in the liquid, the pull decreases until the maximum advancing angle is reached. If the initial θ is obtuse, it may become acute during withdrawal, that is, capillary pull may change its direction from out of to into the liquid; and if the initial θ is acute, it may turn obtuse when the foil is pushed into the liquid.

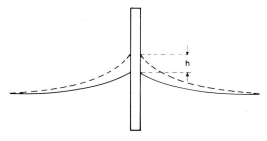

FIG. 24. The capillary-pull method of measuring hysteresis of wetting.

§**28**   The difference between the maximum advancing and the minimum receding contact angle (θ_A and θ_R, respectively) is either zero or positive. It is equal to zero when $\theta_A = 0$, that is when the liquid spontaneously spreads over the solid in a thin film; in this instance also $\theta_R = 0$ and there is no hysteresis. The difference $\theta_A - \theta_R$ may be small (say, 3°) when the solid is particularly smooth and does not swell in the liquid. When the solid is not very smooth, or imbibes some liquid, or both, $\theta_A - \theta_R$ is likely to be great; a hysteresis of wetting amounting to 90° is not at all rare.

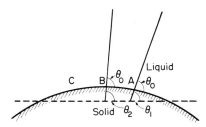

FIG. 25. Hysteresis of wetting caused by surface roughness.

The dependence of hysteresis on surface roughness and swelling is readily understood if the probable mechanisms of the effect are considered. Four such mechanisms are recognized.

1. The first is believed to be operative when there is no intermixing between the solid and the liquid and no macroscopic shift of the three-phase boundary; it is caused by rugosity alone. Figure 25 represents a point of the three-phase boundary and its immediate surroundings. The shaded part is a hill on the solid surface. The true

contact angle, i.e., the angle θ_e between air, liquid, and the true solid surface at a given point, is set equal to 80° in the sketch. The apparent angle, i.e., that between the tangent to the drop and the main plane (discontinuous line) of the solid, is θ_1. When a small volume of the liquid is added to the drop (which is situated to the right of A), the liquid surface moves from A to B, the true contact angle is believed to remain constant, and consequently the apparent angle increases from θ_1 to θ_2. The shift of the three-phase line from A to B is too small to be noticed without special instruments. When the three-phase line, on a further addition of liquid to the drop, moves to the left of the summit (to C), its position can be shown to become unstable and the drop expands until the three-phase boundary reaches or overshoots the bottom of the groove.

2. There is still no intermixing but the drop slides along an inclined plane or a plate is pulled out of a liquid. The liquid present in the grooves of the solid behind the receding three-phase line cannot keep pace with its main volume (see §5). Thus a liquid ribbon remains in the wake of the drop. The rear of the drop acquires a shape illustrated in Fig. 26 and the apparent contact angle may be immeasurably small. When the motion of the drop continues, the ribbon must be extended or ruptured, and the resistance of the ribbon seems to be the main component of the friction observed at every sliding of the three-phase boundary.

FIG. 26. Hysteresis of wetting caused by liquid remaining behind a sliding drop.

3. When the solid swells in, or is in any other manner modified by, the liquid, the front of a moving drop (or a moving meniscus) is in contact with the unaltered solid, while its rear is in contact with the swollen (generally modified) material. Obviously, the advancing and the receding contact angles must in general be different and θ_R be smaller than θ_A (see §23).

4. When the solid is soft, a ridge is raised along the three-phase line (§22). When this line moves over the solid, a ridge must be raised in a new position. The work needed for this deformation is analogous to the work of solid (sliding) friction and may be a cause of the hysteresis of wetting.

Rate of Wetting. Removal of Air

§29   Liquid adhesive usually is spread during application over the whole surface to be joined. This operation, however, does not secure displacement of air from the depressions, crevices, etc., present on the surface (§3). This displacement is achieved by capillary forces and retarded by the viscosity (or more generally, consistency) of the liquid.

The magnitude and direction of capillary forces are given by Laplace's equation of capillary pressure P_c

$$P_c = \gamma \left(\frac{1}{R_1} + \frac{1}{R_2} \right) ; \tag{3}$$

γ is surface tension and R_1 and R_2 are the two principal radii of curvature. The pressure rises by P_c every time the liquid surface is crossed from the convex to the concave side.

This law is sometimes misunderstood. As the pressure under a meniscus such as shown in Fig. 17 is greater than above it, some scientists are tempted to expect that the pressure difference will push the meniscus, that is also the whole liquid mass, up. In reality, no tendency for the meniscus to move is present and Fig. 17 may, and is supposed to, represent an equilibrium state. The apparent contradiction can be resolved in two ways or, more exactly, by resorting to two analogies. The core of the planet Earth is under a very high pressure caused, in common with the capillary pressure, by the mutual attraction of matter; nevertheless, this core exerts no outward force on the exterior stratum of the globe. The pressure in the hollow of a blown-up rubber balloon is greater than that outside, but the balloon wall retains its shape for an indefinite time, because the tension – analogous to surface tension γ – in the rubber exactly compensates the pressure difference.

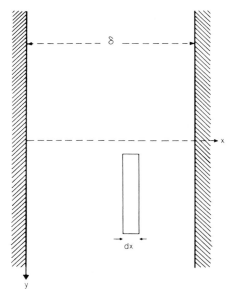

FIG. 27. Laminar flow in a narrow slit.

For viscous forces, in the simplest group of substances, Newton's formula

$$\tau = \eta(du/dx) \tag{4}$$

is valid; τ is shearing stress acting in every plane parallel to the liquid motion and directed opposite to this movement; η is viscosity; u is linear velocity in direction z (normal to the plane of the paper; see Fig. 27), and x is distance in a direction perpendicular to z. In a narrow slit, schematically represented in Fig. 27, every volume of liquid 1 cm long (in the y direction), 1 cm deep (in the z direction), and dx cm wide is subjected to a viscous force $\eta(du/dx)$ at its left and $\eta[(du/dx) + (d^2u/dx^2)\,dx]$ at its right boundary, the resultant force being $\eta(d^2u/dx^2)\,dx$. When liquid moves *without accelera-*

tion, this viscous force is counterbalanced by a force originating from the pressure gradient along the z axis; if this gradient is $\Delta P/\Delta z$, the force on the above described liquid volume is $(\Delta P/\Delta z)$ dx. From the equation

$$\eta \frac{d^2u}{dx^2} = \frac{\Delta P}{\Delta z} \tag{5}$$

it is clear that, as long as $\Delta P/\Delta z$ is constant, d^2u/dx^2 also is constant in the liquid vein under consideration and, consequently, $u = f(x)$ is a parabola. Thus,

$$u = a + bx + cx^2 ,$$

a, b, and c being constants. Obviously, $c = (1/2\eta)(\Delta P/\Delta z)$. At $x = 0$ (see Fig. 27), $u = 0$ because there is no slippage between solid and liquid (§5); hence, $a = 0$. At $x = \delta/2$, i.e., in the plane of symmetry, from symmetry reasons $du/dx = 0$; hence $b = -c\delta$ $= -(\delta/2\eta)(\Delta P/\Delta z)$. Thus,

$$u = -\frac{1}{2\eta}\frac{\Delta P}{\Delta z}(\delta x - x^2) . \tag{6}$$

The volume of liquid moving through the cross section of the slit along 1 cm of its length per second is

$$-\int_0^\delta u \, dx = \frac{\delta^3}{12\eta}\frac{\Delta P}{\Delta z} \tag{7}$$

and the mean linear velocity is

$$u_m = -\frac{\delta^2}{12\eta}\frac{\Delta P}{\Delta z} . \tag{8}$$

The dimensions of the quantities in (8) are: u_m, cm sec^{-1}, δ, cm, η, gm cm^{-1}sec^{-1}, P, g cm^{-1}sec^{-2}, and z, cm.

When pressure difference causing liquid flow in the crack is due

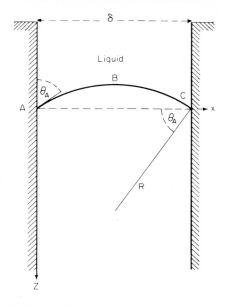

FIG. 28. Flow of liquid into a narrow plane-parallel slit.

to capillarity, $2\gamma \cos \theta_A / \delta$ must be substituted for ΔP. This is made clear by Fig. 28, in which the slit of Fig. 27 is shown in a section perpendicular to the axis of y. The liquid is shown in the upper part of the slit, and its curved meniscus is supposed to advance toward increasing z values. For narrow clearances, gravitation may be neglected in comparison with capillarity; thus the meniscus may be approximated as a part of a cylindrical surface, the axis of the cylinder being normal to the paper and line ABC being an arc of a circle. One of the radii of curvature [see Eq. (3)], namely that swinging in the plane parallel to y and z, is infinitely great. The other radius is in the plane including x and z axes; it is indicated by letter R in the sketch. It is seen that $\delta = 2R \cos \theta_A$, if θ_A is the maximum advancing angle (as the meniscus is supposed to advance). Hence, $1/R = 2 \cos \theta_A / \delta$; Eq. (3) then affords

$$P_c = 2\gamma \cos \theta_A / \delta .$$

This pressure difference exists wholly in the liquid, between the meniscus and the crack orifice at the top of the figure; if the momentary distance between the two levels is z, then z has to be substituted for Δz in Eq. (8). Writing also dz/dt for u_m (t is time), we obtain

$$z \frac{dz}{dt} = \frac{\delta}{6\eta} \gamma \cos \theta_A \qquad (9)$$

and, after integration,

$$z_0{}^2 = \frac{\delta \gamma \cos \theta_A}{3\eta} t , \qquad (10)$$

z_0 being z at the bottom of the crack.

Equation (10) can be written in dimensionless form. Let u be the average velocity of the advance of the meniscus, that is $u = z_0/t$. Then

$$\frac{z_0}{\delta} = \frac{\gamma \cos \theta_A}{3\eta u} . \qquad (11)$$

The ratio of $\gamma \cos \theta$ to ηu is a pure number because γ is measured in gm sec^{-2}, η in gm cm^{-1}sec^{-1}, and u in cm sec^{-1}. This ratio is important in all phenomena determined by an interplay of surface tension and viscosity (see §36). To emphasize the importance of time, the ratio can also be written

$$\frac{\gamma \cos \theta_A t}{\eta l} , \qquad (12)$$

t being the time alloted to the experiment and l the length of the meniscus advance.

In this paragraph, an estimate is made of the time needed to fill a long crevice δ cm wide and z_0 cm deep. An aqueous liquid adhesive usually will have surface tension of about 70 gm/sec^2 while the γ of an organic adhesive will be nearer to 30 gm/sec². The viscosity in the moment of application is likely to be somewhere between 0.01 and 100 gm/cm, sec; thus the range of viscosities is much wider than that of surface tensions. Consider a crevice whose depth is $\sqrt{16.7}$ times its width (i.e., $z_0{}^2 = 16.7\,\delta^2$) and assume $\gamma \cos \theta_A = 50$ gm/sec². Some values are calculated on this basis in Table V.

TABLE V
TIME TO FILL A CREVICE (IN SEC)

δ (cm)	$\eta = 0.01$	$= 1$	$= 100$ gm/cm sec
10^{-5}	10^{-7}	10^{-5}	10^{-3}
10^{-3}	10^{-5}	10^{-3}	10^{-1}
10^{-1}	10^{-3}	10^{-1}	10

If the crack has a V shape (see Fig. 29) the time t needed for filling is, approximately, given by equation

$$z_0 \ln \frac{z_0}{z_0 - z} - z = \frac{\delta_0 \gamma \cos \theta_A}{6 \eta z_0} t. \tag{13}$$

In theory, the crack will never be completely filled but as, in reality, the wedge will be blunt near the apex, the delay will not be dangerous; if, for instance, the bottom is reached at $z = 0.9 z_0$, Eq. (13) is transformed into

$$1.40 z_0{}^2 = \frac{\delta_0 \gamma \cos \theta_A}{6 \eta} t ,$$

which is sufficiently similar to Eq. (10).

§30   The treatment of §29 was based, among others, on three premises.
    (a) The advance of the liquid into the grooves and pores was attributed to P_c only. If also an additional hydrostatic pressure f acts on the adhesive, the relation

$$\frac{dz}{dt} = \frac{\delta^2}{12\eta z}\left(f + \frac{2\gamma \cos \theta_A}{\delta}\right) \tag{14}$$

must be used instead of (9). Its integration affords

$$z_0^2 = \frac{\delta^2}{6\eta}\left(f + \frac{2\gamma \cos \theta_A}{\delta}\right) t \tag{15}$$

or

$$t = \frac{6\eta z_0^2}{f\delta^2 + 2\gamma \cos \theta_A \delta} \cdot \tag{16}$$

A similar equation was published earlier.[29] It is seen that the external pressure is more important than P_c if $f > 2\gamma \cos \theta_A/\delta$. Taking again $\gamma \cos \theta_A = 50$ gm/sec^2 and $\delta = 10^{-5}$ cm, it is found that f has to exceed 10^7 gm/cm sec^2 (or 145 psi) to achieve this condition.

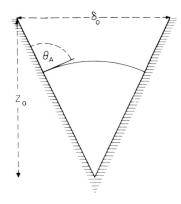

FIG. 29. Flow of liquid into a V-shaped groove.

(b) The adhesive was supposed to be a Newtonian liquid, i.e., a liquid for which Eq. (4) is valid. Very few industrial adhesives belong to this class. Unfortunately, the mathematics involved in calculating the flow of non-Newtonian materials is difficult, and no exact relation between z_0 and t [see Eq. (11)] derived for these

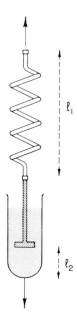

FIG. 30. The Maxwell body.

materials is known to the author. However, it was suggested[29] to write $A + (t/\eta)$ for the ratio t/η appearing in Eq. (10) and expression (12) and to calculate A from a mechanical model suitable for the given adhesive. To understand the method, let us consider the simplest model (a Maxwell body) of a viscoelastic liquid. It consists (Fig. 30) of a spring and a "dashpot" in series. When stress τ extends the spring and gradually lifts the plunger in the viscous liquid, the total length of the system increases by Δl. This quantity is the sum of two length increases. The spring is longer by $\Delta l_1 = \tau l_1/G$, l_1 being its initial length and G the spring constant representing the shear modulus of the adhesive. The rise of the plunger is $\Delta l_2 = (c\tau/\eta)dt$; c is a constant (having the dimension of length) which depends on the design of the "dashpot"; l_2 is the distance between the plunger and the bottom of the vessel. If τ does not vary with time, integration between $t = 0$ and $t = t$ gives $\Delta l_2 = c\tau t/\eta$. The sum of Δl_1 and Δl_2 is equal to Δl. Hence,

$$\Delta l = \frac{\tau l_1}{G} + \frac{c\tau t}{\eta} \, . \tag{17}$$

If the spring did not exist, Δl would be equal to $c\tau t/\eta$, i.e., the viscosity would be equal to $c\tau t/\Delta l$. It is possible to calculate, in the presence of the spring, an analog (η^*) of viscosity (of the same dimension as η) by dividing $c\tau t$ by the above Δl. Thus

$$\eta^* = \frac{cG\eta t}{l_1\eta + cGt} \, . \tag{18}$$

When $l_1 = 0$, i.e., the spring is absent, $\eta^* = \eta$, as it should be. The ratio η/G is the relaxation time t_r of the model; hence,

$$\eta^* = \frac{c\eta t}{l_1 t_r + ct} \, . \tag{19}$$

If η^* is substituted for η in, e.g., Eq. (10), some idea of the flow in viscoelastic liquids may be obtained.

Another approach was advocated in reference 30. Equation (17) is derived for a Maxwell body in which the stress does not vary in time. If τ is a function of t, then

$$\frac{dl}{dt} = \frac{l_1}{G}\frac{d\tau}{dt} + \frac{c}{\eta}\,\tau \, . \tag{20}$$

In a slight simplification of the hypothesis of reference 30, let us assume that

$$\tau = \tau_0 l^{-n} \, ; \tag{21}$$

τ_0 and n are two constants. Equation (20) can be made to agree with (9) by putting $n = 1$, but in non-Newtonian liquids the value of n will be different. Introduction of (21) into (20) results in

$$\frac{dl}{dt} = -\frac{l_1}{G}\,n\tau_0 l^{-n-1}\frac{dl}{dt} + \frac{c}{\eta}\,\tau_0 l^{-n} \tag{22}$$

and integration affords

$$t = \frac{\eta}{c \tau_0 (n+1)} (l^{n+1} - l_0^{n+1}) + \frac{l_1 n \eta}{G c} \ln \frac{l}{l_0}, \tag{23}$$

if l_0 is the value of l at $t = 0$. In Eq. (10), t is proportional to the square of the distance to be covered (z_0 there, l here) but the relation is more complicated if the adhesive is a Maxwell body.

(c) The viscosity of the adhesive was supposed to be constant in time. In reality, it almost always increases because, during the displacement of air, the adhesive cools or loses solvent or is a site of a chemical reaction (see §48). In an example selected in reference 31, viscosity η increased exponentially with time t, i.e., $\eta = \eta_0 e^{bt}$, η_0 and b being constants. If P is the constant pressure difference between the ends of the capillary, then Eq. (9) or Eq. (8) becomes

$$2 \frac{dz}{dt} = \frac{P}{z} \frac{\delta^2}{6 \eta_0} e^{-bt}. \tag{24}$$

If z is the variable length of the adhesive column and z_1 is this length at $t = 0$, integration of (24) results in

$$z^2 - z_1^2 = \frac{P \delta^2}{6 \eta_0 b} (1 - e^{-bt}). \tag{25}$$

When t increases to infinity, the difference $z^2 - z_1^2$ reaches, but never exceeds, the value $P \delta^2 / 6 \eta_0 b$. Thus, if the depth of the groove is greater than $(P \delta^2 / 6 \eta_0 b)^{0.5}$ (the value of z_1 generally may be neglected in comparison with z), the groove is never filled by the adhesive whatever the duration of the contact. In an experimental system, η_0 was 4×10^5 gm/cm sec and b was 0.01 sec^{-1}. Thus, the depth of the valleys must be below $0.006 \delta P^{0.5}$ to achieve a complete displacement of air.

(d) The adhesive was supposed to have a viscosity independent of the pressure f. A process in which this supposition is not valid is outlined in §34.

When it is attempted to apply any of the equations of §§29 and 30 to the flow of real adhesives into the valleys on the adherend surface, at least one additional complication should be remembered (see also §36). The geometry of the valleys, such as z_0 and δ of Eq. (10) may change as a result of swelling or of a release of superficial stresses (see §1).

§31 In the examples of §§29 and 30, $\gamma \cos \theta_A$ was assumed to be 50 gm/sec². When θ_A changes, the time needed to fill the valleys also radically changes. It is very long when $\cos \theta_A$ is very small, i.e., θ_A is almost 90°.

As the maximum advancing contact angle is larger, and can be much larger, than the equilibrium contact angle θ_e (see §28), θ_e should not be permitted to exceed, say, 10° and $\theta_e = 0$ should always be aspired to. When θ_A is greater than 90°, $\cos \theta_A$ is negative and the meniscus tends to get out of any depression. In these instances, air can be removed by applying a vacuum, but this artifice apparently has not been well tested and cannot be relied upon (see §68).

As far as the intended removal of air from the surface of an adherend by the liquid adhesive is concerned, the above review of wetting phenomena leads to the following main conclusions:

1. The viscosity of the adhesive in the first moment of application should be so low that the time of filling is sufficiently short even with due regard to the changes of the adhesive in time.

2. Good wetting, i.e., an equilibrium contact angle of zero or near zero, is essential

3. Because of the sensitivity of contact angles to impurities, the experimenter should not rely on general statements such as "solid A is perfectly wetted by liquid B." This may be true as a rule, but accidental contamination of A in a particular instance may be sufficient to prevent its perfect wetting.

4. Usually, air can be displaced by a liquid adhesive if this contains a solvent of a low surface tension (see §23). However, there is no guarantee that, when the solvent evaporates, the solid ingredients of the adhesive rather than air will take its place (see §53).

5. Surface roughness, generally speaking, does not markedly retard the displacement of air.

§32 The qualitative conclusions of §31 are in agreement with the general experience of the makers of adhesive joints but no quantitative confirmation of the equations of §29 and §30 could be found in the literature. The rate of establishment of a good contact between a liquid or semiliquid adhesive and a solid or semisolid adherend has been estimated many times but a scientific utilization of the results is almost impossible because the geometrical parameters (z_0, δ, and so on) and the rheological properties (such as η and G) were almost never determined.

A modest attempt in the right direction was made[32] with asphalt–granite adhints. A plate of granite was heated to a temperature T_0, taken out of the oven, and asphalt was spread on it. After cooling, as much of the asphalt as possible was scraped off with a razor blade (see §5), and the amount remaining on the stone was determined. When T_0 was above 110°, this amount was independent of T_0. When T_0 was lower, also this amount was smaller. Evidently, the viscosity of the asphalt above 110° or 120° was sufficiently low to achieve complete displacement of air before cooling proceeded so far that the flow almost stopped.

Unfortunately, this displacement has not been determined in many other investigations, and the goodness of contact was estimated from the breaking stress of the adhints produced. The strength of an adhint is related to the area of contact in a qualitative manner only; if there is no contact, the strength will be small (but see §37), and when the contact is perfect, the strength is likely to be higher (but see §69). There is no reason to expect the strength to be proportional to the degree of contact but there are several weighty reasons to believe the relation between the two magnitudes to be far from linear (see Chapter VIII).

In the absence of any better data, the relation between breaking stress f_m on one hand and the time t of contact between the adhesive and adherend and the pressure f assuring the contact on the other hand is illustrated here by several examples. Figure 31 shows[30] the gradual rise of f_m with t for butt joints "metal–rubber vulcanizate–unvulcanized mix–rubber vulcanizate–metal"; the constant pressure f during the establishment of the contact was about 12 bars. In Fig. 32, the increase[30] of f_m with f (at a constant t equal to 3 min) is presented. Data analogous to those of these two graphs are found also in other publications, e.g., references 33 and 34.

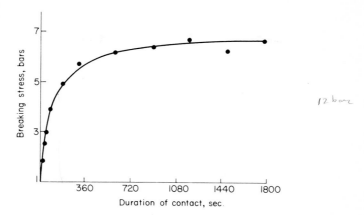

FIG. 31. Effect of duration of contact on breaking stress. Abscissa: duration of contact, in seconds. Ordinate: breaking stress, in bars. Data of reference 30.

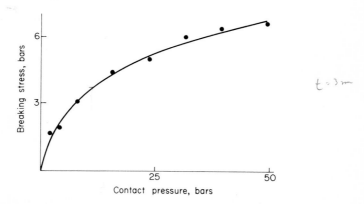

FIG. 32. Effect of contact pressure on breaking stress. Abscissa: contact pressure (bars). Ordinate: breaking stress (bars). Data of reference 30.

A few additional examples may be given here. The stress f_m at an arbitrary but constant rate of separation was[35] for a Hevea rubber pressed against an identical piece of rubber 3.5×10^4 dynes/cm^2 after $t = 1$ sec and 15×10^4 after $t = 25$ sec. As the two pieces were identical, an instance of *autohesion* (so christened in reference 36) was present. In two separate experiments,[37] two polyisobutylene strips were pressed together (by a constant load) for 15 min and for 15 hr; the subsequent peeling required a tension (§92) of 100 kilodynes/cm in the first, and of 220 kilodynes/cm in the second test. When similar strips were pressed for 5 min, once at $f = 5 \times 10^3$ and the other time at $f = 5 \times 10^4$ dynes/cm^2, the peeling tension Γ was 50 and 180 kilodynes/cm, respectively.

When two blocks of rubber were kept together by a force F for time t and then pulled apart by a tensile force F_m such that the time of separation was t_m, then the ratio of $Ft^{0.3}$ to $F_m t_m^{0.3}$ was a nearly linear function of $Ft^{0.3}$; and it was suggested[38] to denote the ratio $F_m t_m^{0.3}/Ft^{0.3}$ extrapolated to $F = 0$ as the "tack index," which was supposed to be characteristic for the rubber used.

The effect of viscosity (or consistency) was determined[39] for several rubbers. A pellet of each elastomer was slowly compressed between two rigid discs, and η (assumed to be constant in each test) was calculated as in §42, for three rates of compression. The tensile strength σ_m of similar pellets, and f_m of pellet pairs pressed together for 30 sec at $f = 0.7$ bar were measured, and the ratio $f_m : \sigma_m$ was computed. In Table VI the values of this ratio are compared with those of η for several elastomers; the experimental range of the η values is indicated.

TABLE VI

VISCOSITY η AND THE RATIO f_m/σ_m OF ADHINT STRENGTH TO
TENSILE STRENGTH

Rubber	η (gm/cm sec)	f_m/σ_m
Plasticized butadiene–styrene	2.6–3.7×10^9	0.98
Butadiene–styrene	4.2–5.5×10^9	0.86
Milled pale crèpe	29–34×10^9	0.53
"Alfin" butadiene–styrene	260–489×10^9	0.42

It is clear that, with the higher consistency of the material, the smaller fraction of the highest possible strength is attained after a compression for 30 sec. After a long contact under pressure, f_m

reached the value of σ_m for all rubbers tested, but the time of contact necessary for this to happen was 3 min for the least, and 17 hr for the most "viscous" rubber.

As the viscosity of Newtonian liquids and the consistency of non-Newtonian solutions decrease when temperature increases, it would be expected that a shorter contact time t will be necessary at a higher temperature to attain a definite value of f_m/σ_m. This expectation was confirmed,[29] for instance, for butt joints "steel–a copolymer of vinyl chloride and vinyl acetate–a poly(vinyl chloride) sheet–the above copolymer–steel." The system was kept for t minutes at a temperature T, cooled, and its f_m determined. The amount of the copolymer was adjusted so that the final thickness of each copolymer layer was about 0.015 cm, independently of t and T; unfortunately, this precaution was disregarded in many other investigations; see §§38 and 104 for the effect of the adhesive layer thickness on f_m. The limiting value of f_m (probably equal to the σ_m of the copolymer) was reached in about 180 min when T was 110°, in about 80 min when T was 130°, 55 min when T was 150°, and 30 min when T was 170°.

Peeling rather than butt joints were used[40] in a similar study on polyethylenes. Two polyethylene films were backed with cloth, pressed together for 15 min at temperature T, cooled to the room temperature, and peeled apart. The work $\mathfrak{W}$ of peeling, equal to peeling tension multiplied with the area delaminated, increased, for instance, in the ratio 1:160:280 when T increased from 110° to 130° and 160°. The gradient $d\mathfrak{W}/dT$ was, as these data show, much greater below than above 132°, and the temperature of this kink was almost identical with the crystalline melting point (136°) of the sample used. For another sample, both the kink temperature and the melting point were found to be 105°. The limiting value of f_m (presumably nearly equal to σ_m) was attained after 5 min pressing when T was 110°–130° and after about 40 min when T was 95°. Description of several analogous experiments can be found in reference 33.

The effects of temperature and viscosity have been made clear also in very different systems, namely those of glass and metals.[41] A glass plate was pressed (with a pressure of about 1 bar) against a metal plate in an oven kept at a temperature T. When the glass temperature also became equal to T (this means that the contact time t was variable), a tensile stress of 0.15 bar was applied. If this stress was sufficient to cause rupture, the oven temperature was raised by 10°, and the test repeated. The lowest temperature T' at which the adhint strength was greater than 0.15 bar depended on both the glass and the metal. If the metal was cast iron, T' was 570°–600° for a glass whose transformation temperature was 515° and the softening point (determined by the dilatometric method) was 563°. For another glass, the three temperatures were 600°, 530°, and 570°; and for a third, 645°, 560°, and 794°. It is seen that they vary in a similar manner, i.e., that the lowest temperature of sticking is higher the greater the viscosity of glass. For a given glass, T' was 660°, 640°, and 620° when the metal (an alloy of platinum) was coarsely abraded, or finely ground, or polished. This observation qualitatively agrees with Eq. (10) or (16); the greater the roughness (i.e., z_0), the smaller must be the viscosity to fill the depressions during a (more or less constant) time.

An effect of roughness could be seen also when a smooth surface of a rubber vulcanizate was compared[42] with one covered with a net of grooves. When a disk of unvulcanized rubber was pressed against these surfaces by a load of 12 bars, the final value of f_m was achieved for the smooth vulcanizate in about 5 min, and for the grooved, in about 20 min.

§**33**   It is implied in the above treatment, §§29 and 30, that, when liquid advances into a valley, air initially present there can escape without experiencing any serious resistance. This assumption presumably is correct as long as the actual displacement of air from the solid surface is considered. However, as soon as this displaced air has formed a bubble fully surrounded by the liquid, surface forces cease to affect its position or its motion, and the bubble can be eliminated from the system only by gravitation or by the moving liquid itself.

The motion of bubbles caused by gravitation may be too slow and often is in a wrong direction. The rate u of ascent of bubbles can crudely be calculated from Stokes' equation

$$u = \frac{2}{9\eta} g \, \rho \, r^2 \; ; \tag{26}$$

g is acceleration due to gravity, ρ is density of liquid minus density of air, and r is the radius of the rising sphere. The equation is not exactly applicable to bubbles because they are not spherical and because the motion considered in Eq. (26) is not the only one taking place during the ascent. If $\rho = 1$ gm/cm³, $r = 0.01$ cm, and $\eta = 1$ gm/cm sec, Eq. (26) affords u of approximately 0.02 cm/sec, and if $\rho = 1$, $r = 0.001$ cm and $\eta = 10$, then $u = 0.00002$ cm/sec. Thus, small bubbles will not travel far in many commercial adhesives during the short time when these are still liquid.

Depending on the kind and the position of an adhint, movement in the gravitational field may be beneficial or detrimental. Thus, if the adherend surfaces are vertical, bubbles will tend to rise between them and to escape; but if these surfaces are horizontal and nonporous, bubbles adjacent to the upper surface will not move and those originating from the lower surface will join them, thus creating an agglomeration of bubbles and, consequently, a weak layer at the boundary of the adhesive film. Observations confirming this description probably have been made by many people experienced in adhints but quantitative studies of the effect seem to be lacking. If at least the upper adherend is porous, bubbles may escape through it.

Bubbles in a rubber lowered[39] its tensile strength, as would be expected from §53, but had no effect on the breaking stress f_m after a contact for 30 sec (§32). Perhaps, the volume of air still remaining between the two mating surfaces after 30 sec was so considerable that a few preexisting bubbles were of little importance.

§**34**   Displacement of bubbles with the excess of the adhesive probably is the most common method of their removal. As long as the bubbles are small and not too numerous, they do not significantly upset the pattern of flow of the liquid adhesive when its excess is being squeezed out by the outside pressure. A calculation of this flow is given here in some detail because it is important not only for bubble elimination but also for (the simplest instance of) tackiness (§36).

Consider two parallel rectangular plates, as in Fig. 33; the lower plate is pressed upward with force F. The liquid adhesive between the plates will gradually be forced out. We assume that whatever happens to the adhesive outside the slit between the plates is of no importance; or, in other words, that only a negligible fraction of force F is used up on changing the shape and position of the excess adhesive A, A.

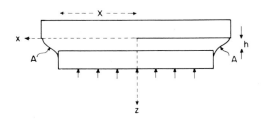

FIG. 33. Squeezing of liquid between two parallel plates.

Force F is needed to overcome the viscous forces in the adhesive during its flow. Assume the adhesive to have a viscosity η independent of the rate of flow as in §29. Let, for simplicity's sake, the plates be so long in the y direction (normal to x and z) that the flow along this direction may be disregarded in comparison with that along the x axis. Denote the pressure on the plate, that is F divided by the area of the plate, by letter f. As liquid flows between two parallel plates, Eq. (7) is valid here; to conform to Fig. 33 we write it as volume velocity $= (h^3/12\eta)(dP/dx)$. Another expression for this quantity is arrived at as follows. The volume of liquid between the median plane (in which $x = 0$) and the plane of any other x is xh per unit length of the plate (in the y direction); h is the variable distance between the plates. Thus, the volume of liquid flowing outward through any plane perpendicular to the x axis (per unit length of y and unit time) is $-x(dh/dt)$, t being time. Hence,

$$x \frac{dh}{dt} = \frac{h^3}{12\eta} \frac{dP}{dx}. \qquad (27)$$

Equation (27) is concerned only with the movement parallel to the x axis; obviously there must be some movement of the liquid upward from the vicinity of the rising plate, but we neglect it here. Abbreviate

$$\frac{12\eta}{h^3}\frac{dh}{dt} = -2K ; \tag{28}$$

this quantity is independent of x. Consequently,

$$-\frac{dP}{dx} = 2\,Kx$$

can be integrated to $P = -Kx^2 + K_1$. The integration constant K_1 is found from the condition that the pressure at the edge of the plates must be equal to the atmospheric pressure. If only the excess of the pressure in the liquid over that outside is counted, then $P = 0$ at $x = X$, if X is the half-width of the plates. Thus $K_1 = KX^2$ and

$$P = K(X^2 - x^2) . \tag{29}$$

As long as liquid flows with a negligible acceleration, the integral $\int_0^X P\,dx$ must be equal to $-Xf$; f must be considered a negative quantity as P is treated as a positive pressure. Thus,

$$-Xf = K \int_0^X (X^2 - x^2)\,dx = \frac{2}{3}\,KX^3 \tag{30}$$

or

$$-K = \frac{3}{2}\frac{f}{X^2} . \tag{31}$$

Substituting (31) into (28), we obtain

$$\frac{dh}{h^3} = \frac{f}{4\eta X^2}\,dt , \tag{32}$$

whence

$$\frac{1}{h_2^2} - \frac{1}{h_1^2} = -\frac{ft}{2\eta X^2} \quad \text{or} \quad -ft = 2\eta X^2 \left(\frac{1}{h_2^2} - \frac{1}{h_1^2} \right). \tag{33}$$

Equation (33) permits calculation of the time needed for pressure f to diminish the distance between the plates from h_1 to h_2. Three numerical examples will illustrate the meaning of Eq. (33).

1. $-f = 10^6$ baryes (i.e., approximately 14 psi), $\eta = 1$ gm/cm sec, $X = 1$ cm, $h_1 = 0.1$ cm, $h_2 = 0.01$ cm. Time $t = 0.02$ sec.

2. $-f = 10^5$ baryes (i.e., approximately 1.4 psi), $\eta = 10$ gm/cm sec, $X = 10$ cm, $h_1 = 0.1$ cm, $h_2 = 0.01$ cm. Time $t = 198$ sec.

3. $-f = 10^5$ baryes, $\eta = 10$ gm/cm sec, $X = 10$ cm, $h_1 = 0.1$ cm, $h_2 = 0.001$ cm. Time $t = 19,998$ sec.

If the plates are circular rather than rectangular and a is their radius, Eq. (34) results[43, 44]

$$-ft = \frac{3}{4} \eta a^2 \left(\frac{1}{h_2^2} - \frac{1}{h_1^2} \right) \tag{34}$$

or

$$-Ft = \frac{3}{4} \pi \eta a^4 \left(\frac{1}{h_2^2} - \frac{1}{h_1^2} \right), \tag{35}$$

as in this instance $F = \pi a^2 f$. When $h_2 \ll h_1$,

$$-ft = \frac{3}{4} \eta \frac{a^2}{h_2^2} \tag{36}$$

and

$$-Ft = \frac{3}{4} \pi \eta \frac{a^4}{h_2^2}. \tag{37}$$

Any of the relations (34) to (37) is referred to as Stefan's equation. A comparison of (33) and (34) demonstrates that the radius of a circular plate in this phenomenon is equivalent to $\sqrt{8/3} \, X$.

If the plates are elliptical, with the half-axes a and b, then

$$-Ft = \frac{3\pi\eta a^3 b^3}{2(a^2 + b^2)} \left(\frac{1}{h_2^2} - \frac{1}{h_1^2} \right); \tag{38}$$

the equation given by Reynolds[45] has another numerical factor and must be the result of an error in calculation.

If the viscosity is a function of pressure (see §30), so that

$$\eta = \eta_0 e^{mP},$$

η_0 and m being constant, then Eq. (27) is transformed into [46]

$$x \frac{dh}{dt} = \frac{h^3}{12 \eta_0} e^{-mP} \frac{dP}{dx}. \tag{39}$$

Integration of this equation between X where $P = 0$ and x, where the excess pressure is P, affords

$$X^2 - x^2 = -\frac{h^3}{6\eta_0} \frac{dt}{dh} \frac{(1 - e^{-mP})}{m},$$

i.e.,

$$e^{-mP} = 1 + \frac{6\eta_0}{h^3} \frac{dh}{dt} m(X^2 - x^2). \tag{40}$$

The pressure has the highest value at $x = 0$. There,

$$e^{-mP} = 1 + \frac{6\eta_0}{h^3} \frac{dh}{dt} mX^2.$$

If the rate dh/dt of the approach of the plates is so high that $(6\eta_0 mX^2/h^3)(dh/dt) = -1$, then $e^{-mP} = 0$, i.e., P is infinitely large. Thus, if the viscosity increases with pressure, the above rate cannot increase indefinitely.

For the limits of validity of the reasoning presented in this section see §§39 to 42. Here only the effect of surface roughness on the rate of descent of a horizontal plate is considered.

When such a plate slowly descends onto another in a viscous liquid, the distance h between them should be inversely proportional to $\sqrt{t}$ [see Eq. (37)]. This expectation is fulfilled as long as h is considerably greater than the height of elevations on the two solid surfaces (but, of course, much smaller than the initial distance h_1).

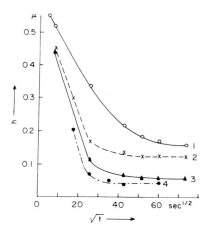

FIG. 34. Rate of descent of a horizontal plate in a liquid. Abscissa: square root of time (sec). Ordinate: distance (in microns) between the descending upper and stationary lower plate. Curves 1 and 3: steel plate in transformer oil. Curves 2 and 4: quartz plate in 0.01 N NaCl solution. Curves 1 and 2: pressure = 0.2 bar. Curves 3 and 4: pressure = 4 bars. From reference 47.

When h becomes commensurable with h_{max} (§3), the decrease of h is slowed down. An example of this behavior is presented in Fig. 34 taken from Fuks.[47] Its ordinate is h in microns, its abscissa is $\sqrt{t}$ in seconds, Curves 1 and 3 are for a transformer oil apparently between two steel plates, Curves 2 and 4 are for 0.01 N aqueous sodium chloride solution apparently between two quartz plates, and the pressure on the upper plate is 0.2 bar for Curves 1 and 2, and 4 bars for Curves 3 and 4. The leveling off of the curves below about 0.1 μ is undoubtedly due mainly to rugosity but two additional effects may be suspected. The transformer oil apparently contained impurities which reacted with the steel, and the true viscosity of the liquid next to the adherends was raised by the reaction products. Quartz on the other hand must have swelled in the aqueous solution, thus forming a very viscous boundary layer. Analogous increases in the true viscosity of the liquid near the interface presumably take place also when tackiness, i.e., time of separation rather than time of approach, is measured.

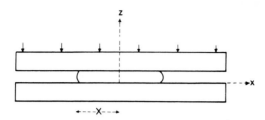

FIG. 35. Spreading of a drop by pressure between two parallel plates.

Observations similar to those of Fig. 34 have been recorded, for instance, by Needs.[48]

If the adhesive initially was present as a drop between the two adherends (see Fig. 35), time t is needed to spread the adhesive over the whole surface by pressing the plates together. Let again the mathematically simplest instance be considered, namely gradual spreading of a drop very long in the y direction (normal to the plane of the paper) and short in the x direction. Equations (28) and (29) are still valid but now the half-width of the drop, that is X, is a function of the distance h between the plates. Let V be the constant volume of the drop spread over the length l in the y direction. Then, whatever the value of t,

$$V = hXl. \tag{41}$$

Analogously to (30),

$$-F = Kl \int_0^X (X^2 - x^2)\, dx = \frac{2}{3} KX^3l\,. \tag{42}$$

When (41) is combined with (42), the equation

$$K = -\frac{3Fh^3l^2}{2V^3}\,. \tag{43}$$

results. Its comparison with Eq. (28) affords

$$\frac{4\eta}{h^3}\frac{dh}{dt} = \frac{Fh^3l^2}{V^3}\,. \tag{44}$$

Integration leads to

$$\frac{1}{h_2^5} - \frac{1}{h_1^5} = -\frac{5}{4}\frac{Fl^2}{\eta V^3}t, \tag{45}$$

if again h_1 is the initial and h_2 the final distance between the plates. Usually, $h_1 \gg h_2$ and $(1/h_1^5)$ may be neglected in comparison with $(1/h_2^5)$. In the final state, $F = flX_2 = fV/h_2$, if X_2 is the final width of the drop and f is the average pressure as in Eq. (33). Thus,

$$-ft = \frac{4\eta V^2}{5h_2^4 l^2} = \frac{4\eta X_2^2}{5h_2^2} = \frac{4\eta X_2^4 l^2}{5V^2}. \tag{46}$$

The second form of Eq. (46) is strikingly similar to Eq. (33).

If the plates are circular,

$$-Ft = \frac{3\eta V^2}{8\pi}\left(\frac{1}{h_2^4} - \frac{1}{h_1^4}\right). \tag{47}$$

If a is the radius of the plates, $V = \pi a^2 h_2$ at the moment when the drop has spread over the whole plate area. Hence, neglecting $1/h_1^4$ in comparison with $1/h_2^4$,

$$-Ft = \frac{3\pi\eta a^4}{8h_2^2}; \tag{48}$$

here [49] the product Ft is one-half that given by Eq. (37).

§35   The exact mechanism of the elimination of air dislodged from the adherend surface must depend on the porosity (or its absence) of the adherends and on the mode of application of the adhesive, but apparently, no systematic study of the phenomenon has been made yet.

A particularly simple experiment on the effect of bubble removal by the adhesive flow may be described here.[50] Polyethylene powder was spread on an aluminum foil either along the periphery of a rectangle as in Fig. 36b or along its middle as in Fig. 36a, a glass plate was placed on each foil, and the sandwiches were heated above the melting range of the polyethylene under a small pressure. It is clear that in the arrangement of Fig. 36b, air is likely to be trapped between aluminum, glass, and the wall of molten polyethylene, while in the other arrangement spreading melt will readily push air out of the clearance between foil and plate. In accord with the expectation, joints of the a-kind showed no large bubbles after setting, while the b-type joints had visible bubbles the largest of which was 0.8 cm long. The peeling resistance of the b joints was 1.6×10^5 and 1.9×10^5, and that of the a joints 2.6×10^5 and 3.6×10^5 dynes per centimeter width.

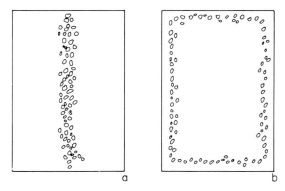

FIG. 36. Importance of air removal in the application of an adhesive. In b air was entrapped, and in a its escape was easy. From reference 50.

A similar observation was made by Bredzs.[51] Two horizontal steel cylinders were placed along one axis so that the clearance between the two bases facing each other was a fraction of a millimeter thick. Then a loop of solder wire was put around the clearance and the system was heated. The solder melted and advanced into the slit because of capillary pressure. However, since penetration occurred simultaneously along the whole periphery, an air bubble remained entrapped near the center of the clearance thus giving rise to weak joints. To prevent void formation, the axial part of the steel cylinders was kept hotter than the peripheral part, and the solder was maintained at a temperature high enough, i.e., at a viscosity low enough, for the bubble to escape because of gravitation.

In some special instances removal of air is achieved by submerging the two adherends in a liquid. Thus, the safety glass of 20 years ago was made in an "assembly bath" of dimethyl phthalate or a similar liquid, in which the two glass plates and the cellulose acetate interlayer were pressed together.

REFERENCES

1. Smirnov, N. S., and Prostakov, M. E., "Cleaning Steel Surfaces." Metallurgiya, Moscow, 1965 (in Russian).
2. "Metals Handbook," Vol. 2, p. 307. Am. Soc. Metals, Metals Park, Ohio, 1964.
3. Zherebkov, S. K., "Attachment of Rubber to Metals," p. 16. GNTIKhL., Moscow, 1956 (in Russian).
4. Rogers, N. L., *J. Appl. Polymer Sci., Appl. Polymer Symp.* No. 3, 327 (1966).
5. Abbey, W. F., *Rubber World* 134, 87 (1956).
6. Fiske, R. L., *Adhesives Age* 4, No. 10, 33 (1961).
7. Wegman, R. F., *Adhesives Age* 10, No. 1, 20 (1967).
8. Bullett, T. R., and Prosser, J. L., *Trans. Inst. Metal Finishing* 41, 112 (1964).
9. Kleinert, H., and Krimmling, W., *Plaste Kautschuk* 12, 472 (1965).
10. Smirnov, N. S., and Prostakov, M. E., "Cleaning Steel Surfaces," p. 80. Metallurgiya. Moscow, 1965 (in Russian).
11. Belyi, V. A., and Rutto, R. A., *Dokl. Akad. Nauk Belorussk. SSR* 9, 34 (1965).
12. Chessin, N., and Curran, V., *J. Appl. Polymer.Sci., Appl. Polymer Symp.* No. 3, 319 (1966).
13. Mittrop, F., *Z. Metallk.* 56, 622 (1965).
14. Stuart, N., *Proc. 4th Rubber Technol. Conf., London, 1962*. Inst. Rubber Ind., London, 1962.
15. Krotova, N. A., Morozova, L. P., and Sokolina, G. A., *Vortraege Originalfassung Intern. Kongr. Grenzflaechenaktive Stoffe 3, Cologne, 1960* 2, 368.
16. Hoefling, E., and Breu, H. *Adhaesion* 10, No. 6, 252 (1966).
17. Hothersall, A. W., and Hammond, R. A. F., *Trans. Electrochem. Soc.* 73, 449 (1938).
18. White, M. L., and Drobek, J., *J. Phys. Chem.* 70, 3432 (1966).
19. Bikerman, J. J., "Contributions to the Thermodynamics of Surfaces," Cambridge 1961, pp. 38 and 65.
20. Bikerman, J. J., *Kolloid-Z. Z. Polym.* 218, 52 (1967).
21. Bikerman, J. J., "The Science of Adhesive Joints," p. 34. Academic Press, New York, 1961.
22. Bikerman, J. J. *Kolloid-Z. Z. Polym.* 201, 48 (1965).
23. Bartell, F. E., and Bristol, K. E., *J. Phys. Chem.* 44, 86 (1940).
24. Bikerman, J. J., *Ind. Eng. Chem., Anal. Ed.* 13, 443 (1941).
25. Blaisdell, B. E., *J. Math. Phys.* 19, 186 (1940).
26. Voet, A., and van Eltern, J. F. *Rec. Trav. Chim.* 56, 923 (1937).
27. Shafrin, E. G., and Zisman, W. A., *J. Colloid Sci.* 4, 571 (1949).
28. Bikerman, J. J., "Surface Chemistry," 2nd ed. Academic Press, New York, 1958.
29. Kanamaru, K., *Kolloid-Z. Z. Polym.* 192, 51 (1963).
30. Kamenskii, B. Z., Vostroknutov, E. G., and Reznikovskii, M. M., *Kauchuk i Rezina* 23, No. 8, 35 (1964).
31. DeBruyne, N. A., *Trans. Plastics Inst. (London)* 27, 140 (1959).
32. Bikerman, J. J., *J. Mater.* 1, 34 (1966).

33. Voyutskii, S. S., "Autogeziya i Adgeziya Vysokopolimerov." Rostekhizdat., Moscow, 1960 (also an English translation).
34. Pickup, B., *Trans. Inst. Rubber Ind.* **33,** 58 (1957).
35. Beaven, E. W. J., Croft-White, P. G., Garner, P. J., and Rooney, G., *Proc. 2nd Rubber Technol. Conf., London, 1948* p. 224. Inst. Rubber Ind., London, 1948.
36. Zhukov, I. I., and Talmud, S. L., *J. Rubber Ind. (USSR)* **12,** 1005 (1935); *Chem. Abstr.* **30,** 6982 (1936).
37. Voyutskii, S. S., and Zamazii, V. M., *Dokl. Akad. Nauk SSSR* **81,** 63 (1951).
38. Skewis, J. D., *Rubber Chem. Technol.* **38,** 689 (1965).
39. Forbes, W. G., and McLeod, L. A., *Trans. Inst. Rubber Ind.* **34,** 154 (1958).
40. Shtarkman, B. P., Voyutskii, S. S., and Kargin, V. A., *Vysokomolekul. Soedin.* **7,** 135 (1965).
41. Oel, H. J., and Gottschalk, A., *Glasstech. Ber.* **39,** 319 (1966).
42. Reznikovskii, M. M., and Kamenskii, B. Z., *Dokl. Akad. Nauk SSSR* **155,** 924 (1964).
43. Stefan, J., *Sitzber. Akad. Wiss. Wien, Math.-Naturw. Kl.* Abt. II **69,** 713 (1874).
44. Bikerman, J. J., *J. Colloid Sci.* **2,** 163 (1947).
45. Reynolds, O., *Phil. Trans. Roy. Soc. London* **177,** I, 157 (1866).
46. Butler, L. H., *J. Inst. Petrol.* **46,** 63 (1960).
47. Fuks, G. I., *Dokl. Akad. Nauk SSSR* **113,** 635 (1957).
48. Needs, S. J., *Trans. ASME* **62,** 331 (1940).
49. Healey, A., *Trans. Inst. Rubber Ind.* **1,** 334 (1926).
50. Bikerman, J. J., *J. Appl. Polymer Sci.* **2,** 216 (1959).
51. Bredzs, N., *Welding J. (N.Y.)* **33,** 545-s (1954).

CHAPTER IV / TACK

§**36**   As soon as the clearance between two adherends has been filled with a liquid adhesive, an effort is needed to separate the two solids again. The resistance to separation, manifested by the system when the adhesive is still liquid, is known as tack or tackiness. In §32 its symbol (for butt joints and for a unit area) is f_m but it is denoted simply by f in this chapter as the pressure during the formation of an adhint is not discussed here.

The usual meaning of *tack* implies also (a) that only a weak external force was applied when making the joint and (b) that the measurement of the above resistance was made very soon after the application of the adhesive. In §37 the common observation is referred to that two flat solids pressed and wrung together (without any visible adhesive between them) require a considerable force to bring them apart; these solids would not be considered tacky because their contact was achieved after significant work by the experimenter. If a drop of water is permitted to fall on a horizontal solid plate and the plate is at once turned upside down, the test would comply with the two conditions (a) and (b) and water would be declared nontacky because gravitational force acting on a large drop is sufficient to cause its downfall. A similar concept was presented in reference 1; and a less specific definition may be found in ASTM D 907-64a (The 1966 Book of ASTM Standards **16,** 280).

The gradual growth of tack during an adhesive–adherend or adhesive–adhesive contact is described in §32. From §§29 and 30 it is clear that the ratio $\gamma \cos \theta_A/\eta u$, or an analogous ratio for non-Newtonian liquids, is, as a rule, the quantity determining what degree of the maximum possible tack will be achieved in a given test. In many instances, however, the predictions based on the equations of §§29 and 30 will be found incorrect. Probably the most common cause of this discrepancy is the fact that viscosity measurements are performed on well-stirred samples, while in the measurement of tack the adhesive is almost undisturbed. Consequently, it may have a thin solid crust on its surface; this would almost eliminate tack but would have hardly any effect on viscosity.

A crust of this kind was deliberately produced[2] by exposing specimens of various rubbers to ozone for 10 min. This treatment reduced f (after a contact for 30 sec) from 3.0 to 1.7 bars for a "butyl rubber," from 3.1 to 0.35 bar for a butadiene–styrene copolymer, from 4.2 to 0.25 bar for a butadiene–acrylonitrile, and from 2.3 to 1.0 bar for natural rubber. Subsequent roughening of the surface, i.e., partial removal of the oxidized layer, almost restored the previous tackiness.

Apparently, an opposite effect also is possible. A "butyl rubber" pressed to polystyrene manifested[3] considerable tackiness. When it was heated to, e.g., 100°, cooled, and again pressed to a polystyrene panel, the tack had only about half the previous magnitude. Abrasion of the preheated specimen restored its tackiness. The author believes that, at 100°, an oil migrated from the bulk to the surface, i.e., a weak boundary layer formed.

§37   Before reviewing typical tack phenomena, it is necessary to discuss the often quoted example of two flat and smooth solid surfaces which, after being pressed together in air, can be separated only with a considerable effort. This effect, and the "solid-to-solid adhesion" of §15 are sometimes still confused with tack, as defined in §36.

Polished steel prisms, often called Johansson blocks, are choice objects for the above tests. Three reasons for the "attraction" between the two surfaces are known.

1. Even when the surface appears clean, it may be contaminated with an oil or with water condensed from the atmosphere. As all solid surfaces, including those of Johansson blocks, are rough, they can touch each other at discrete points only. Let Fig. 37 represent one of these points; the shaded areas are solids. If there are traces of a liquid between the blocks, they will tend to form droplets around the points of contact because the vapor pressure above a

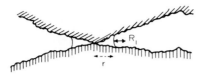

FIG. 37. Droplet of liquid surrounding protuberances on two solid surfaces in contact.

concave meniscus is less than that above a flat or convex liquid surface. If the radius of curvature of the menisci, such as indicated in Fig. 37, is R_1 in the plane of the paper and R_2 in a plane normal to it and parallel to the main planes of the solids, the value of R_1 usually will be considerably smaller than that of R_2, and the capillary pressure in the drop will be approximately γ/R_1. The magnitude of R_1 should not be very different from the height of hills in contact; for a polished metal surface we may assume R_1 to be of the order of 10^{-6} cm (see §7). For $\gamma = 50$ gm/sec^2 and $R_1 = 10^{-6}$ cm, γ/R_1 is 5×10^7 gm/cm sec^2 (or 50 bars). The attractive force exerted by the meniscus is approximately $\pi r^2 \gamma/R_1$ because the underpressure γ/R_1 acts on the whole horizontal cross section ($= \pi r^2$) of the drop, Fig. 37. Assume r to be 10^{-4} cm; the force comes out to be over 1.5 dyne. If there are, say, 600 contact points, the total attractive force would be near 1000 dynes.

Should the volume of the liquid be so great as to form a continuous film between the two surfaces, and if this film is 2×10^{-6} cm thick, the attractive force would be 50 bars times the area of the block surface; γ is again supposed to be 50 gm/sec^2.

The capillary attraction discussed in the two preceding paragraphs has been studied many times by, and since, Laplace. Recent publications in which it was "rediscovered" will not be named here.

2. If no fluid of a low electric resistivity is present between or around the blocks, they are mutually attracted because of electrostatic forces, even when the materials of the blocks are supposedly identical. This is caused by the fact that the work function of a solid depends not only on its overall chemical composition but also on the cleanness of its surface, the crystallographic orientation of its surface layers, and the state of stress of the latter. As it is practically impossible to prepare two surfaces identical in all these respects,

one of the two will lose electrons more readily than the other; thus the first body will carry a positive, and the second, a negative charge. These charges, naturally, will be concentrated on the two opposite surfaces and thus give rise to Coulombic attraction between the two blocks. The attraction will lessen if the atmosphere surrounding the blocks is ionized (for instance, by a radioactive substance) or its humidity is high.

§38   3. The third of the reasons referred to in the beginning of §37 presumably is the main cause of the tackiness of adhesives and sometimes accounts also for the major part of the difficulty of separating two flat polished solids without an adhesive between them. In §34 the time needed to press two plates together was calculated. An equal time is needed for removing them from each other by reversing the motion; mathematically speaking, we simply exchange the two integration limits. Thus,

$$Ft = \frac{3}{4} \pi \eta a^4 \left(\frac{1}{h_1{}^2} - \frac{1}{h_2{}^2} \right) \tag{49}$$

and, in analogy to (36),

$$ft = \frac{3}{4} \eta \frac{a^2}{h_1{}^2} . \tag{50}$$

In this case the initial clearance (h_1) is smaller than the final (h_2).

As is clear from these equations, no real attraction between the two solids exists. When they are being gradually removed from each other, air or another fluid streams into the growing clearance, and the external force is needed to keep this stream up. This explanation was given first by Galilei,[4] but the equations are due to Stefan.[5]

In the instance of two polished discs in air, as the viscosity of air is about 1.8×10^{-4} gm/cm sec, Eq. (50) gives $Ft = 1.8 \times 10^{10}$ gm cm/sec for discs of $a = 2.55$ cm and $h_1 = 10^{-6}$ cm. Thus, a disc weighing 100 gm would remain suspended in the gravitational field of our earth (which would make F a little smaller than 10^5 gm cm/ sec^2) for about 1.8×10^5 sec (≈ 50 hr). When a liquid adhesive fills the space between the plates, the duration of the disengagement process is much longer. An identical disc in water, instead of air, would continue to hang for 10^7 sec (i.e., 116 days), the viscosity of water being 0.01 gm/cm sec at 20°.

An experimental confirmation of Eq. (49) was supplied by Stefan[5] himself, and results in a satisfactory accord with the theory were obtained several times afterwards; see, for instance, references 6, 7, and 8. A few data[8] may be reproduced here to illustrate the degree of agreement between theory and experiment. As the right-hand side of Eq. (50) is independent of f, the product ft must remain constant when f varies. Table VII corroborates this conclusion.

TABLE VII
PRODUCT ft IS INDEPENDENT OF f
STEEL PLATES, $h_{rms} = 8 \times 10^{-6}$ CM PARAFFIN OIL. TEMPERATURE 28.1°

f (gm/cm sec²)	135	246	472	736	1060	1715	3830×10^2
ft (gm/cm sec)	23	23	20	19	20	21	18×10^6

As no property of the solid is referred to in Eq. (50), ft should be independent of the material of the plates; this was verified for nickel, stainless steel, and copper. The temperature coefficient of ft was equal to that of the viscosity of the liquid between the discs; no other quantity appearing in the equation has a temperature coefficient significant in this connection. The magnitude of the initial clearance h_1 was measured directly (as the thickness of the capacitor formed by the two metal discs) and found, within the experimental error, equal to h_1 calculated from the product ft.

The considerations of this section and of §29 indicate an important condition which must be fulfilled by an adhesive to be tacky. To achieve a "quick grab," i.e., to attain a reasonable value of f in a reasonable time, the viscosity of the adhesive should be low. On the other hand, when η is small, also the final value f of tack is small. Thus, a compromise is needed. Viscosity should not be too high, to avoid long waiting times, and not too low, to avoid rapid separation at weak stresses. It seems that the most convenient value of viscosity is of the order of magnitude of 10^6 gm/cm sec, although much smaller viscosities were recommended earlier.[1]

Equation (32) of §34, with the opposite sign, i.e., $dh/h^3 = f\, dt/4\eta X^2$ is valid for the rate of separation of two discs. It shows that the linear velocity dh/dt should be proportional to f, as long as the adhesive is a Newtonian liquid. Unfortunately, experimental data are available chiefly for rubbers whose rheological behavior is more complicated. When two pieces of natural rubber[2] were pressed together and then pulled apart at a speed of 0.2 cm/sec, the resistance (i.e., tack) was about 1.9 bar, and when the velocity was 0.85 cm/sec, the tack was 3.3 bars, i.e., it increased with dh/dt more slowly than predicted. A "butyl rubber" apparently was nearer to a Newtonian liquid; when it was pressed[3] to a nonspecified solid for 40 sec and then lifted at a velocity ranging from 39 to 89 cm/sec, f rose from 2.0 to 4.8 bars.

The answers given by Eqs. (49) and (50) are, or may be, incorrect when (a) the plates are not immersed, (b) air has not been removed, (c) the solid surfaces are very rough, (d) force F (or rather stress f) is too great or time t is too short, (e) viscosity η is too great, or (f) viscosity is not independent of the rate of shear. These limitations are discussed in the above order in §§39 to 42; some of them apply also to the problem of two plates approaching each other (see §29), but are treated here because they are particularly important in the study of tackiness. Some of the experiments on tack were vitiated by trivial mistakes, such as poor alignment and wedge-shaped clearances between the plates, and the effect of these asymmetries is considered in §45.

§39   (a) When the plates are not immersed or, more exactly, when a meniscus exists around the clearance, capillary pressure acts as indicated in §37. Thus, the value of f to be inserted in, e.g., Eq. (50) is not the whole external (negative) pressure f but only $f - (2\gamma/h)$ assuming that the liquid perfectly wets the two surfaces; h is the variable distance between the plates. However, this system is analogous to that shown in Fig. 35 rather than to that of Fig. 33 because the area occupied by the liquid varies with time; in §29 it increased; here, in a symmetrical manner, it decreases. Instead of Eq. (44), the equation

$$\frac{4\eta}{h^3}\frac{dh}{dt} = \frac{Fh^3l^2}{V^3} - \frac{2\gamma hl^2}{V^2} \tag{51}$$

is obtained. The integrated expression

$$t = \frac{\eta}{l^2}\left(\frac{F^3 V}{2\gamma^5}\right)^{0.5} \arctan\left(\frac{F}{2\gamma V}\right)^{0.5} h + \frac{\eta F V}{2\gamma^2 l^2 h} + \frac{2\eta V^2}{3\gamma l^2 h^3} \tag{52}$$

may at some future date prove useful. For the meaning of the symbols see §34.

It follows from Eq. (51) that the rate dh/dt is zero when $2\gamma = Fh^2/V$. A suggestion was made[9] that human dentures were retained in the mouth by this mechanism.

(b) The proof reproduced in §29 makes use of the assumption, among others, that the pressure difference P can be relieved only by the centripetal flow of the liquid adhesive. This assumption is invalid if the liquid does not wet well the two (or one of the) solids. In the absence of complete wetting, some air remains between the solid and the liquid, mainly in the valleys on the solid surface. When the external load creates a space of low pressure near the axis of the system, the outside air flows in at the same time as liquid does. As the viscosity of air is about one-fiftieth that of water and, perhaps, 0.0001th of that of an industrial adhesive, even a narrow channel open to air and leading toward the center of the plates may cause a marked diminution of the time t of separation. When metal plates were polished with an aqueous abrasive, washed with water, and only superficially dried before being immersed in a hydrocarbon oil (viscosity $= 1.9$ gm/cm sec), t was about one-fourth the time observed when the plates were well-dried and rinsed with trichloroethylene prior to the application of the oil.[8]

As usual liquid adhesives are more or less saturated with air or may contain volatile solvents, air or solvent vapor will tend to form bubbles near the axis of the joint where the pressure deficiency has the highest value. If these bubbles can grow at a considerable rate, they may relieve the pressure difference in yet another manner.[10-13]

§40   (c) The effect of surface roughness was studied[8] in an arrangement similar to that of Fig. 33. The lower plate was well polished in all instances while the mean-square-root of the elevations (§3) on the upper plate varied within a wide range. The two plates (with an oil in between) were pressed together with a definite force for a definite time, and both force and time were kept constant, i.e., not adjusted for roughness changes. When, then, loads were suspended

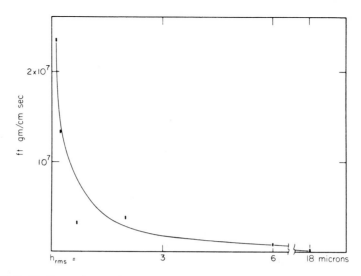

FIG. 38. Dependence of product ft (= stress × time) on surface roughness for a Newtonian liquid. Abscissa: h_{rms} of the coarse surface (μ). Ordinate: ft (gm/cm sec). Data of reference 8.

from the bottom plate, the product ft proved to be approximately inversely proportional to the height h_{rms} of the upper surface, as determined with a stylus instrument (§3). Figure 38 illustrates this behavior.

Roughness should not be disregarded in the determination of the initial clearance h_1. Thus, it was assumed[14] that, when the two plates are kept "in contact" until the product ft ceases to increase, this limiting value of ft has a molecular significance. In reality[15] the value of h_1 achieved after prolonged contact must be approximately equal to the height of a few tallest hills on the two surfaces; as soon as the upper plate rests on these hills, no further approach to the lower plate is possible (see §5).

§41   (d) When the mutual detachment of the two plates proceeds too rapidly, i.e., when the applied stress f is too great, Eqs. (49) and (50) cease to be applicable because the liquid flows with an acceleration which cannot be neglected (see §29). This source of error is more dangerous for fluids of a relatively low viscosity, such as water or lubricating oils, then for typical tacky adhesives. For the latter materials, limitation (e) is more important.

(e) When viscosity η is great, the adhesive may have no time to form the parabolic pattern of flow derived in §29 before it ruptures in the manner characteristic for brittle solids. Some kinds of rosin and asphalt are nearly Newtonian liquids; that is, their viscosity, although very high, is practically independent of the gradient of velocity as long as this gradient is small, but they break rather than flow if an excessive stress is applied to them. These materials may have viscosity of, say, 1000 gm/cm sec. If $a^2 = 13.33$ cm^2 and $h_1^2 = 10^{-8}$ cm^2, Eq. (50) gives $ft = 10^{12}$ gm/cm sec. Thus, two metal discs of the radius 3.65 cm, glued together with a rosin, would support a stress of 10^{10} gm/cm sec^2 (or about 10^4 atm corresponding to approximately 140,000 psi) for 100 sec. In reality, the tensile stress of such a rosin would be, perhaps, 10^8 gm/cm sec^2 and it would crack immediately after the application of the stress.

In less extreme cases, apparently, some flow takes place but instead of being all from the periphery of the adhint toward its axis, it proceeds toward many points or lines. When the detachment is complete, these points remain visible on the adhesive film as protuberances, and the lines are visible as ridges. Call the distance between two nearest protuberances $2a_0$; then Eq. (50) with a_0 substituted for a, may be used. In other words, we treat the liquid film of radius a as a sum of small films, all in parallel and having each a radius a_0; these elementary films flow independently of their neighbors. As a_0 is likely to be between one-tenth and one-hundredth part of a, the product ft would be 0.01 to 0.0001 that calculated from the original equation.

Perhaps, some observations[16] on the tack at high velocities may be considered as a confirmation of this hypothesis. A drop of viscous polymer liquid (which in many instances was non-Newtonian) was placed between two metal blocks, and the upper block was lifted so that the distance between the two reached 1 or 2 cm in 0.004 to 0.016 sec. A fluid which, in its Newtonian range, had η of 60 gm/cm sec produced a single column of liquid near the center of the block. A viscoelastic polymer, whose η in the Newtonian range was about 10^6 gm/cm sec, gave rise to multiple filaments which contracted after the rupture; the contraction was attributed to elastic rather than to capillary forces.

At these high speeds, vibrations are initiated. When the upper block was rising up, the adhesive followed it, and the bottom block (for a few milliseconds) followed the adhesive; the acceleration of the latter did not stay constant or vary monotonously with time, but rather showed maxima and minima.

§42   (f) When the viscosity of the adhesive is a function of the rate of shear (or, in another terminology, of the velocity gradient), the physical picture is little changed but mathematical difficulties at once become serious. In §30b an analog of viscosity for the Maxwell body is derived but, apparently, it has never been checked whether the equations of §38 could be rendered valid for materials of this type simply by inserting η^* for η. The equations of §30c ought to be correct also for the separation of two parallel plates. Two other rheological systems have been treated by Scott[17], and his theory, slightly modified, is given in the following.

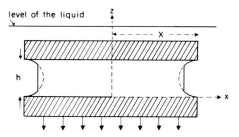

FIG. 39. Separation of two parallel plates in a Bingham body.

Figure 39, analogous to Fig. 33, represents the system. If the adhesive is a "Bingham body,"

$$\frac{du}{dz} = \varphi(\tau - \tau_0) \tag{53}$$

instead of $(du/dz) = \tau$, as in a Newtonian liquid, §29. Stress τ_0 (gm/cm sec^2) and quantity φ (cm sec/gm) are material constants; to account for the rheological behavior of a Bingham body both are needed, while in the analogous problems dealing with Newtonian liquids viscosity alone is sufficient. Equation (53) is valid as long as $\tau > \tau_0$; when $\tau \leqslant \tau_0$, $du/dz = 0$. The viscous stress τ is least at $x = X$ and $z = h/2$ (see §29). In the regions where both these conditions are satisfied, i.e., in the middle between the plates at the edge of the adhesive film, the τ is most likely to be less than τ_0; where $\tau < \tau_0$, u is independent of z; thus the profile of the inflowing liquid (when a tensile force is applied to the plates; see the arrows in Fig. 39) is a truncated parabola (the continuous line) instead of a parabola (dashes) valid for Newtonian liquids.

The viscous force acting on a slab, 1 cm in the x direction, 1 cm in the y direction, and dz cm in the z direction, is $(d\tau/dz)\, dz$; as long as flow takes place without acceleration, it is balanced by force $(dp/dx)\, dz$, p being the difference between the variable pressure in the adhesive and the atmospheric pressure outside. Thus, analogously to (5), we have

$$\frac{d\tau}{dz} = \frac{dp}{dx}. \tag{54}$$

For a Newtonian liquid, dp/dx is independent of z; we assume that this is true also in the present instance. Hence, u is a parabolic function of z as long as τ remains greater than τ_0; if $\tau \leqslant \tau_0$ between $z = z_0$ and $z = h - z_0$, then $u = u_1 = Az^2 + Bz + C$ between $z = 0$ and $z = z_0$ and between $z = h - z_0$ and $z = h$, and $u = u_0 = $ const. elsewhere. The constants A, B, and C are easily determined by the method sketched in §29; and it is found that

$$u_1 = \frac{\varphi}{2} \frac{dp}{dx} (z^2 - 2zz_0)$$

in the lower half of the clearance,

$$u_1 = \frac{\varphi}{2} \frac{dp}{dx} (z^2 + h^2 + 2zz_0 - 2z_0 h - 2hz)$$

in the upper half, and

$$u_0 = -\frac{\varphi}{2} \frac{dp}{dx} z_0{}^2 .$$

The volume V of the adhesive moving from the periphery toward the axis (at $x = 0$) of the system in unit time is

$$V = -2 \int_0^{z_0} u_1 \, dz + 2 \int_{z_0}^{h/2} u_0 \, dz = y\varphi z_0{}^2 \frac{dp}{dx} \left(\frac{h}{2} - \frac{z_0}{3} \right),$$

if the depth of the plate (in the y direction, normal to the plane of the paper) is y. Now an approximation is introduced. If the region of constant velocity is thin, the value of $(h/2) - z_0$ is considerably smaller than that of $h/2$; if we neglect $[(h/2) - z_0]^3$ compared with $(h/2)^3$, the above expression is reduced to

$$V = \frac{1}{12} y\varphi \frac{dp}{dx} h^2 \left[h - 3 \left(\frac{h}{2} - z_0 \right) \right].$$

Since

$$\frac{h}{2} - z_0 = \frac{\tau_0}{dp/dx},$$

we may write

$$V = \frac{y\varphi h^3}{12} \frac{dp}{dx} - \frac{y\varphi h^2 \tau_0}{4}. \tag{55}$$

This quantity must be equal to $yx(dh/dt)$. Hence, p, which is zero at $x = X$ and negative everywhere else, is

$$p = \frac{6}{\varphi h^3} \frac{dh}{dt} (x^2 - X^2) + \frac{3\tau_0}{h} (x - X).$$

As the plates are in contact with a liquid layer (i.e., the zone of constant velocity u_0 does not extend to the plates), Pascal's law is still valid and so is the equation

$$F = -y \int_0^X p \, dx,$$

F being the external force acting on the right-hand side of the plates. Hence,

$$F = -y \frac{4}{\varphi h^3} \frac{dh}{dt} X^3 + y \frac{3\tau_0}{2h} X^2 \tag{56}$$

and

$$f = \frac{F}{yX} = \frac{4X^2}{\varphi h^3} \frac{dh}{dt} + \frac{3\tau_0}{2h} X . \tag{57}$$

It is seen that Eq. (32) is obtained if $\tau_0 = 0$ and η is written for $1/\varphi$. Integration of Eq. (57) affords

$$X \left(\frac{1}{h_1} - \frac{1}{h_2} \right) + \frac{2f}{3\tau_0} \ln \frac{h_2(2fh_1 - 3\tau_0 X)}{h_1(2fh_2 - 3\tau_0 X)} = \frac{3\varphi\tau_0}{8} t . \tag{58}$$

Obviously, this equation cannot be correct unless f is greater than $3\tau_0 X/2h$; when $f < 3\tau_0 X/2h$, then $dh/dt < 0$, that is, no separation occurs, but in this instance the above condition of $\tau_0/(dp/dx)$ being much smaller than $h/2$ is invalid.

If, instead of Eq. (53),

$$\frac{du}{dz} = \varphi\tau^n , \tag{59}$$

n being a numerical constant, and if $(d\tau/dz) = (dp/dx)$ is again independent of z, then

$$\frac{du}{dz} = \varphi \left(\frac{dp}{dx} \right)^n \left(z - \frac{h}{2} \right)^n$$

and

$$u = \frac{\varphi}{n+1} \left(\frac{dp}{dx} \right)^n \left[\left(z - \frac{h}{2} \right)^{n+1} - \left(\frac{h}{2} \right)^{n+1} \right]$$

for that half of the clearance between $z = (h/2)$ and $z = h$; compare Eq. (6). The volume

$$V = 2y \frac{\varphi}{n+2} \left(\frac{dp}{dx} \right)^n \left(\frac{h}{2} \right)^{n+2} \tag{60}$$

must be equal to $yx(dh/dt)$. Hence,

$$p = \frac{2^{(n + 1)/n}n(n + 2)^{1/n}}{(n + 1)\varphi^{1/n}} h^{-(n + 2)/n}\left(\frac{dh}{dt}\right)^{1/n}$$

$$\times [x^{(n + 1)/n} - X^{(n + 1)/n}] ; \tag{61}$$

if $n = 1$, Eq. (61) becomes identical with (27), since in this instance $\varphi = (1/\eta)$ and $p = -P$. As $\int_0^X p\, dx = Xf$,

$$f = \frac{2^{(n + 1)/n}n(n + 2)^{1/n}}{(2n + 1)\varphi^{1/n}} h^{-(n + 2)/n}\left(\frac{dh}{dt}\right)^{1/n}X^{(n + 1)/n} \tag{62}$$

[see Eq. (32)], and

$$\frac{1}{h_1^{n + 1}} - \frac{1}{h_2^{n + 1}} = \frac{(n + 1)(2n + 1)^n}{2^{n + 1}(n + 2)n^n}\frac{\varphi f^n t}{X^{n + 1}}, \tag{63}$$

which becomes identical with (33) when $n = 1$.

It is also possible, without specifying the relation between du/dz and τ, to measure the apparent tensional modulus of the adhesive at different rates of deformation and to use the value obtained to account for the rate of separation at a given load.[18]

§43   In §§38 to 42, the rate of detachment normally to the plane of the adhesive film was considered. Often, tackiness is judged by pressing the coated side of a flexible ribbon (which carries adhesive on one side) to a rigid plate and then peeling (or stripping) the tape off. In the more common variant of this method, detachment starts from one end of the tape; see Fig. 101, §92, in which P is the rigid plate, R the flexible ribbon, and A the adhesive film. In one series of experiments,[19] the symmetrical arrangement of Fig. 40 was employed.

When the adhesive is a Newtonian liquid, the mechanism of peeling is fully analogous to that treated in §38. As soon as the weight (or weights) is (are) applied, underpressure is established in the liquid and this starts to flow away from the points of application of external force, i.e., to the right in Fig. 101 and from the

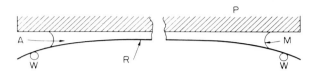

FIG. 40. Peeling in a system consisting of a rigid plate, P, a liquid film, A and a flexible ribbon, R. M is the meniscus, W is the weight. From reference 19.

suspended ends to the still attached middle in Fig. 40. The main difference between this flow and that studied by Stefan is that in the latter case the liquid maintains its cylindrical shape and only the height of the cylinder increases during the experiment, while in the process of peeling the shape of the liquid is more like a wedge (or two wedges) and, for the instance of Fig. 40, the shape of the wedges continuously changes during the test.

The difference in geometry renders the mathematical problem more difficult than that of §38, and no exact equation for the rate of stripping has yet been derived even for Hookean solids as ribbons and Newtonian liquids as adhesives.[20] An approximate equation is

$$\frac{dl}{dt} = \frac{c\Gamma^2 y_0}{\eta E \delta^3};$$ (64)

l is the length of the ribbon detached during time t, Γ is the peeling tension (equal to weight W divided by the width w of the ribbon; w is perpendicular to the plane of paper), y_0 is the initial thickness of the liquid film, η its viscosity, and δ and E are the thickness and the modulus of elasticity of the ribbon (for instance, of the backing of the adhesive tape). The constant c, whose dimension is length, must be calculated from the experimental data. For the time t_m required for the ribbon of Fig. 40 to fall off, the approximate expression is[19]

$$t_m = \kappa \frac{\eta E \delta^3}{\Gamma^2 y_0};$$ (65)

the empirical constant κ is a pure number.

When η is relatively small, less than, say, 1000 gm/cm sec, two additional effects take place during the detachment. (a) Liquid flows not only from the two ends of the ribbon toward the middle but also from the two long edges of the ribbon toward the centroid line (i.e., in the two directions perpendicular to the plane of paper). (b) Because menisci (M in Fig. 40) exist near the two ends of the ribbon, the pressure in the liquid is less than atmospheric not only in consequence of the weights attached but also as a result of capillary pressure, which for a well wetting liquid would be about $-2\gamma/y_0$ in the beginning of the experiment but less important afterward; as before, γ is surface tension. It is difficult to improve the theory by considering these two effects, but apparently they can be corrected for in the following manner. When the experimental values of $(1/t_m)$ are plotted as a function of W^2, a straight line is obtained which crosses the abscissa (i.e., the coordinate of W^2) at a value which we may denote by W_0^2. Then, Γ in Eq. (65) is $(W - W_0)/w$.

Constant κ was about 0.2 in the experiments of reference 19, in which the ribbon was of aluminum, steel, or copper (0.005 to 0.008 cm thick) and hydrocarbon polymers (with viscosities of 75 and 300 gm/cm sec) were used as tacky adhesives.

In these experiments the angle of peeling was indefinite. In the customary peeling experiments, this angle is either 90° as in Fig. 101 or 180°. Observations on 90° peeling and a Newtonian adhesive are available.[21] The rigid solid was a stone (e.g., granite), the ribbon was an aluminum foil, and the liquid was an asphalt at 25° whose η at this temperature was 8×10^6 gm/cm sec. It was found that dl/dt was proportional to Γ^2 as long as δ was 0.0025 or 0.0050 cm. Contrary to Eq. (64), the ratio of dl/dt to Γ^2 was almost independent of y_0 (when this varied between 45 and 135 μ) and of δ. The "constant" c was about 20 cm. The two additional effects referred to above apparently were insignificant in the instance of a liquid as viscous as this asphalt, as no correction for the weights W was needed.

After the completion of the peeling, the asphalt coating which remained on the aluminum foil was, with due regard to surface roughness, just as thick as the asphalt residue on the stone. This is in accord with the mechanism postulated above: when a Newtonian liquid flows in and out of a slit, the maximum velocity is observed in the central plane of the latter [see Eq. (6) in §29]; hence, the plane of separation should coincide with this central plane.

A theory of peeling through a viscoelastic adhesive (a Maxwell body, §30) has been published.[22] It includes the two extreme cases of purely viscous and purely elastic interlayers. Apparently, no attempt has been made yet to compare the mathematical predictions of the theory with the experimental results.

§**44** The tack of many rubbers and adhesive tapes was determined by peeling but the significance of the results obtained is difficult to judge as the rheological properties of the adhesives were not known. In almost all instances, however, these adhesives probably were not Newtonian liquids and, consequently, there was no reason to expect any compliance with Eqs. (64) and (65).

Figure 41, based on a graph of reference 23, represents the

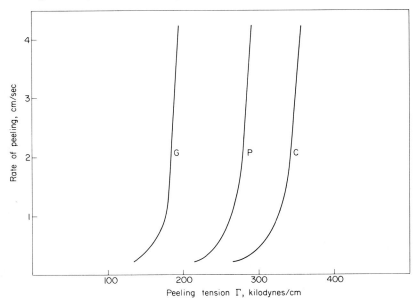

FIG. 41. Peeling rate of adhesive tapes as a function of peeling tension. Abscissa: peeling tension, in kilodynes/cm. Ordinate: peeling rate (cm/sec). G: on glass; P: on polyester; C: on cellophane. Data of reference 23.

typical behavior of adhesive tapes, as far as the relation between the rate dl/dt and the tension Γ is concerned. The adhesive was a copolymer of 60 parts of octyl acrylate and 40 parts of vinyl acetate. The tape was left in contact with glass (curve G), a polyester (curve P), and cellophane (curve C) for a time (not specified in the original) and then peeled. It is seen that dl/dt increases with Γ more steeply than Eq. (64) would predict; one is tempted to conclude that a "yield tension" (see τ_0 in §42) is necessary before any stripping would start.

Figure 41 shows also that, at a given rate of separation, a higher Γ is needed for cellophane than for polyester, while peeling from glass is the easiest. This order, however, varies with the adhesive used; for instance, a tape whose adhesive was mainly natural rubber "stuck a little stronger" to polyester than to cellophane. In another series of experiments,[24] at a given rate dl/dt, the Γ was greatest for "moisture-proof" cellophane and decreased from it to cellulose acetate, ordinary cellophane, and cellulose laurate. The adhesive on the tape consisted mainly of natural rubber and a rosin ester. An explanation for this effect of the adherend on the ease of peeling is not available at present.

The unexpectedly small effect of the backing thickness δ, observed for Newtonian liquids (§43), is encountered also in adhesive tapes. With peeling angle maintained at 90°, Γ was[25] independent of δ when this varied from 0.0025 to 0.03 cm; the material of the backing was aluminum or terephthalate ester polymer. A clear increase of Γ with δ occurred only when a hard aluminum foil (0.0025 or 0.012 cm thick), covered with a permanently tacky adhesive, was peeled off at an angle of 180°. When the adhesive was made softer, or the thickness y_0 of the adhesive layer was made greater, higher values of Γ resulted.

In many instances, the tack was determined as a function not of the external variables (rate of peeling, y_0, δ, etc.) or of the rheological properties of the adhesive, but rather of the chemical composition of the latter; for instance, the effect of the ratio of butadiene to acrylonitrile (in the copolymer rubber[26]) and of the molecular weight of this copolymer[27] on Γ was ascertained. These results often are difficult to interpret. An example may be narrated here.

Two sheets of a copolymer of divinyl with 2-methyl-5-vinyl-pyridine were pressed together[28] for 15 sec by 1 kg weight and immediately peeled apart by a load of 300 gm. The time t_m of complete separation was 18 min when the two sheets were 2 hr old, and only 1 min when 24 hr have passed between the last mastication and the test. This weakening of the tack may have been caused by diffusion of a low-molecular-weight impurity to the surface (see §69), or by a gradual hardening of the surface layer, as in §36, or by another factor; no study of the problem was made. Instead, the authors added a condensation product of p-nonylphenol and formaldehyde to the copolymer and found that t_m was raised to 40 min and 8 min for specimens 2 and 24 hr old. Did the addition retard the above diffusion, or the above hardening, or what?

§45 An important reason for the deviation of experimental detachment times from the values predicted by theory has not been mentioned in §38 because it was not as "scientific" as the others were. This reason is absence of symmetry in the experimental arrangement.

If, for instance, the two plates of Fig. 33 are not parallel, time t is smaller than calculated from their *average* mutual distance because, in liquid flow, the importance of a channel increases more rapidly than in linear manner with the diameter of the channel. Imagine a set of n parallel slits of equal width and of thicknesses $\delta_1, \delta_2, \ldots, \delta_n$. The average thickness would be $\delta_{av} = (1/n)(\delta_1 + \delta_2 + \ldots \delta_n)$ but the volume V of liquid moving through the set would be proportional to $(\delta_1^3 + \delta_2^3 + \ldots + \delta_n^3)$ [see Eq. (7), §29]; thus the contribution of narrow slits is less important for V than for δ_{av}. When the clearance between two discs was 5 μ at one end of a diameter and 23 μ at the opposite end (5 cm away), the t was about one-third of what it should be.[8] If one of the plates is flat and the other concave, convex or, generally, wavy (see §6), the asymmetry would be as damaging as when the plates are both flat but not mutually parallel.

Similar effects presumably would be observed if, instead of the clearance, the plates themselves would have no cylindrical symmetry; if, say, the bottom plate of Fig. 33 had the shape outlined in

Fig. 42 instead of being circular. An analogous phenomenon, due
to accidental asymmetry, was noticed when an instrument depicted
in Fig. 43 was used.[29] This is simply a glass tube (1) partly filled with

FIG. 42. An asymmetrical plate.

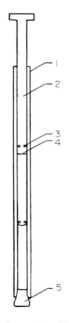

FIG. 43. A penetroviscometer. From reference 29.

an adhesive (whose upper level is at 4), into which a coaxial metal
rod (2) slowly sinks under its own weight; from the rate of descent

the viscosity (or consistency) of the adhesive can be calculated. When, after the descent, the instrument is turned upside down and the rate of emersion of the rod is measured, the experiment is a determination of the tackiness of the adhesive in a tubular lap joint. In a perfectly symmetrical system the two rates (in and out) would be identical. In reality[30] the rod falls out more rapidly than it pene-

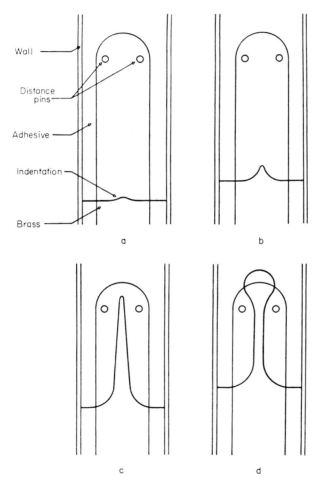

FIG. 44. Effect of asymmetry on time of separation (or tackiness). From reference 30.

trated into the adhesive. Figure 44 shows the reason for the discrepancy. When the adhesive-air surface is not flat, the distance
between the region of atomospheric pressure and that of the underpressure above the inverted rod is not identical around the rod; the
Δz of §29 is smaller at the indentation indicated in Fig. 44 than elsewhere. Consequently, $\Delta P/\Delta z$ is greater at the indentation than in
other points; hence, the inward flow is more rapid here than elsewhere and the indentation gets deeper. This even more accentuates
the difference between Δz at the indentation and far from it; thus
the effect is self-accelerating.

§46   Many instruments have been suggested for measuring tack. As is
clear from the previous sections of this chapter, the property (or
the complex of properties) which they determine is almost identical
with viscosity for Newtonian liquids or with consistency for the
others. Thus it may be argued that these instruments are, fundamentally, viscometers and do not deserve a description in a book on
adhesive joints. The excuse for giving such a description here is
that, at present, the geometry of tack-testing methods usually is
too complicated for predicting the results from viscosity considerations and that the rheological behavior of commercial adhesives
usually is too complex to predict the test results even when the
geometry is particularly simple.

Two essential stages are present in each measurement of tack,
namely, making and breaking contact.

The method of establishing contact often is selected to be similar
to that in the actual use. Thus, an adhesive tape may be allowed to
settle on a solid under its own weight, if it is intended for an application excluding an external pressure.[31] If the adhesive is supposed
to be called into action after t seconds, also in the test it is kept in
contact with the adherend for t seconds before detachment is
attempted. The requirement of a minimum tack after t seconds is
quite common. Suppose, for instance, that we have to bend a sheet
of paper and to glue the ends together. The stress produced in the
sheet by the bending will tend to open the seam; thus, an outside
force is needed to prevent unbending until tackiness is strong
enough to overcome the tendency to unbend; and production is

speeded up when this force is applied for a shorter time. This problem arises, for instance, in the glueing of the flaps of cardboard boxes (see §55). Presumably, time needed for air to escape greatly influences test results, but this idea has not yet been considered by experimenters.

In another test for adhesive tapes (ASTM D 1000−65), the tape is placed on a steel plate and a roller of standard shape and weight is twice passed over the backing of the tape at a prescribed speed; presumably further rolling would not markedly enhance the tackiness.

An example in which "autohesion," (§32) was determined may be mentioned here. A roller covered with synthetic rubber was pressed into a plate of the same rubber for a definite time by a definite force, after which the force needed for separation was measured.[32] Similar devices have been constructed and tested later.[33]

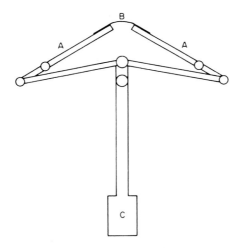

FIG. 45. Tack tester of the type of ASTM D 773-47 (1961). From reference 34. A and A are hinged plates, B is a ribbon glued to them, and C is a weight.

In the above instances, the properties of the tacky adhesive were relatively independent of time so that the age of the adhesive material was not critical. A more sensitive system is present in the common gummed tape which is not tacky when dry, becomes tacky when moistened, and ceases to be tacky when moisture evaporates. Evidently, the rheology of this substance in its tacky state varies from second to second. In ASTM test D 773 − 47 (1961), Fig. 45, moisture is applied with a standardized brush and the resistance to separation is measured after a standardized lapse of time; and apparently this degree of standardization is satisfactory for industrial testing.

§**47**   As far as breaking the contact is concerned, the majority of the methods may be classified as follows:

(a) Determination of the force needed

    (1) in butt joints
    (2) in lap joints
    (3) by peeling (a) at 90°; (b) at 180°
    (4) in more complex arrangements

(b) Determination of the work needed

    (1) by a swinging pendulum
    (2) by a rolling cylinder

A scheme of the butt joint is shown in Fig. 33. Instruments of this type have been used by Stefan himself and many times since. Types for routine testing are described, for instance, in references 7, 33, and 35.

The apparatus depicted in Fig. 43, when turned upside down, is an example of tubular lap joint.

Among the many devices suggested for the determination of peeling strength, those in which the angle of peeling (§98) is maintained constant are more likely to afford reproducible results. In the machine outlined in Fig. 46[36] this angle is 90°. Ribbon B is glued to rigid plate A which is mounted on a cart which can roll along the horizontal beam C practically without friction. When C is gradually lifted, B causes an extension of the calibrated spring E, and this extension is recorded on drum D. As there is no friction, B is always perpendicular to A. An instrument of this type was

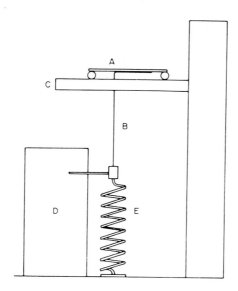

FIG. 46. Tack tester by Orlov.[36] From reference 34.

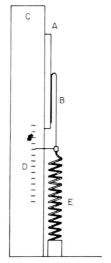

FIG. 47. Tack tester of the ASTM D 1000-65 type. From reference 34.

found very convenient in the laboratory of the author of this monograph.[37]

Peeling at 180° is carried out in several arrangements such as that recommended in the ASTM test D 1000−65. The essential features of the instrument are shown in Fig. 47. In it again A is a rigid plate, B a flexible ribbon, D a scale, and E a calibrated spring, while C is a stand. In other variants the force is measured by the inclination of a heavy pendulum rather than by the extension of a spring.

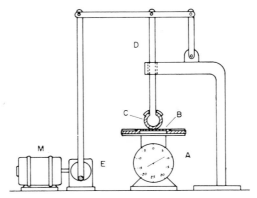

FIG. 48. Tack tester by Busse *et al.*[32]

An arrangement,[32] which mechanically is as simple as the foregoing devices but would offer considerable obstacles to a theoretical treatment, is illustrated in Fig. 48. Here a lying cylinder (C) is being lifted from a plate (B) in the direction normal to the plate. The force with which C lifts B is read on the dial of the spring scale A. The rate of movement of C is determined by the speed of motor M and the geometry of the transmitting members D and E.

A machine named *inkometer* was devised to measure the tack of printing inks spread on rollers. Only the principle of its essential part is indicated[34] in Fig. 49. The adhesive is spread over drum A kept in rotation by a motor. The "friction" between drums A and B causes a tilt of the pendulumlike system consisting of a bar to which drums B and D and sidearm E are firmly attached. A load is suspended on E to restore the initial position of the bar; the value of this load is a measure of the tack of the adhesive. More on the tack of the printing ink will be found in reference 38.

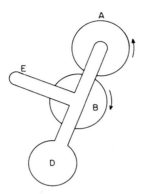

FIG. 49. The essential part of an inkometer. From reference 34.

When work, rather than force, of separation is to be measured, a pendulum is a suitable device. For instance, the bottom of a freely swinging pendulum is pressed against a vertical plate coated with the tacky material. The plate is h_0 centimeters above the lowest position of the pendulum. When the pendulum is released, it does not rise h_0 high on its upswing but only, say, h_1 centimeters high. If F is the weight of the pendulum, the work done against the tack of the adhesive is simply $F(h_0 - h_1)$. This method has been employed, for instance, in reference 39.

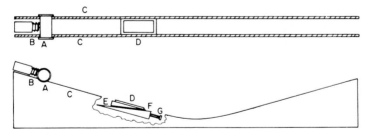

FIG. 50. The tack tester by Voet and Geffken. From reference 40.

Figure 50 is a diagram of an apparatus[40] consisting of two bent rails (C) over which a cylinder (A) can roll down (from the release device B) and up the opposite slope. On its downward path the roller passes an inked plate D, loses some of its momentum because of the tackiness of the printing ink, and therefore reaches, in its subsequent ascent, a point (h_1) which is lower than point h_0 from which it started. Letters E, F, and G indicate members serving to adjust the height of the inked plate relative to the rails. The work against tack again is $F(h_0 - h_1)$ and the "specific work" is $F(h_0 - h_1)/A$, A being the area of the plate and F the weight of the roller. It is interesting that this specific work increases with the depth of the ink layer but manifests no definite correlation with the viscosity (or consistency) of the ink. Apparently, the greater the viscosity η, the more shallow is the layer disturbed by the rolling cylinder but at the same time the work required to achieve a given disturbance is greater the greater η. A theory of the resistance to rolling a cylinder along a surface covered with a viscous liquid has been given by Kapitsa,[41] and its extension to viscoplastic materials was published by Kotova.[42]

REFERENCES

1. Josefowitz, D., and Mark, H., *India Rubber World* **106**, 33 (1942).
2. Forbes, W. G., and McLeod, L. A., *Trans. Inst. Rubber Ind.* **34**, 154 (1958).
3. Vickers, H. H., *J. Appl. Polymer Sci.* **6**, 316 (1962).
4. Galilei, G., "Two New Sciences," p. 11. Dover, New York.
5. Stefan, J. *Sitzber. Akad. Wiss. Wien, Math.-Naturw. Kl.* Abt. II **69**, 713 (1874).
6. Ormandy, E., *Engineer* **143**, 362 and 393 (1927).
7. Green, H., *Ind. Eng. Chem., Anal. Ed.* **13**, 632 (1941).
8. Bikerman, J. J., *Trans. Soc. Rheol.* **1**, 3 (1957).
9. Roydhouse, R. H., *J. Am. Dental Assoc.* **60**, 159 (1960).
10. Banks, W. H., and Mill, C. C., *J. Colloid Sci.* **8**, 137 (1953).
11. Strasburger, H., *J. Colloid Sci.* **13**, 218 (1958).
12. Oberth, A. E., and Bruenner, R. S., *Trans. Soc. Rheol.* **9**, Part 2, 165 (1965).
13. McEwan, A. D., *Rheol. Acta* **5**, 205 (1966).
14. Heidebroek, E., *Ber. Verhandl. Saechs. Akad. Wiss. Leipzig, Math.-Naturw. Kl.* **97**, No. 6, 20 (1952).
15. Bikerman, J. J., *J. Soc. Chem. Ind. (London)* **62**, 41 (1943).
16. Erb, R. A., and Hanson, R. S., *Trans. Soc. Rheol.* **4**, 91 (1960).
17. Scott, J. R., *Trans. Inst. Rubber Ind.* **7**, 169 (1931).
18. Dahlquist, C. A., *Adhesives Age* **2**, No. 10, 25 (1959).
19. Bikerman, J. J., and Yap, W., *Trans. Soc. Rheol.* **2**, 9 (1958).
20. McEwan, A. D., and Taylor, G. I., *J. Fluid Mech.* **26**, 1 (1966).

21. Bikerman, J. J., *J. Mater.* **1**, 34 (1966).
22. Truman, A. B., *Appl. Sci. Res.* **A11**, 401 and 415 (1962).
23. Weidner, C. L., *Adhesives Age* **6**, No. 7, 30 (1963).
24. Dahlquist, C. A., *Am. Soc. Testing Mater., Spec. Tech. Publ.* No. **360**, 46 (1964).
25. Satas, D., and Egan, F., *Adhesives Age* **9**, No. 8, 22 (1966).
26. Voyutskii, S. S., and Shtarkh, B. V., *Kolloidn. Zh.* **16**, 3 (1954).
27. Voyutskii, S. S., and Vakula, V. L., *J. Appl. Polymer Sci.* **7**, 475 (1963).
28. Kopylov, E. P., Lazaryanz, E. G., and Epshtein, V. G., *Kolloidn. Zh.* **28**, 675 (1966).
29. Bikerman, J. J., *J. Collod Sci.* **3**, 75 (1948).
30. Bikerman, J. J., *J. Colloid Sci.* **2**, 163 (1947).
31. Chang, F. S. C., *Rubber Chem. Technol.* **30**, 847 (1957).
32. Busse, W. F., Lambert, J. M., and Verdery, R. B., *J. Appl. Phys.* **17**, 336 (1946).
33. Pickup, B., *Trans. Inst. Rubber Ind.* **33**, 58 (1957).
34. Bikerman, J. J., "A Review of Adhesion Tests," PATRA Packaging Bull. No. 2 (1945).
35. Hammond, F. H., *Am. Soc. Testing Mater., Spec. Tech. Publ.* No. **360**, 123 (1964).
36. Orlov, A. I., *Zavodsk. Lab.* **7**, 977 (1938).
37. Bikerman, J. J., and Whitney, W., *Tappi* **46**, 420 (1963).
38. Voet, A., "Ink and Paper in the Printing Process," p. 56. Wiley (Interscience), New York, 1952.
39. Deryagin, B. V., and Sorokin, S. M., *in* "Physico-chemical Fundamentals of Printing Processes," p. 207. Moscow, 1937.
40. Voet, A., and Geffken, C. F., *Ind. Eng. Chem.* **43**, 1614 (1951).
41. Kapitsa, P. L., *Z. Tekhn. Fiz.* **25**, 747 (1955).
42. Kotova, L. I., *Zh. Tekhn. Fiz.* **27**, 1540 (1957).

CHAPTER V / **SETTING**

§48   As mentioned in §17, some commercial adhesives are permanently tacky but the majority of cements lose their tack and become definitely solid soon after application. This phenomenon is called setting. Three main mechanisms of setting are known: (a) by cooling, (b) by solvent removal, and (c) by a chemical reaction.

(a) Many substances, which are never thought of as adhesives, can act as such if they can be molten and then solidified by cooling between two adherends.[1] Apparently there is another more or less necessary condition. If the rate of nucleation is great compared with the rate of crystal growth, the adhesive film after setting is more likely to be continuous and therefore strong than when the crystal growth is rapid, the nucleation is slow, and the large crystals formed may be separated by voids or greatly contaminated regions. Polymers usually do not form separate crystals on cooling; thus, they make good adhesives if they do not decompose before melting. Common is also the utilization of thermoplastic polymers as coatings; the adherence of a coating to a substrate is, of course, not seriously different from that of an adhesive to an adherend.

For research, hot-melt adhesives offer important advantages. They are, or can be, individual compounds. As such, they can be purified before application. Their rate of setting can readily be controlled and, in this manner, their degree of crystallinity and crystal size can be varied almost at will. An investigator who wants to know what his adhesive really is, will think of this type first.

In industry, hot-melt adhesives and coatings often are preferred because their rate of setting, as a rule, exceeds that of the other types. The absence of solvents, many of which are toxic or have to be recovered, or both, is another advantage. Coatings that are

120

applied molten can be made thicker in one pass than those applied as a solution because, in the former, no danger of solvent entrapment exists. Some adhesives and coating materials cannot be used as solutes, e.g., solders or poly(tetrafluoroethylene); and they must be applied in a liquid or softened form. Adhesives which solidify on cooling are usable between both porous and nonporous adherends (e.g., paper and steel) since no route for the escape of the solvent is needed; on the other hand, only those adherends which are not weakened or deformed by the high temperature during the application of these adhesives are suitable.

The two oldest hot-melt adhesives are probably also the most important; they are solders and asphalts (bitumens); their properties are reviewed, for instance, in references 2 and 3. The use of fluxes before soldering is a particularly interesting example of controlling the wetting conditions to remove weak boundary layers. Molten solders do not wet the oxide on the metal surface. Fluxes dissolve the oxide and form a coating (of, for instance, copper abietate if rosin is the flux and copper the metal) that can be displaced by the solder according to the mechanism (b) of §23. Because of the good heat conductance of the usual metals, the adherends, as a rule, have to be heated (e.g., with a soldering iron) together with the solder.

Asphalts often are applied hot to cold solids, such as gravel (known as the aggregate) and masonry. If the asphalt too rapidly loses heat to the solid, its viscosity increases too early, and its penetration into the valleys and pores of the solid remains incomplete, as in Bikerman's experiments of §32, when the granite temperature was below 110°. Sometimes, additional substances are incorporated in the asphalt; their function is reputed to be "increasing the adhesion" between the bitumen and the stone; it is not known what they really achieve.

Various asphalts are used for impregnating paper, paperboard, and cloth. Paraffin wax was the favorite impregnating material for milk cartons; at present, some polyethylene often is added to it as the wax–polyethylene mixtures are less brittle than the wax alone. Paper saturated with polyethylene alone serves for food packaging, wire insulation, as a dielectric in capacitors, and many other purposes. Molten polyethylene is applied to wires and cables, and forms, after solidification, a protective sleeve.

For many years now, poly(vinyl butyral) has remained a preferred adhesive for the windshields of passenger automobiles. Since the windshields are big and curved, their manufacture is not easy. Obviously, no solvent cement, §49, would be suitable for this system.

Many other polymers and copolymers are main constituents of hot-melt adhesives. No attempt is made here to discuss, or even to mention, all of them. This information can best be obtained from the free technical pamphlets offered by the manufacturers; there is no better way to judge the present state of the art. Books are of necessity a little behind the time but give a condensed review of the main adhesives available; see, e.g., references 4 and 5. The following examples are intended only to illustrate the variety of materials which give rise to satisfactory adhints; it will be clear that adhesiveness has no chemical connotation. All commercial adhesives are mixtures, and the chemical formulas given below refer to their main component only.

Polyethylenes are commonly divided into high-pressure and low-pressure species. The latter are chiefly linear, i.e., their main ingredients are chains $(-CH_2-CH_2-)_n$. The former are branched, i.e., their chains, in addition to many links of the above kind, contain also links similar to

$$(-CH_2-\underset{\underset{\displaystyle CH_2-CH_3}{|}}{CH}-CH_2-CH_2-)_n .$$

The literature on polyethylenes has been summarized more than once, for instance, in references 6 and 7.

Polymers of vinyl chloride $(-CH_2-CHCl-)_n$, vinyl fluoride $(-CH_2-CHF-)_n$, vinylidene chloride $(-CH_2-CCl_2-)_n$, vinylidene fluoride $(-CH_2-CF_2-)_n$, vinyl alcohol $(-CH_2-CHOH-)_n$, and vinyl acetate $(-CH_2-CHOCOCH_3-)_n$ are used as such or as copolymers with each other, with ethyl cellulose, and so on.[8]

The above-mentioned poly(vinyl butyral) is mainly

$$\left[\begin{array}{c} -CH-CH_2-CH-CH_2- \\ \;\;\mid\qquad\quad\;\; \mid \\ O\; -\; CH\; -\; O \\ \mid \\ C_3H_7 \end{array}\right]_n$$

and partly $(-CHOH-CH_2-CHOH-CH_2-)_n$.

Alkyd resins are esters of polyhydric alcohols and polycarboxylic acids. If glycerol and phthalic acid are chosen, the polymer may be schematically represented as

Coumarone–indene resins are mainly polymers of indene, and their formation may be visualized as

Perhaps we are entitled to say that in the innumerable igneous rocks (basalt, granite, etc.) those minerals which solidified last acted as the hot-melt adhesive for the other minerals.

§49 (b) Solvent removal is the main or the sole process by which, probably, the majority of commercial, especially the household, adhesives solidify. These are sometimes denoted as solvent cements. It may be asked: What properties must a solid A, a solvent B, and solutions of A in B possess for these solutions to be usable as cements? Apparently no answer to this question is available in the literature. Presumably here again formation of separate crystals is the danger to be avoided. Thus, aqueous solution of sodium chloride is not an adhesive because the salt crystallizes out as separate cubes. If the solution during its evaporation becomes very viscous before crystallization starts, the danger has almost passed as high viscosity depresses crystal growth.

Solvent can be removed not only by evaporation but also by imbibition by porous adsorbents such as wood or paper. The separation of solute and solvent by filter paper is a well-known phenomenon; a successful method of analysis ("capillary analysis") is based on it; see, e.g., reference 9. Apparently, a similar separation of the adhesive and its solvent took place[10] in dextrin solutions applied to paper (§19); dextrin remained attached to the cellulose fibers, water between them migrated into the bulk of the fiber mat and, eventually, evaporated, and the interfacial layer became a mixture of paper fibers, dextrin, and air.

It is clear that solvent cements can be used only as long as at least one of the two adherends is porous (or otherwise permeable for the solvent). The evaporation of solvent from a narrow space between two nonporous solids (such as metals or glasses) would take too long; sometimes it is not completed several months after the preparation of the adhint. This, and some other disadvantages of solvent cements are mentioned in §48. An additional difficulty is encountered when these adhesives are applied to many adherends in succession. The solvent, which must be volatile, tends to evaporate also before the adhesive is applied; this raises the viscosity of the latter and may result in clogging the brush, the application rollers, and so on. The evaporation may lead to skin formation on the surface of the solution.

All these handicaps are often outweighed by the two fundamental advantages of solvent cements; they can be applied at room temperature and consequently do not require any heating equipment, and only they render possible the utilization of numerous good and abundant adhesive materials which decompose before they melt. Examples of such materials are mentioned in the following paragraphs.

Whenever possible, aqueous solutions are preferred. Carpenter's glue, fish glue, and their relatives are colloidal solutions of proteins of animal origin of a relatively low molecular weight. They often are applied hot and solidify not only by losing the solvent (water) but also by cooling. This process is often described as a sol–gel transformation. These animal glues are very strong in the absence of water and microorganisms but soften in rain (i.e., revert to the sol state) and are subject to putrefaction. Casein, a protein of milk, is more water-resistant. Its setting also is due not only to the removal of water; the chemical reaction sodium caseinate→calcium caseinate greatly contributes to setting. Starches, dextrins, and natural gums (exemplified by gum arabic) are strong enough for paper gluing (envelopes, postal stamps, etc.). Also soluble silicates, such as "water glass," are adhesives for paper and many other materials.

Organic solvents are resorted to for polymers insoluble in water. These polymers include, for instance, natural and reclaimed rubber, many types of synthetic elastomers (such as Neoprene), and a large number of thermoplastic high-molecular-weight materials, e.g., poly(vinyl chloride) and polystyrene. Probably, all commercial adhesives with an organic vehicle contain more than one polymer. Numerous recipes for solvent cements have been published in trade literature.

In many instances, emulsions or latexes are more convenient to apply than true solvent cements. The former are dispersions of an organic phase, typically consisting of at least a polymer, a plasticizer, and an emulsifying agent, in water or a dilute aqueous solution. They set when water evaporates and the remaining globules give rise, by coalescence, to a coherent polymer film on the adherend surface. This coalescence is a less reliable process than evaporation; some literature on it exists.[11]

§**50**   (c) Setting as a result of a chemical reaction also is not always dependable. After the solidification of a melt, at least the chemical composition (if not the degree of crystallinity, the crystal orientation, etc.) of the solid is certain. In group (c), it is often difficult to predict (or, after the fact, ascertain) in what direction and to what extent the reactions will (or did) proceed. On the other hand, the popular adhesives of this group are still solid and strong at the temperatures at which their hot-melt brethren are already soft or even liquid. Also at room temperature the adhesives of group (c) usually are stronger than those of the other groups. Many chemically setting adhesives solidify simply on mixing the ingredients, but many others call for a high-temperature curing so that the convenience of working without heating devices is not always present.

Compared with solvent cements, an important advantage of

these adhesives is that substances insoluble in any liquid can be employed; as a result, also the completed adhint is little affected by solvents. The absence of volatile components is a benefit common with the hot-melt adhesives, if no gaseous products form in the chemical reaction of setting.

If there are no (or almost no) gaseous by-products, the adhesive is suitable for both porous and nonporous adherends; otherwise, it would be recommended for porous solids only.

The venerable plaster of Paris is an example of bonding agents appropriate to both kinds of adherend. Calcium sulfate hemihydrate is mixed with water, reacts with it, and forms an agglomerate of calcium sulfate dihydrate crystals, strong enough for many purposes; no by-product, ideally, is evolved. The reactions causing the hardening of portland cement are similar but, in spite of its name, portland cement probably would not qualify as an adhesive.

Organic reactions resulting in setting of adhesives, as a rule, are polymerization or addition or condensation phenomena. In the first type two identical or nearly identical molecules unite, and in the second type the two combining molecules are quite different, but in both cases no other product results except the double molecule. In the third type, water or another small molecule forms as a by-product.

As in the previous sections, no listing of the adhesives of each subgroup can be given here; a few examples must suffice. Cross-linking of two polymeric esters of maleic acid and ethylene glycol is a typical polymerization reaction:

$$
\begin{array}{c}
-O-CH_2-CH_2-O-CO-CH \\
\qquad\qquad\qquad\qquad \parallel \\
-O-CH_2-CH_2-O-CO-CH
\end{array}
\;+\;
\begin{array}{c}
HC-CO-O-CH_2-CH_2-O- \\
\parallel \\
HC-CO-O-CH_2-CH_2-O-
\end{array}
\;=
$$

$$
\begin{array}{c}
-O-CH_2-CH_2-O-CO-CH-CH-CO-O-CH_2-CH_2-O- \\
\qquad\qquad\qquad\qquad\quad |\quad | \\
-O-CH_2-CH_2-O-CO-CH-CH-CO-O-CH_2-CH_2-O-
\end{array}
$$

The cross-linking of rubber is a much older instance.

Addition reactions may be exemplified by the curing of epoxy resins and of urethanes:

$$-O-\text{⬡}-C(CH_3)_2-\text{⬡}-O-CH_2-CHOH-CH_2-NH$$
$$\underset{\text{CH}_2}{\overset{|}{}}$$
$$\underset{\text{CH}_2}{\overset{|}{}}$$
$$-O-\text{⬡}-C(CH_3)_2-\text{⬡}-O-CH_2-CHOH-CH_2^{\nearrow NH}$$

and

$$\overset{CH_3}{\text{⬡}}\overset{NCO}{}_{NCO} + 2HOCH_2\cdot CH_2OH = \overset{CH_3}{\text{⬡}}\overset{NH\cdot CO\cdot O\cdot CH_2\cdot CH_2OH}{}_{NH\cdot CO\cdot O\cdot CH_2\cdot CH_2OH}$$

Depending on the ratio of formaldehyde to phenol and the acidity or alkalinity of the mixture, one of the following (or analogous) condensations preferentially occurs:

$$2HOCH_2 \quad + \quad CH_2O =$$

$$HOCH_2 \quad\quad + \quad H_2O$$

$$2 \quad\quad + \quad CH_2O =$$

$$\quad\quad + \quad H_2O$$

The product of many such condensations is a resol (the upper scheme) or a novolac (the lower scheme). These resols and novolacs are subjected to further condensation between two adherends to produce adhints popular mainly in the wood industry. For water-proof adhints, resorcinol rather than phenol is the starting material. It is seen that water forms during the condensation reaction. As long as wood is the adherend, this is no drawback. In some systems the amount of water liberated is so small that phenol-formaldehyde and analogous polymers, usually mixed with other ingredients, are usable between two metals also.

§51   If solidification of adhesives occurred without any associated change, that is if their viscosity and yield stress increased during setting while all other physical and chemical properties remained unaltered, both study and use of adhints would have been greatly simplified. Of the numberless changes accompanying the setting of adhesives, those that lower the final strength of adhints (see §17) may, for convenience, be classified in three divisions:

(1) changes resulting in weak boundary layers; these are treated partly in Chapter VII and partly in §§52–53;

(2) changes resulting in unfavorable stress concentrations; see §§75 to 78;

(3) changes resulting in flaws in the bulk of adhesive; see §54.

Weakness Caused by Setting

§52   In this and the next section some phenomena are outlined which are particularly dangerous if they result in the formation of weak boundary layers. They are caused by the contraction which usually accompanies setting.

Of the three groups of adhesives described in §§48–50, solvent cements and latexes, as a rule, suffer the greatest shrinkage during solidification. They usually contain 20–60 wt % of solids which, on the average, would be equivalent to 15 to 50 vol %. This means that a liquid adhesive completely filling the space between two rigid adherends would fill only 15% to 50% of the space after solidification, thus leaving up to 85% voids. Evidently a system thus constructed would not be strong.

The contraction associated with the other two classes of adhesives is smaller but still can be dangerous. The volume of solid adhesive at room temperature divided by its volume above the softening and melting range is, or would be, for instance, for polyethylenes: 0.86,[12] 0.80,[13] 0.85,[14] and for polystyrenes: about 0.95.[12, 15]

The polymerization, addition, and condensation processes of the third class cause similar shrinkages. Thus a unit volume of a liquid polyester may result in a volume of 0.90, and a liquid volume of an epoxy resin may give a volume of 0.95–0.97 after setting.[16] The small contraction of epoxy adhesives is believed to be an important factor in their popularity.

For manufacturers of plastic goods, another shrinkage coefficient is important. If a plastic material is compressed in a mold whose interior length is l and if the molded part, after cooling, has the length $(1-z)l$, then the coefficient z is, for instance, 0.001 to 0.015 for phenol-formaldehyde and related condensation products, 0.05 for a polyethylene, 0.04 for a nylon, 0.003 for a polystyrene, and so on. The values of z have to be multiplied by 3 to obtain the minimum values of the volume contraction quoted in the preceding paragraph; if, for instance, $z = 0.05$, then the volume after setting is less than 0.85 that before.

In industry, some adhesives are classified as sealers. The shrinkage of some of these materials is very small but a volume contraction of about 4% seems to be more common, and some sealers shrink by as much as 18%. Nevertheless, they can be successfully used to fill clearances of predetermined dimensions. Apparently, stress concentrations caused by shrinkage (§75) are small in typical sealers because these are still relatively mobile when the main contraction takes place.

As adhesives which would not markedly contract during solidification appear so desirable, it is a little surprising that no attempt is known to devise an adhesive material from this point of view. Long ago physical-organic chemists determined the effect of particular radicals or functions on the density of carbon compounds. Thus, Partington[17] quotes, among many others, the following values of the "atomic volumes," that is the volumes (cm³) which a gram-atom seems to occupy in a gram-molecule: oxygen in OH, 5.6 to 6.4; oxygen in ethers (except methyl ethers), 9.5 to 11. Rings take less space than a straight-chain compound of an identical composition, and the difference per "gram-ring" is said to be 6.4 cm³ for 3-atom

rings, 15 cm^3 for six-atom rings, and so on. (The density of cyclohexane at 20° is 0.7791; of 1-hexene, 0.6732; and of hexane,
0.6603). Hence, if ether formation is induced *in situ* (i.e., between
two adherends) and the water liberated is bound to another molecule
without an expansion, then a volume gain of about 4 cm^3 per gram-
molecule is obtained. If a polymer containing several cyclopropane
rings (C_3H_6) can be polymerized *in situ* to polypropylene (whose
monomer also is C_3H_6), the volume would increase by 6.4 cm^3 for
each gram-molecule of the monomer.

Some inorganic substances are exceptionally good, as far as
shrinkage is concerned, since they expand during freezing. The
volume increase observed in the transformation water → ice presumably is an important reason for the unexpected adherence of
ice to every kind of solid including those not wetted by water.[18]

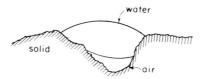

FIG. 51. Mechanical attachment of ice to a rough surface.

Suppose that liquid water is forced into a depression on a poorly
wettable surface, as indicated in Fig. 51 which is similar to Fig. 11
in §15. When the drop solidifies, it expands, pushes the hills apart,
and is gripped by them, analogously to the snap fastener effect of
§15. Perhaps this mechanism might be responsible for the marked
difference between the forces needed to shear off a cake of ice from
a stainless steel or from a polystyrene surface.[19] This force, divided
by the apparent area of the ice–adherend contact, was about 10 bars
for steel and less than 0.3 bar for polystyrene, both at −10°. Was
the grip of steel so much stronger than that of polystyrene? Unfortunately, also the other experimental results were difficult to
account for, thus the strength of the steel adhints was high and almost constant below −13°, while that of the polystyrene adhints
(also as butt joints, §79) linearly increased when the temperature
was lowered over the whole range between 0° and −25°.

Solders containing bismuth and/or antimony expand on solidification in some range of composition. Thus, many alloys containing

lead, tin, antimony, cadmium, and indium increase in volume during the liquid → solid transformation as long as bismuth content is 55% or greater[20]; when this content is 48–55% there is no measurable volume change on freezing.

Shrinkage of many adhesives can be reduced by mixing the liquid adhesive with a solid powder whose volume remains almost constant during setting. If, for instance, the volume percentage of this powder (usually denoted by the term *filler*) is $x\%$ and the relative shrinkage of pure adhesive is $y\%$, then the relative shrinkage of the filled adhesive is approximately $(1 - x)y\%$.

The common way of avoiding coarsely porous adhints is to maintain a constant pressure on the assembly during the main part of its solidification process and to eliminate anything that can prevent gradual coming together of the adherends during the rest of the setting time. If this is not done, the final strength of an adhint usually is impaired. If the clearance between two solids is filled with a liquid adhesive and the dimensions of the former are kept constant while the latter sets, the breaking stress of the joint (as a rule) first increases (because of increase in viscosity or consistency), reaches a maximum, and then decreases (because of void formation).[21]

§53   When void formation is not completely averted, its deleterious effect on the strength of an adhint depends both on the shape and size of the void and on its position. Stress concentration around voids is discussed in §§63 to 65. Here the position of the bubbles is considered. As no deliberate experiments concerning the matter are known to the author, only general and tentative statements are possible.

Presumably, a bubble is most dangerous when it is situated at the three-phase line (see, for instance, §77), as high stress concentrations are likely to exist there. It is less to fear when it clings to the adherend–adhesive boundary far from the air phase but many bubbles at the interface would be equivalent to a weak boundary layer of the first kind (§67). A bubble is relatively innocuous when it is surrounded by the adhesive; in Fig. 52 the weakening effect decreases from a to b to c.

The next question, namely what conditions of setting give rise preferentially to bubbles in a, b, or c position, also can be answered in very general terms only. It is known that *growth* of a solid (from a melt below the freezing temperature or from a supersaturated solution) is easier than the *start* of a new crystal or a disconnected chunk of amorphous solid. Thus, when an adhesive film sets, there will be a tendency for the solid phase to concentrate around the regions in which nucleation started and for the voids to be as far from these regions as possible.

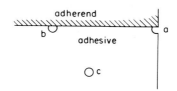

FIG. 52. The weakening effect of a bubble is greatest in position a and least in position c.

From this point of view, adhesives fall again in the same three groups as mentioned in §48. Those that set by cooling will have their voids in the region which cooled last. Usually, this means the center of the adhesive film. Only when the heat conductance of the adherends is considerably less than that of the adhesive, would bubbles of the b type be most probable. Solvent cements lose their solvent to the atmosphere and, consequently, also start solidifying around the periphery of the adhint. However, voids in position b are more likely in this than in the preceding class because diffusion of the solvent from the bottom of a narrow crack such as illustrated in Fig. 29, is a relatively slow process; the adhesive just outside the crack will set before that in the crack and, finally, there will be a bubble of solvent vapor in the depth of the crack. In the third class, the rate of solidification, at least as a first approximation, is identical over the adhesive film and no position of a bubble is more probable than any other.

Hardly any experimental proof exists for the conclusions arrived at in the preceding paragraph. If these conclusions are correct, then the most dangerous voids (position a) form not because of the preferred direction of crystal growth but because of shrinkage stresses (§75).

The higher probability of voids in the regions of latest solidification may supply a satisfactory explanation for the observation which was believed[22] to prove the existence of "specific adhesion." When animal glue is poured on wood, it is seen that the liquid fills the pores of the solid. After the setting, solid glue usually is visible as a coating on the internal pore walls. It may be asked why the solid does not remain as a bar or a blob somewhere in the middle of the pore. The answer given in earlier times was that pore walls "specifically attracted" the glue. An answer which at present appears more convincing is based on the rule that solidification tends to proceed around the first nuclei. If the pressure of water vapor above the wood in the state it was used for glueing was smaller than that of the glue solution, the solution lost its water to the wood, solidification of the glue started at the wood surface, and a glue coat remained on the pore walls after complete removal of water.

Shrinkage is not the only physical change which may cause formation of weak boundary layers. If the adhesive is a suspension, it has a tendency to settle and the upper adherend may be in contact with a more dilute suspension than the bottom member. This effect is said to be important for the adherence of portland cement to metal bars used for reinforcing.[23]

Flaws in the Bulk of the Adhesive

§54   These flaws increase the factor β of Eq. (68), §61, and thus lower the breaking stress of an adhint. They always appear during setting but usually are particularly conspicuous when (1) impurities are pushed toward the center of the adhesive layer in the course of solidification (see §53), or (2) the number of crystallization nuclei is relatively small and the rate of crystal growth is great (see §48).

There are two main devices for retarding crystal growth: one consists in adding impurities which concentrate at the crystal–liquid boundary, and the other depends on an increase in the viscosity of the liquid. In some instances, the two procedures are entirely different, but in other cases one addition combines both mechanisms.

When a dye is added to a supersaturated solution of a salt, such as NaCl, the resulting salt crystals often are more numerous and less bulky than when the dye was absent; and they are dyed. The amounts of dye introduced usually are so small that they do not markedly affect the viscosity of the solution; thus in these systems the impurity retards crystal growth because the large ion of the dye tries to substitute for the small ion (of the same sign) in the inorganic salt and in this manner disrupts the crystal lattice so badly that this ceases to grow.

The two effects are combined in the retardation of crystal growth by substances of the gelatin type. Also gelatin is an electrolyte, and the gelatin ion (positive or negative, depending on the acidity of the solution) may tend to substitute for the equally charged ion of the salt. But the viscosity effect also will be felt. When a crystal grows, it pushes the liquid with whatever is in it away from the crystal nucleus. Those molecules whose rate of diffusion is great compared with the rate of crystal growth will have time to spread over the bulk of the solution. On the other hand, gelatin molecules, whose diffusion coefficient is extremely small, will not move far. Hence, if the weight-to-volume concentration of gelatin in the solution is x gm/cm^3 and the volume of the crystal at any stage of its growth is v cm^3, then an amount xv gm of gelatin will be found around the crystal. The viscosity of this layer may be so high that convection currents are suppressed and the supply of supersaturated solution to the growing crystal retarded.

When there is no adsorption of the impurity, the effect of the latter is all due to viscosity changes.

The above reasoning explains the fact that the vast majority of adhesives are mixtures. When the least soluble ingredient starts crystallizing on evaporation of the solvent, the other components act as the dye or gelatin in the above examples. An analogous effect takes place when an ingredient starts crystallization during the cooling of a melt. High viscosity or consistency of commercial adhesives, in addition to rendering them tacky, hinders crystallization in them. Many solders are neither polycomponent mixtures nor very viscous in the molten state; they are (after setting) micro-crystalline because they are cooled so rapidly that a very large number of nuclei grows at once; thus there are many crystals and, consequently, the average crystal must be small.

Time of Set

§**55** In some industrial applications the achievement of a suitable *rate* of setting is more difficult than that of a satisfactory final strength. Thus, in automatic glueing of cartons (see §46), the adhesive is applied to one flap or both flaps, the flaps are pressed together and are kept under pressure for, say, 5 sec. Then the carton is pushed away on the conveyer belt. The setting must progress so far in these 5 sec that bent flaps do not open up as soon as pressure is removed. The tendency of the flaps to unbend can be depressed by moistening the folds with water but this device apparently is not used in industry; when a higher speed of glueing is required, an adhesive which sets more rapidly is selected.

In other applications the rate of setting should not be too rapid. Time of set should be long enough to enable the operator to place all members of the adhint in the correct position. Application of wall paper is a familiar example of this requirement.

From the point of view of the time of set, the classification of adhesives would be almost identical with that given in §48. Adhesives which solidify on cooling usually have the greatest rate of setting; those solidifying because of a chemical reaction generally need more time, and solvent cements often have the longest time of set.

It does not seem advisable to discuss the rate of setting in detail because it so greatly depends on the composition of the adhesive and on external circumstances.

The rate of cooling is determined above all by the heat conductivities of the materials of the adhint and by the geometry of the system. In theory, the final strength of a bond should depend on the rate of solidification because the tensile (or shear) strength of a solid usually is a function of this rate. Experimentally, this effect seems to be insignificant in the usual adhints.

The rate of chemical reactions which lead to solidification of an adhesive has been measured many times and for many systems. Considerable literature exists on the time of setting of plaster of Paris and of portland cement, and it is known by what additions this time can be extended or shortened. Time needed for optimum curing of innumerable rubber mixes, at many different temperatures, also has been ascertained. Many data are available also on the rate of condensation of phenol-formaldehyde and other polymeric adhesives.

The rapidity of evaporation of solvent from a solvent cement depends on the vapor pressure of the solvent, the ease of convection, the rate of diffusion of solvent molecules through the surface layer of the drying adhesive, and many other variables. If solvent can be lost by imbibition also, the pore number, the pore diameter, the wettability, and other properties of the adherend also will affect the rate of setting.

REFERENCES

1. McBain, J. W., and Lee, W. B., *J. Phys. Chem.* **31,** 1674 (1927).
2. Nightingale, S. J., "Tin Solders," Brit. Non-Ferrous Metals Res. Assoc., London, 1932.
3. Abraham, H., "Asphalts and Allied Substances," 6th ed. Van Nostrand, Princeton, New Jersey, 1960–62.
4. Skeist, I., "Handbook of Adhesives." Reinhold, New York, 1962.
5. Parker, D. H., "Principles of Surface Coating Technology." Wiley (Interscience), New York, 1965.
6. Renfrew, A., and Morgan, P., "Polythene." Wiley (Interscience), New York, 1960.
7. Boenig, H. V., "Polyolefins." Elsevier, Amsterdam, 1966.
8. Kainer, H., "Polyvinylchlorid und Vinylchlorid-Mischpolymerisate." Springer, Berlin, 1965.
9. Bikerman, J. J., "Surface Chemistry," 2nd ed., p. 31. Academic Press, New York, 1958.
10. Bikerman, J. J., and Whitney, W., *Tappi* **46,** 420 (1963).
11. Voyutskii, S. S., "Autohesion and Adhesion of High Polymers." Wiley (Interscience), New York, 1963.
12. Clash, R. F., and Rynkiewicz, L. M., *Ind. Eng. Chem.* **36,** 279 (1944).
13. Hunter, E., and Oakes, W. G., *Trans. Faraday Soc.* **41,** 49 (1945).
14. Hahn, F. C., Macht, M. L., and Fletcher, D. A., *Ind. Eng. Chem.* **37,** 526 (1945).
15. Alfrey, T., Goldfinger, G., and Mark, H., *J. Appl. Phys.* **14,** 700 (1943).
16. Sorg, E. H., and Breslau, A. J., *SPE Journal* **13,** No. 6, 115 (1957).
17. Partington, J. R., "An Advanced Treatise on Physical Chemistry," Vol. 2, p. 17. Wiley, New York, 1955.
18. Loughborough, D. L., and Haas, E. G., *J. Aeron. Sci.* **13,** No. 3, 126 (1946).
19. Jellinek, H. H. G., *J. Colloid Sci.* **14,** 268 (1959).
20. Tin Research Institute, "Fusible Alloys Containing Tin." Greenford, England, 1949.
21. Hinken, E., and Marra, A. A., *Forest Prods. J.* **7,** 286 (1957).
22. Truax, T. R., *U.S. Dept. Agr., Bull.* **1500** (1929).
23. Belykh, I. N., *Stroit. Prom.* **32,** No. 11, 38 (1954); *Chem. Abstr.* **49,** 4255 (1955).

CHAPTER VI / **FINAL STRENGTH OF ADHINTS**

Improbability of True Adhesional Failures

§56   Physical and chemical processes in an adhint, which generally are rapid immediately after the application of the adhesive, sometimes continue as long as the assembly exists. However, the rate of this aging as a rule decreases in time (see §17) so that it is possible mentally to separate the state of setting (during which the above processes are quick) from the final state when the properties of the adhint may, at a sufficient approximation, be treated as independent of the age of the system.

The final strength of an adhint is its mechanical strength in the final state. The most general statement which can be made concerning ruptures in the final state is that failure occurs where and when the *local stress* exceeds the *local strength*. This can happen in an adherend, a boundary layer, or in the adhesive.

Failures exactly along the adherend–adhesive interface were often postulated in the past. As far as we know now, they occur, if at all, so rarely as to be of no practical importance for the mechanical behavior of adhints. Several suggestions have been made to force a true "failure in adhesion" on an adhint. Although they are not likely to be successful, their principles are pointed out in §58.

It is clear that clean mechanical separation of unchanged adhesive from unchanged adherend is unthinkable wherever there is no sharp (atomically sharp) frontier between the two in the completed joint. Consider, for instance, the transition between copper and a tin-rich solder in a soldered copper joint. At the temperature of soldering, tin is markedly soluble in copper; the equilibrium solubility is[1] approximately 6 gm of tin in 94 gm of copper at 300°. At the same temperature, the two metals are capable of forming several solid phases, of which two have a definite chemical composition, namely Cu_3Sn and Cu_6Sn_5 (see §72); often, these phases can be detected on the cross-sections of copper–solder interfaces. If the transition layer between copper and solder is examined starting from the deep strata of copper and progressing to unchanged solder, the first substance encountered will be copper. Then the limit of the diffusion of tin into copper during the soldering operation will be reached, and the material will contain some tin. The concentration of tin will gradually increase, and crystals first of Cu_3Sn and then of Cu_6Sn_5 will be met before the copper concentration decreases to zero. If only the ratio of Cu to Sn, without any regard to the structure, is considered, this ratio is infinity in the bulk copper, starts to decrease as soon as the above diffusion layer is reached, and then decreases in a gradual manner to zero. There is no geometrical plane separating a material which is all copper from one which is all tin; and rupture cannot proceed along a nonexisting plane.

The diffusion and crystallization process described in the preceding paragraph is used deliberately in the so-called diffusion bonding whose literature was reviewed, e.g., in reference 2.

When a polymer adhesive is employed between two polymer adherends, intermixing occurs across the two interfaces; this, apparently, is observed also when the two polymers are incompatible in bulk experiments. The extent of intermixing is relatively easy to judge when both polymers luminesce in the ultraviolet light, and the luminescence colors are different. It was found in this manner[3] that the transition layer was about 60 μ thick when a solution of a synthetic rubber (apparently, a copolymer of butadiene, styrene, and acrylonitrile) was poured, and permitted to set, on a plate of paraffin wax. When guttapercha was substituted for the wax, the thickness of the transition zone was about 1 μ, and similar values were obtained for a few other combinations of synthetic rubbers, vinyl polymers, and so on.

In many instances, the transition zone between adherend and adhesive is, on the whole, stratified; for instance, a stratum of metal oxide as a rule is interposed between a metal substrate and a polymeric adhesive.

The oxide is a boundary layer but may also be treated as a primer, and a break between metal and oxide or between oxide and polymer still might be an instance of an adhesion failure. In reality, however, a sharp frontier between metal and its oxide usually does not exist; first because oxide films on metals are likely to be nonstoichiometric (thus, in aluminum oxide on aluminum, the ratio of Al to O gradually decreases from metal to air) and, secondly, because the two lattices (of metal and oxide, respectively) are likely to be distorted for the depth of several atoms on both sides of the imaginary frontier. Thus, instead of a plane interface between a perfect metal lattice and a perfect oxide lattice, as postulated in the "molecular" theories of adhesion, a layer of distorted structure exists, and crack starts where this distortion is particularly severe.

In some instances (see §§70 and 72), the weakest spot of the boundary layer is present not in the defective zone between two phases but is situated definitely in the bulk of the crystals between the metal and the adhesive. That this is "failure in cohesion" cannot be doubted.

§**57**   In the preceding section, systems were discussed in which no interfacial separation was possible simply because no interface was present. Here it is explained why a clean rupture between two materials practically never takes place even if the boundary between them is perfectly sharp. The interface between a metal oxide and a polymer, mentioned in §56, is an example. The essential difference between this boundary and the metal–oxide boundary described above is that there is practically no intermixing between oxide (or glass and many other materials) and the polymer and, as far as known, no significant distortion of the lattice of the adherend; the common polymers usually are to a considerable extent amorphous, that is, they do not have a definite structure which might be upset by contact with a crystal of another composition. Thus in the instance of metal oxide (or glass, etc.) in contact with a chemically inactive polymer (such as polyethylene) a true interface presumably exists. However, mechanical separation does not progress along this boundary.

In Fig. 53 white circles represent atoms of the adherend and black circles, those of the adhesive. If stress is applied normally to the

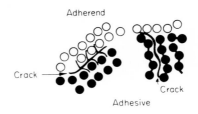

FIG. 53. A proof of the improbability of true failures in adhesion.

main plane of phase boundary (§2), a crack will start at a point where local stress exceeds local strength. Let us assume that this point is situated between the adherend and the adhesive, as shown at the left end of the sketch. The crack propagates toward the right, and it can continue either between two atoms of the adherend, or between an atom of the adherend and an atom of the adhesive, or between two atoms of the latter. If these three paths are equally probable, the probability of a crack (which started between two materials) to continue in the phase boundary for two atoms is 1/3. The probability of an interfacial crack three atoms long is $(1/3)^2$, and that of an interfacial crack extending over $n + 1$ atoms is $(1/3)^n$. If n is, for instance, 10, this probability is about 1/59,000; in other words, only in one adhint for 59,000 will a phase separation 11 atoms long be found. Thus, no rupture on a microscopic or a macroscopic scale can ever occur between two phases.

The above calculation can be refined in three respects, and each refinement lowers the probability of interfacial detachment. The factor 1/3 above was arrived at because only three alternative paths were considered. However, more than one path between adherend and adherend or between adhesive and adhesive corresponds to each path between adherend and adhesive; this is better seen on three-dimensional models. Thus, still confining ourselves to geometry, we may say that a factor of 1/7 would be more realistic than that of 1/3; for each way between two different atoms we consider three ways between identical atoms (along three faces of a cube) in each of the two phases.

The second refinement concerns the molecular structure of adhesives. Usually, they are polymers and their representation as an agglomeration of independent atoms is misleading. The right-hand half of Fig. 53 takes the long-chain nature of the adhesives into account. As a rule, it is easier to separate two molecules of a polymer than to break one of the chains. Thus, as soon as the crack reaches the space between two polymer molecules, it will advance in this space until the space between two other polymer chains is reached, and so on; it is clear that in its progress from one inter-molecular clearance to another the crack will practically never return to the two-phase boundary.

The third refinement refers to the relatve intensity of inter-molecular forces between equal and unequal substances. In the van der Waals equation for one mole of gas

$$\left(p + \frac{a}{v^2}\right)(v - b) = RT \tag{66}$$

p is gas pressure, v its volume, T absolute temperature, R the gas constant, and a and b are constants characteristic for each gas. In particular, a is a measure of intermolecular attraction. It has been known for many years (see, e.g., Beattie[4]) that Eq. (66) is applicable to gas mixtures also and that a simple (approximate) relation exists between the a values for the mixture and for its components. Let a_1 be the attraction constant for gas No. 1 and a_2 that for gas No. 2. Then the attraction (a_{12}) between molecules of gas No. 1 and those of gas No. 2 is given by the equation

$$\frac{a_1}{a_{12}} = \frac{a_{12}}{a_2}. \tag{67}$$

This relation is not exact but, at any rate, it shows that attraction between two dissimilar molecules is smaller than between two identical "stronger" molecules but greater than between two "weak" molecules. In the instance of a metal–polymer adhint we may con-clude that attraction between metal and polymer is greater than be-tween polymer and polymer; hence the bond between two polymer molecules is more likely to be severed than any other bond; thus molecular forces favor rupture in cohesion in the adhesive layer.

An equation analogous to (67) is obtained also when molecular forces are considered in more detail. If the polarizability of molecule No. 1 is α_1, and of molecule No. 2, α_2, then the attraction between two molecules of the first kind is proportional to α_1^2, between two No. 2 molecules it is proportional to α_2^2, and between No. 1 and No. 2 it is proportional to $\alpha_1\alpha_2$. If $\alpha_1 > \alpha_2$, then $\alpha_1\alpha_2 > \alpha_2^2$. If the molecules have permanent dipoles, again an analogous relation results.

As in this section molecular forces occupy our attention, the answer to the frequent question — "What keeps an adhint together?" — may be supplied here. When no external force (not even that of gravitation) acts on an adhesive joint, no internal force is needed to preserve its integrity. Each atom oscillates about its equilibrium position in which it is equally attracted by all its neighbors and thus is subjected to no resultant force. When an external force acts but it is too weak to start rupture, when, for instance, a butt joint is suspended vertically in the Earth's gravitational field, then the distances between the neighbors increase in the vertical and decrease in the horizontal directions, and forces proportional to a_1 and a_2 start acting between identical, and those proportional to a_{12} between different atoms. In this respect there is no difference between an adhint and any other solid object.

A somewhat different proof of the improbability of failure in adhesion can be formulated as follows.

In §62 the probability theory of the tensile strength of brittle solids is outlined. A consequence, supported by experiment, of this theory is that larger samples are weaker than smaller specimens. Thus, the breaking stress of a short wire or filament is greater than that of a longer piece of an identical material. The numerical value of this difference cannot be stated in precise terms because every sample has its own distribution of flaws. However in many instances the breaking stress decreases to one-half when the filament length increases ten to a hundred-fold.

As the "thickness of the interface" is very much smaller than the thickness of an adhesive film, breaking stress of the interface must be greater than that of the adhesive. It is, of course, difficult to assess the thickness of the interface, i.e., the thickness of the space between the adjacent rows of adherend and adhesive atoms, but a value near 10^{-9} cm seems reasonable. The minimum thickness of industrial or household adhesive films may be put equal to 10^{-3} cm. Thus it is 10^6 times as great as the thickness of the interface. With the above-mentioned dependence of breaking stress on thickness, the interface would be between 2^6 and 2^3 times as strong as the bulk. Even if the lowest estimate is accepted, it is clear that in a sandwich of material A and material B, the strength of A being 8 times that of B, material B rather than A regularly will be broken.

If the "three-dimensional interface" and the adhesive film are perfectly plastic rather than brittle bodies, their yield stress at a first approximation would be inversely proportional to their thicknesses (see §80.3); thus adhesive film will yield at a stress one-millionth the yield stress of the "interface."

The third refinement mentioned above in this section would apply to the present reasoning also and would further decrease the probability of rupture between adherend and adhesive.

A cruder method of accounting for the absence of true interfacial ruptures is based on surface roughness (§3). Because of roughness, a butt joint (§79) in the immediate vicinity of the interface is a multitude of scarf joints (§89). As scarf joints are relatively strong, adhesive breaks in a space in which a butt joint still may be considered as such, i.e., where rupture still may progress approximately normally to the external force.

It is interesting to note that, when the growth of a crack exactly along a perfectly smooth interface between two different elastic solids is treated in the classic manner of the theory of elasticity, the results are inadmissible from the physical viewpoint[5-7]; no such difficulty arises when the crack proceeds *in* a solid rather than between two solids.

§**58**   The odds against a clean interfacial separation are overwhelming and a true failure in adhesion cannot be expected to occur in ordinary tests on the breaking stress of adhints. A few suggestions[8] have been made to concentrate the stress exactly along the interface and, in this manner, to induce the rupture to advance between two solids rather than in one solid. Surface roughness seems to invalidate all these proposals.

Let ρ_1 be the density of the adherends and ρ_2 the density of the adhesive. Let the adhint be immersed in a liquid of density ρ_0 such that $\rho_1 > \rho_0 > \rho_2$. Gravitation would try to push the adherend down and the adhesive up, and the force would reverse its direction at the phase boundary. Centrifugal force may be used instead of gravitation.

Analogously, let μ_1 and μ_2 be the magnetic permeability of adherend and adhesive, respectively. If the adhint is immersed in a liquid of magnetic permeability μ_0 and if $\mu_1 > \mu_0 > \mu_2$, then the adherend will tend to move toward a more intensive, and the adhesive toward the less intensive magnetic field. Evidently, dielectric constant and an inhomogeneous electrostatic field can be substituted for magnetic permeability and magnetic field.

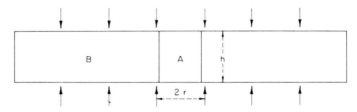

FIG. 54. Rupture of an adhint caused by a difference in the Poisson ratios.

Purely mechanical forces also may change their directions by 180° at the boundary between two phases. Let A be a cylinder (of radius r) embedded in a disc B; see Fig. 54. If the composite disc is compressed as shown, both A and B tend to expand in the horizontal directions but the spreadings are different if the Poisson ratios ν_1 and ν_2 of the two materials are different. In the absence of B, the radius of the cylinder would increase to $r + \Delta_1 r = r[1 - \nu_1(\Delta h/h)]$, assuming Hooke's law to be valid and denoting the relative vertical compression by $\Delta h/h$. In the absence of A, the round hole in the disc would expand to $r + \Delta_2 r = r[1 - \nu_2(\Delta h/h)]$. If $\nu_2 > \nu_1$, the superficial atoms of A at the A/B interface are pulled inward, and the superficial atoms of B at the same boundary are pushed outward, as the actual radius must be a compromise between $r + \Delta_1 r$ and $r + \Delta_2 r$.

Unfortunately, because of surface roughness, the macroscopic stresses caused by the differences between the densities, the magnetic susceptibilities, or the Poisson ratios of the two solids are not perpendicular to the actual interfaces. The stress patterns in the tests of the three preceding paragraphs would not be significantly different from those present in a common butt joint.

It is important to know where rupture occurs because this knowledge indicates what forces have to be overcome in breaking an adhint. If the locus of separation is not between two different materials, then evidently the attractive forces between these two solids are not involved in the fracture and need not be scrutinized when the final strength of adhints is reviewed.

§**59**   Joints failing in adhesion have often been mentioned in the literature. As §§56–57 demonstrate, these statements cannot be correct. Failure occurred either in a weak boundary layer or in the adhesive near the interface. In both instances some foreign matter must have remained on both adherends. Unfortunately the adherends, as a rule, were subjected to a cursory visual inspection only, and adhesion failure was believed to happen if no adhesive was visible on one of the solids. An examination of this kind is inadequate. It is very easy to miss a coating as thick as 20 μ if it is transparent. "Moisture-proof" cellophane is coated on both sides with films about 2 μ thick but it looks exactly like regular cellophane.

There are several methods known for detecting small amounts of foreign matter on a solid. In some instances, the contact angle of water (or another liquid) in air is suitable; this is so when the wettabilities of the adhesive or the boundary substance are different from that of the adherend. The coefficient of friction between, say, two metal plates, is significantly altered when one of these plates is contaminated with as little as 0.000001 gm of a lubricant per square centimeter. When the area of the adherend-adhesive boundary is not too small, the amounts of the adhesive remaining on the solid may be sufficient for quantitative or at least qualitative chemical analysis. Electron diffraction is sensitive enough to detect latex imprints on a glass which was touched with an adhesive tape.

Seven experimental attempts to decide whether a true failure in adhesion exists are reported in this section. No complete record of an early use[15] of radioactive isotopes is available.

The clearance between a steel bar and a poly(methyl methacrylate) plug was filled with methyl methacrylate monomer, and the monomer was polymerized *in situ,* e.g., by ultraviolet irradiation.[9] Probably the polymerization was incomplete because, on centrifuging the assembly, rupture took place in the polymer but very near to the interface, and the breaking stress was only about one-sixth the tensile strength of the bulk polymer. After the rupture the steel surface was examined with an ellipsometer, and the conclusion reached that "in no case was the thickness" of foreign matter on the metal "less than the monolayer."

In another study,[10] the two fracture surfaces were abraded with potassium bromide crystals (see §10), and the debris subjected to an infrared analysis. If the two infrared spectra obtained are identical, it is clear that the rupture took place in one material, not between two materials. The first system consisted of a lacquer film coated over a primer. The breaking stress was very small and the failure appeared to be "in adhesion." However, the two spectra proved to be identical and to belong to the phthalate plasticizer used. Apparently, the plasticizer "bled" to the interface (see §69), formed a nearly liquid layer between the two solids, and separation proceeded in this layer. In the second system, two unplasticized polymer films were placed in contact and heated together. After peeling, the two spectra were almost identical and corresponded to one polymer slightly contaminated with the other. The third system was a polymer film coated over a pigmented primer, and peeling produced two surfaces whose spectra did not agree with each other.

Both electron microscopy and contact angles were used[11] to detect the adhesive residue on glass. The amount of the residue seemed to increase with the temperature during contact and with the breaking stress.

Films of poly(isobutylene), about 25 μ thick, were cast[12] from a solution onto thin films (about 4 μ) of an alkyd resin, dried at room temperature, and peeled off. The thickness of the alkyd film was measured before and after, and no change was noticed. It was not ascertained whether the substrate was affected by the solvent, whether any of it was transferred to the poly(isobutylene), etc., and no regard was paid to surface roughness.

Four commercial adhesive tapes were applied[13] to six adherends each and then peeled off at two rates of separation (0.0042 and 0.42 cm/sec). The contact angles θ for air (at 50% relative humidity)–water–adherend were determined before and after the application and removal of the tape. One of the adherends gave unreliable results, but the data for the other five are shown in Table VIII. PTFE is poly(tetrafluoroethylene). The adhesive on Tape No. 1 was of the acrylic type; on Tape No. 2, a poly(vinyl ethyl ether); on

TABLE VIII

CONTACT ANGLES BEFORE AND AFTER APPLICATION OF ADHESIVE TAPES

Adherend		Contact angles							
	Before	After							
		Tape No. 1		Tape No. 2		Tape No. 3		Tape No. 4	
		0.42	0.0042	0.42	0.0042	0.42	0.0042	0.42	0.0042
Cellophane	23°	35°	57°	75°	79°	52°	52°	30°	45°
Glass	11°	36°	44°	33°	39°	29°	42°	74°	83°
Treated PTFE	35°	65°	84°	61°	73°	45°	59°	86°	92°
Polyamide	59°	76°	82°	87°	91°	82°	82°	90°	99°
Polyester	61°	60°	72°	76°	80°	55°	72°	73°	92°
Adhesive tape		92°		85°		77°		107°	

No 3, a natural rubber composition; and on No. 4, a silicon rubber. The lowest line of the Table lists the θ values for air–water–tape. Although the absolute values of θ are inexact (see $\theta = 23°$ for cellophane), the tendency of the data is clear: a touch of an adhesive tape alters the wetting properties of every solid tested and does it in the direction indicating the presence of some adhesive on the solid surface. The change in θ is greater the slower the peeling, i.e., the more time the adhesive has to displace air from the adherend surface.

The meaning of the results is obvious whenever the compositions of the two fracture surfaces are identical or adhesive residues are definitely detected on the adherend surface. When the compositions appear to be different, two possible sources of error must be considered. The method of detection may not be sensitive enough. Thus in the abrasion method[10] a few hundred ångströms of the surface layer usually are removed; if the adhesive residue is only, say, 50 ångströms thick, the spectrum of a layer consisting of, e.g., 300 Å of adherend + 50 Å of adhesive naturally appears different from that of the adhesive only. Another potential source of error is the presence of a weak boundary layer not detectable by infrared spectra, ellipsometry, and so on. If air or atmospheric moisture was the main ingredient of this layer, it would be missed in the post-mortem examination of the fracture surfaces. A test (admittedly imperfect, see §32) for the presence of a weak boundary layer is determination of the breaking stress f_m of the adhint; if f_m is much smaller than the tensile strength of both the adherend and the adhesive, a weak boundary layer is almost certainly there. Consequently, experiments in which both f_m and the adhesive residue were determined[11] are particularly welcome. The experiments of reference 14 are a good example.

Polypropylene, in which the middle atom was the radioactive ^{14}C (i.e., a polymer of $CH_3 \cdot C^*H : CH_2$, C^* being radioactive), was dissolved[14] in benzene, a strip of fabric was saturated with the benzene solution, the solvent was removed by evaporation, and the remaining ribbon of reinforced polypropylene, whose molecular weight was about 30,000, was pressed to an adherend for time t at a temperature T. Then it was peeled off, and the peeling tension Γ recorded. From the radioactivity of the adherend, the amount of polypropylene remaining on it after separation was calculated.

Figure 55 indicates the results obtained when an inactive polypropylene was the adherend and the temperature during the contact period was 22°. The left-hand ordinate and curve 1 refer to the peeling tension Γ, and curve 2 (with the right-hand ordinate) shows the average thickness τ of the tracer residue on the adherend; τ is expressed in "unimolecular layers" which, apparently, are believed to be about 3 Å thick. The abscissa is the time of contact. It is seen that Γ reaches an almost constant value when τ exceeds about 15 monolayers.

In the experiments of Fig. 55 presumably gradual intermixing of the two polypropylenes took place. No intermixing can be believed in the system of radioactive polypropylene and glass. Table IX collects the data recorded[14] when the contact temperature was 60°

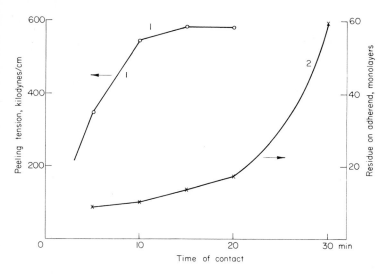

FIG. 55. Peeling tension (left-hand ordinate) and adhesive residue on adherend (right-hand ordinate) as a function of the time of contact (abscissa). Data of reference 14.

but peeling was performed at room temperature. When a copper foil was the adherend, Γ was 98 kilodynes/cm and τ was 0.6; and when the foil was oxidized at 200° before the contact, the Γ increased to 237 and τ to 2.4 monolayers. The difference between these two sets of results may have been caused, at least partly, by the greater roughness of the oxidized foil.

The effect of roughness was noticed[16] also in tests on peeling of labeled polyurethane films from aluminum panels. The films were

TABLE IX

PEELING TENSION Γ AND ADHESIVE RESIDUE THICKNESS τ —
GLASS AND POLYPROPYLENE

Time of contact at 60° (min)	Γ (kilodynes/cm)	τ (monolayers)
10	113	2.4
60	236	3.4
120	226	5.5

deposited from a solution and cured at 55–60° for about 16 hr. When the roughness of the panel (determined apparently with a gas-leakage instrument, Fig. 4) was 0.76 to 1.02 μ, the residual amount of radio-active polyurethane was 2.3×10^{-6} gm/cm^2, corresponding to about 200 Å. When the roughness was 0.38 to 0.51 μ, the residue was 1.4×10^{-6}; and at the roughness of 0.13 to 0.25 μ it was 0.9×10^{-6} gm/cm^2.

It appears that the theoretical conclusions of §§56–57 are in agreement with the experimental findings. Apparently, the theory is applicable also to the adhesion of living cells to solids.[17]

Older Theories

§60   The improbability of a true adhesional failure was first pointed out relatively recently.[18] Long before this, and repeatedly since, it was claimed that molecular attraction $\mathfrak{A}$ between adherend and adhesive directly determined the breaking stress f_m of an adhint. In many instances f_m was treated as if it were simply equal to $\mathfrak{A}$. The equation $f_m = \mathfrak{A}$ is totally wrong because of two fundamental reasons (and a few less weighty considerations which are not mentioned here). One of these is that rupture does not proceed be-tween two different materials and, consequently, interfacial forces are not involved at all. The other is that breaking stress is not a reliable measure of the intensity of any molecular forces, either in one solid or between two solids. The former reason is discussed in §§56 to 59, and the latter, in §61. In the following, four more specific hypotheses for adhesion are briefly outlined, and their specific weak-nesses are pointed out.

1. According the the first hypothesis, the work which must be spent to break an adhint is determined by the various surface energies of the system. Let γ_3 be the free surface energy of the unit area of the adherend, γ_2 the analogous quantity for the solid ad-hesive, and γ_{23} the energy of the adherend–adhesive interface. If the adhint is broken and rupture proceeds exactly along the interface, then the process of rupture results in disappearance of the interface and formation of two solid–air surfaces. For unit area the change in the free surface energy is thus $\Delta\Omega = \gamma_2 + \gamma_3 - \gamma_{23}$.

None of the values γ_2, γ_3, and γ_{23} can be measured.[19] However, if Young's equation of wetting (§22), $\gamma_3 = \gamma_{23} + \gamma_2 \cos \theta_e$, is invoked, the relation $\Delta\Omega = \gamma_2(1 + \cos \theta_e)$ is obtained. As explained in §31, $\cos \theta_e$ for all (liquid !) adhesives suitable for a given adherend must be near 1 so that $1 + \cos \theta_e$ is practically equal to 2. Thus, $\Delta\Omega = 2\gamma_2$. If a further hypothesis is introduced, namely that the surface energy of a solid is not significantly different from that of its melt, then γ_2 can be found. For polymeric adhesives, 30 gm/sec² or 30 ergs/cm² is a reasonable value for it. Thus, the conclusion is reached that the work of rupturing an adhint should be about 60 ergs/cm².

The experimental work $\mathfrak{M}$ needed to break 1 cm² of an adhint is almost always much greater. To calculate it, we consider a butt joint between two cylinders (basis to basis), each 5 cm long and made of a material whose modulus of elasticity is 7×10^{11} dynes/cm² ($\approx 10^7$ psi) as for aluminum. If the breaking stress of the joint is 7×10^8 baryes ($\approx 10^3$ psi), the cylinders are extended by 0.01%, i.e., both cylinders together are in the moment of rupture by 0.001 cm longer than before the application of the load. Hence, $\mathfrak{W}$ per unit area is $7 \times 10^8 \times 10^{-3} = 700 \times 10^3$ ergs/cm² and $\mathfrak{M} = 12 \times 10^3 \mathfrak{A}$.

It is plain that the hypothesis $\Delta\Omega = \mathfrak{W}$ is wrong not only because there is no separation between two different materials but also because the work of breaking an adhint is spent above all on the deformation of the system before actual rupture takes place. This statement is true also for peeling and other types of rupture. Also, Young's equation is incorrect (see §22), and there is no justification for assuming the surface energies of a solid and its melt to be identical.

The considerations of the four preceding paragraphs evidently are applicable to a uniform solid (such as a metal bar or a glass plate) to the same extent as to an adhint. In this instance, the theory assumes a much more sophisticated form but is still not more convincing than in the crude example above.[20]

2. Many investigators believed (and still believe) that a strong attraction between the molecules of the adherend and those of the adhesive is required for a strong bond. A valence bond between an adherend atom and an adhesive atom would be ideal but interaction between dipoles in the two phases also would be admissible. Con-

sequently, the formulators of industrial adhesives were urged to introduce "more polar" components into their mixtures. Apparently, the polarity which was believed so beneficial was never adequately defined. Was it necessary for the whole molecule to be a permanent dipole? Toluene is one, but somehow was classed by many advisers as a nonpolar compound. Was the absolute value of the dipole moment important? It is almost identical for water and cetyl alcohol. Perhaps, the dipole moment divided by the volume of the molecule would be a better indication?

The attraction hypothesis is easily refuted by the observation that substances (such as polyethylene) which contain no dipoles perfectly adhere to solids (such as glasses, metals, polymers) with which no chemical reaction is possible (see §69). When a chemical reaction undoubtedly occurs, it may result in a weakening of adhints (see §70). When a brittle polar, a brittle nonpolar, and a ductile nonpolar adhesive are compared, the two brittle materials behave similarly, while there is no similarity in the behavior of the two nonpolar substances (see §96).

The surface energy hypothesis which gives unreasonably low values for $\mathfrak{W}$ usually leads to excessive results for the breaking stress. If the attraction $\mathfrak{A}$ between adherend and adhesive linearly decreases, when the distance between the two solids increases from zero to 3×10^{-8} cm, and is negligibly small at larger distances, then the highest value of $\mathfrak{A}$ is equal to $2 \Delta\Omega/3 \times 10^{-8}$ baryes if $\Delta\Omega$ is in ergs.cm^{-2}. With $\Delta\Omega = 60$, $\mathfrak{A}$ becomes 4×10^9 or 58,000 psi. More detailed calculations[21] of molecular attractions afforded even higher values for $\mathfrak{A}$ (e.g., 5×10^{10} baryes) which thus are even further from the experimental data for f_m. In the terms of Eq. (68), §61, these computations are erroneous because they take cognizance of the cohesion ξ but forget the factor β.

3. Electrostatic attraction between adherend and adhesive was supposed to be responsible for the major part of the final strength of an adhint. However, in peeling tests, irradiation of the three-phase line with X rays or with the rays of radioactive thorium usually increased the work of peeling.[22] As such an irradiation ionizes air around the adhint and thus suppresses the effects of static electricity, it would reduce the resistance to peeling to almost nothing if this

resistance were of electrostatic origin. If the hypothesis were correct, the strength of adhints would have been markedly greater in dry than in humid air; unless the adhesive itself is moisture-sensitive no such effect has been detected yet. There was no definite difference[23] in peeling tensions between rubbers which did, and those that did not, emit radiation when stripped off a steel drum.

Another argument against the electrostatic theory is that, according to it, the cause of strength of adhints is totally different from that of ordinary solids. It is impossible to believe that the strength of, say, glass and polyethylene is due to intermolecular forces but the strength of glass–polyethylene–glass sandwiches is determined by static charges.

4. Intermixing of adherend and adhesive along their common boundary was believed to be essential. As mentioned in §56, this intermixing certainly takes place in numberless adhints, but it is not necessary because joints between mutually immiscible solids are, if they are proper joints, just as strong as those in which mixing is manifest.

The Breaking Stress

§**61**   If the concept on which this monograph is based is correct, that is, if practically every failure of an adhint takes place *in* a material rather than *between* two different materials, then the breaking stress of the adhint must be related to the strength of its weakest phase. This conclusion is confirmed by many observations but, unfortunately, the relation between the strength of a system and that of the weakest material in it is complex and varies from instance to instance. The discussion of this relation may be based on the equation

$$\xi = (\alpha f_m + s)\beta , \qquad (68)$$

although this is rather a mnemonic help than mathematical truth; ξ is molecular cohesion, f_m is breaking stress, s is "frozen stress," and α and β are stress concentration factors defined in the following.

Molecular cohesion ξ is the maximum attractice stress acting across a plane perpendicular to an external force when the distance between the atoms on both sides of the plane gradually increases as a result of the force. It is a property of the composition and the molecular (or atomic) structure of the solid and in the simplest instances can be calculated. The difference between ξ and the $\mathfrak{A}$ of §60 is that ξ acts between identical, and $\mathfrak{A}$ between different atoms or molecules.

The calculation is relatively straightforward for the simple ionic crystals such as those of sodium chloride. If only the electrostatic forces acting between ions at all distances and the repulsive forces forces significant at distances less than 1 Å are considered, cohesion comes out equal to 2.3×10^{10} baryes (330,000 psi) for NaCl; if also dispersion forces are taken into account, the result is 2.6×10^{10} baryes.[24]

The shear strength of sodium chloride and similar simple crystals should be approximately equal to $0.25G$ (G is the shear modulus), i.e., to about 3×10^{10} baryes. Similar values are obtained by setting ξ equal to the heat of sublimation of 1 cm^3 of sodium chloride at room temperature; this magnitude is usually denoted by the term "cohesive energy density" and has the dimension of erg/cm^3, i.e., that of pressure or stress. The usual experimental values of tensile strength of NaCl are confined between 4×10^7 and 6×10^7 baryes, that is are about 500 times as small as expected. The elastic limit of single crystals of silver is about $0.00002G$ instead of $0.25G$, and even for polycrystalline metals it is usually less than $0.01G$.

For polymers, different values are obtained according to whether rupture involves breaking of a primary valence bond or can proceed between molecules. In the first alternative, tensile strength would be as high as 4.3×10^{11} baryes (6,000,000 psi) for a phenol-formalde-hyde resin[24] and 1.5×10^{11} baryes for a cellulose fiber.[25] If no degradation of molecular chains takes place, the theoretical cohesion may be about 4×10^9 baryes for phenol-formaldehyde condensation products and near 3×10^9 for cellulose, that is, of the experimental order of magnitude. However, the idealized structure postulated for the calculation of strength without intramolecular rupture probably never occurs in real polymers. Thus, in general, ξ is much greater than the experimental breaking stress averaged over the affected area (see also §100).

The sign f_m in Eq. (68) denotes this stress. In the instance of butt joints $f_m = F_m/A_1$, F_m being the external force and A_1 the cross section of the adhint in a plane perpendicular to F_m. For lap joints stressed in tension, $f_m = F_m/A_2$, F_m having the previous meaning and A_2 being the area of the overlap. The values of f_m for some other types of adhint are given in Chapter VIII.

The factor α is different from unity because the stress pattern in an adhint is different from that in a grossly uniform body of identical dimensions, subjected to an identical system of forces and moments. The value of α, as a rule, is greater the greater the difference between the mechanical constants (such as modulus of elasticity) of the adherend and the adhesive (or the weak boundary layer) (see Chapter VIII).

In Chapter VIII also the "frozen stress" s is discussed in detail. It has to be vectorially added to, or vectorially subtracted from, stress αf_m caused by the external force F_m.

The sum $\alpha f_m + s$ would be equal to molecular cohesion if the adhesive were uniform down to molecular dimensions. It has to be multiplied by factor β because no solid is truly uniform. The discrepancy between the theoretical values of cohesion, as stated above in this section, and the experimental breaking stresses of solids has been accounted for by flaws in real solids. It is believed that every rupture originates at a bad flaw or a particularly weak spot, and that weak spots are distributed in the solid more or less at random.

Thus the theory has two aspects. First, we must render the existence of flaws probable and gain a knowledge of their distribution. Secondly, we must consider the possible nature of these flaws and prove that flaws which are likely to be present can be the cause of the striking difference between theoretical and experimental strength.

§62   The probability theory of strength is at least as old as Plateau's work. (Leonardo da Vinci is said to have forecast it but no clear indication of the theory could be found by the present author in

Leonardo's available notes.) Plateau[26] noticed that big foam films lasted for a shorter time than small films from an identical solution and concluded that this size effect presumably was due simply to the greater probability of a weak spot (caused by an external agent) in a larger specimen.

An early mathematical treatment of the theory was published by Peirce.[27] Suppose that N_0 samples were tested and N of these broke at stresses between f and $f + df$. (The subscript m used in §60 to remind the reader that we were dealing with the maximum possible stresses is omitted here.) Evidently, $(N/N_0) = \varphi(f)$ is a function of f. The probability that the strength of one of these samples is equal to, or greater than, f is $\int_f^\infty \varphi(f) \, df$. Let the length of each sample be l cm. If we now consider a sample nl cm long, we can apply this reasoning to each part, l cm long, of the large specimen. The probability Π that none of the n regions of this specimen will break at a stress below f is equal to the product of the probabilities for each region. Thus

$$\Pi = \left[\int_f^\infty \varphi(f) \, df \right]^n$$

or, if N_0 specimens of length nl are tested, the number breaking at a stress between f and $f + df$ is given by

$$dN = \varphi(f) \left[\int_f^\infty \varphi(f) \, df \right]^n df.$$

The function $\varphi(f)$ can either be postulated or can be derived from experiments; for instance, for cotton fibers, it was found that

$$f_{nl} - f_l = -4.2(1 - n^{-0.2})\sigma_l \, ,$$

σ_l being the standard deviation of the breaking stresses found for length l; f_{nl} is the mean breaking stress of specimens nl cm long and f_l that for l cm long specimens.

A particularly simple test of the probability theory of fracture is conducted as follows.[28, 29] Determine the *average* breaking stress of samples nl cm long (or adhints nh cm thick). Determine the minimum breaking stress in a group of n samples, each l cm long, or h cm thick. These two stresses should be equal because in each set of experiments the strength of the weakest spot along nl (or nh) cm is measured. Experimental results confirmed the expectation for glass fibers and also for many other substances (see, e.g., reference 30) so that the theory may be considered a reliable guide. Of the many additional publications on the statistical theory of strength only one[31] can be referred to here.

§**63**　　The degree of weakening caused by flaws requires a somewhat more extended treatment. This treatment leads to quantitative results if the adhesive is a Hookean solid or behaves as a Hookean solid after the deformation caused by an external force (see §65). Tables for stress concentration factors at notches, holes, and so on can be found, for instance, in reference 32. The following treatment is based mainly on the book by Savin.[33] The solid containing flaws is supposed to be practically two-dimensional as the mathematics becomes prohibitively difficult as soon as the third dimension is involved.

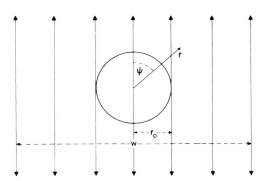

FIG. 56. Stress concentration at a circular hole.

Imagine, therefore, a thin foil (of width w) in which a circle of radius r_0 has been cut out (see Fig. 56); w is supposed to be greater than about $5r_0$. If the foil is stretched by force $F = fw\delta$, δ being the thickness of the foil ($w \gg \delta$), then stress σ_ρ normal to the circumference is given by

$$\sigma_\rho = 0.5f[(1 - \rho^2) + (1 - 4\rho^2 + 3\rho^4) \cos 2\psi];\qquad (69)$$

ρ is r_0/r, if r is the distance of a point in the foil from the center of the circle and ψ is the angle between the direction of the external force and the radius connecting the center of the circle with the point for which Eq. (69) is valid. When $r = r_0$ and $\rho = 1$, that is, at the phase boundary, $\sigma_\rho = 0$ as we assume that the inside of the hole cannot support any stress; if the hole is filled with a material weaker than the foil but still able to transmit stresses the equation must be modified. At $r \gg r_0$ the value of ρ is negligibly small and stress $\sigma_\rho = (f/2)(1 + \cos 2\psi)$; thus stress in the direction of the external force (i.e., at $\psi = 0$) is equal to f as it should be. At $\psi = 0$, stress σ_ρ rapidly decreases from f to zero on nearing the hole; at $\rho = 0.5$, σ_ρ is still $0.47f$, at $\rho = 0.8$ it is $0.34f$, and so on.

Stress σ_ψ along the circumference of the hole and along circles concentric with it is given by the equation

$$\sigma_\psi = 0.5f[(1 + \rho^2) - (1 + 3\rho^4) \cos 2\psi].\qquad (70)$$

It is, when $\psi = 0$, zero at $\rho = 0$, i.e., far from the hole. At the phase boundary (that is at $\rho = 1$) $\sigma_\psi = f(1 - 2 \cos 2\psi)$ and at the right-hand and the left-hand ends of the circle (see Fig. 56)

$$\sigma_\psi = 3f.\qquad (71)$$

Thus the pull in the direction of the external force at the points where the tangents to the circle are parallel to this force is three times as great as the average pull. In this instance, β of §61 is equal to 3. If r_0 is not much smaller than w, then

$$\beta = 3w/(w - r_0).\qquad (72)$$

Figure 57 demonstrates an experimental confirmation of Eq.

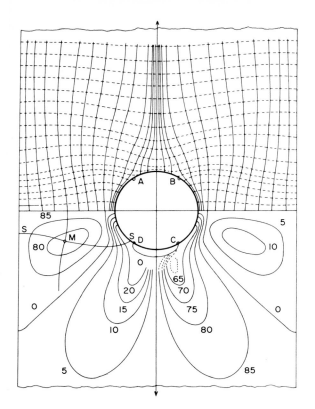

FIG. 57. Experimental stress concentration at a circular hole. From reference 33.

(70). It was prepared on the basis of an optical examination of a polymer plate, 2.64 cm wide, having a round hole of 0.8 cm diameter and stressed in the direction of the arrows. The upper half of the figure shows the direction of the principal stresses, and in the lower half the isoclines are drawn; the direction of the principal stress is constant along each isocline. The numbers at the isoclines mean the deviation of this direction (in degrees of an angle) from the direction of the external force. Thus the (solid) lines of the principal stress in the right-hand upper quarter of the figure are inclined from SW to

NE near the equatorial line, and from SE to NW near the top; somewhere in between they are directed from N to S, and the line marked 0 in the bottom half is the locus of these points.

Shear stress τ is

$$\tau = 0.5f(1 + 2\rho^2 - 3\rho^4) \sin 2\psi . \tag{73}$$

It is zero along the circumference of the hole because of its symmetry. It is greatest at $\sin 2\psi = 1$, i.e., at $\psi = 45°$ and at $\rho = \sqrt{\tfrac{1}{3}}$, i.e., at $r = 1.73 r_0$.

§64   The greatest stress concentration factor at a circular flaw is equal to 3. Much greater factors are possible when the hole is elliptical.

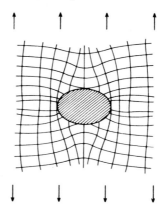

FIG. 58. Stress concentration at an elliptical hole. From reference 33.

In Fig. 58 the principal stress lines in the vicinity of such a hole are illustrated. If a is the half-axis of the ellipse perpendicular to the external force and b the half-axis parallel to the latter, then stress σ_ψ at the right-hand and the left-hand extremes of the ellipse is

$$\sigma_\psi = f\left(1 + \frac{2a}{b}\right) . \tag{74}$$

As a may be much greater than b (as in a crack), the stress concentration factor

$$\beta = 1 + \frac{2a}{b} \qquad (75)$$

may be a large number. If, for instance, $a = 100b$, then $\beta = 201$, that is, the maximum stress acting in the adhesive is 201 times the average stress. As the radius R of curvature at the ends of the major axis is b^2/a, an approximation of Eq. (75) is $\beta = 2(a/R)^{1/2}$.

If the ellipse is extended in the direction of the external force, rather than normal to it as in Fig. 58, then a is smaller than b and the stress concentration is less significant. If $a \ll b$, the value of β is practically equal to unity. Thus a crack along the line of pull has no harmful effect.

§65 If the hole is a square, the highest β is observed at the corners. The actual values of β depend on the sharpness of these corners (which cannot be infinitely sharp because of the molecular structure of matter). Thus, when the radius of curvature at the corners decreases from $0.060l$ to $0.014l$, l being the length of a side of the square, β near the corners increases from 3.9 to 6.2.

If the hole is a rectangle, the greatest β depends on the ratio of its length to its width and also on the angle ψ between the longer

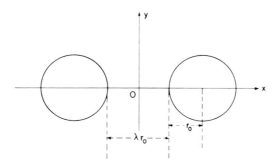

FIG. 59. Stresses in a plate perforated with two circular holes.

side of the rectangle and the direction of force. If, for instance, this angle increases from 30° to 60°, the maximum β (for the above ratio equal to 5) increases from 7 to 12.

If there are two circular holes in the plate, their effect depends on their mutual distance $2\lambda r_0$ (see Fig. 59) and on the direction of the external force. When the force acts parallel to $0y$, two holes weaken the plate more than one hole does but the difference is small if λ is greater than 1.5; at $\lambda = 1.5$ the greatest β is 3.26 but at $\lambda = 2.0$ it is 3.02, that is, practically equal to that at $\lambda = \infty$. When the force acts along $0x$, two holes are less dangerous than one because they are like an ellipse elongated parallel to the pull direction (§64). Thus, the maximum value of β is 2.57 for $\lambda = 1$.

§66   The conclusions reported in §§63 to 65 are derived from equilibrium equations. In other words, it is assumed that no movement occurs and that the shape of the holes is that *after,* not before the application of the external force.

It would be advantageous to be able to predict the difference between the two shapes but the present theories apparently cannot give final answers to this problem. It is clear, however, that both elastic and plastic changes tend to reduce the value of β. If, for instance, the hole was a circle before the application of stress, either elastic or plastic deformation will alter it to an ellipse elongated in the pull direction, that is, will render a smaller than b (see §64), and thus lower the value of β under its initial magnitude of 3.0. If the total elongation is large, say over 100%, every circular or quadratic hole will be extended into an ellipselike hole directed along the lines of force, so that flaws present in the adhesive before the tension was applied will be made innocuous. If, on the other hand, the total relative elongation is small, say less than 3%, the deformation occurring before the rupture will not be able markedly to influence the shape of the weak spots, and stress concentrations will be approximately as great as calculated in §§63 to 65.

REFERENCES

1. Hansen, M., and Anderko, K., "Constitution of Binary Alloys," p. 634. McGraw-Hill, New York, 1958.

2. Bernstein, L., *J. Electrochem. Soc.* **113,** 1282 (1966).
3. Krotova, N. A., and Morozova, L. P., *Dokl. Akad. Nauk SSSR* **127,** 141 (1959); "Research in Surface Forces" (B. V. Deryagin, ed.), p. 36. Consultants Bureau, New York, 1962.
4. Beattie, J. A., *Chem. Rev.* **44,** 141 (1949).
5. Salganik, R. L., *J. Appl. Math. Mech.* **27,** 1468 (1963).
6. England, A. H., *J. Appl. Mech.* **32,** 400 (1965).
7. Malyshev, B. M., and Salganik, R. L., *Intern. J. Fracture Mech.* **1,** 114 (1965).
8. Bikerman, J. J., *in* "Adhesion and Adhesives. Fundamentals and Practice," p. 72, Wiley, New York, 1954.
9. Patrick, R. L., Doede, C. M., and Vaughan, W. A., *J. Phys. Chem.* **61,** 1036 (1957).
10. Johnson, W. T. M., *Offic. Dig., Federation Soc. Paint Technol.* **33,** 1489 (1961).
11. Gul, V. E., Chzhan, In-si, Vakula, V. L., and Voyutskii, S. S., *Vysokomolekul. Soedin.* **4,** 294 (1962).
12. Huntsberger, J. R., *J. Polymer Sci.* **A1,** 1339 (1963).
13. Weidner, C. L., *Adhesives Age* **6,** No. 7, 30 (1963).
14. Gromov, V. K., Neiman, M. B., Vakula, V. L., and Voyutskii, S. S., *Zh. Fiz. Khim.* **37,** 2077 (1963); *Intern. J. Appl. Radiation Isotopes* **14,** 351 (1963).
15. Bright, W. M., *in* "Adhesion and Adhesives. Fundamentals and Practice," p. 33. Wiley, New York, 1954.
16. Reegen, S. L., *J. Appl. Polymer Sci.* **10,** 1247 (1966).
17. Weiss, L., *J. Theoret. Biol.* **2,** 236 (1962).
18. Bikerman, J. J., *J. Colloid Sci.* **2,** 163 (1947).
19. Bikerman, J. J., *Phys. Status Solidi* **10,** 3 (1965); **12,** K 127 (1965).
20. Bikerman, J. J., *SPE Trans.* **4,** 290 (1964).
21. Taylor, D., and Rutzler, J. E., *Ind. Eng. Chem.* **50,** 928 (1958).
22. Deryagin, B. V., and Krotova, N. A., "Adgeziya," p. 73. Acad. Sci. U.S.S.R., Moscow, 1949.
23. Deryagin, B. V., Karasev, V. V., Medvedeva, A. M., and Zherebkov, S. K., *Kolloid. Zhur.* **27,** 35 (1965).
24. deBoer, J. H., *Trans. Faraday Soc.* **32,** 10 (1938).
25. Mark, H., *in* "Cellulose and Cellulose Derivatives" (E. Ott, ed.), p. 1000. Wiley (Interscience), New York, 1943.
26. Plateau, J., *Mem. Acad. Roy. Sci. Belg.* **37,** 9th ser., 7 (1869).
27. Peirce, F. T., *Textile Inst. J.* **17,** T 355 (1926).
28. Bikerman, J. J., *J. Soc. Chem. Ind. (London)* **60,** 23 (1941).
29. Bikerman, J. J., and Passmore, G. H., *Glass Ind.* **29,** 144 (1948).
30. Greene, C. H., *J. Am. Ceram. Soc.* **39,** 66 (1956).
31. Weil, N. A., Bortz, S. A., and Firestone, R. F., *Mater. Sci. Res.* **1,** 291 (1963).
32. Roark, R. J., "Formulas for Stress and Strain," 4th ed. McGraw-Hill, New York, 1965.
33. Savin, G. N., "Kontsentratsiya Napryazhenii okolo Otverstii," GITTL, Moscow-Leningrad, 1951; "Stress Concentration Around Holes," Pergamon Press, New York, 1961.

CHAPTER VII / IMPROPER ADHINTS

Weak Boundary Layers

§67   Improper adhints contain a zone of weakness between (at least one) adherend and the adhesive; when a sufficient external force is applied, rupture proceeds within this zone. The failure is still "in cohesion," that is, the same (weak) material is present on both fracture surfaces (see §59).

It is convenient to classify improper adhints according to the origin of the material making up the weak boundary layer. As three phases (the medium in which the joint is being made, the adhesive, and the adherend) are present during the formation of an adhint, seven classes of these layers are possible; in the following air is supposed to be the above medium. The weak material can come from

(1) the air
(2) the adhesive
(3) the adherend (or both adherends)
(4) the air and the adhesive
(5) the air and the adherend(s)
(6) the adhesive and the adherend(s); and
(7) all three phases.

Instances of improper adhints of all these classes are given in §§68 to 73.

§68   Weak boundary layers of the first class are very common. They always occur when the adhesive does not wet the adherend and air pockets remain between the two after the solidification of the adhesive. Water-repellent fabrics are an example of systems, and lithography is an example of processes, in which this phenomenon is utilized. Figure 60 is a schematic representation of an adhesive–adherend boundary from which air was not completely removed; seven air pockets are shown between the two solid phases. The contact angle is approximately 90°. If a stress perpendicular to the main plane of the adhesive–adherend interface is applied, each air pocket acts as a bubble a or a bubble b of Fig. 52 (§53). For a spherical bubble in position b, the stress concentration factor would have been $3w/(w - r_o)$ [See Eq. (72), §63]; in the instance of Fig. 60, w means the distance between the midpoint of the adhesive separating a first from a second bubble and the analogous midpoint of the adhesive separating the second from the third bubble.

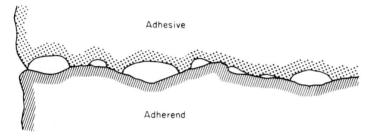

Adhesive

Adherend

FIG. 60. Air pockets in the boundary between an adhesive and an adherend poorly wetted by it.

If the adherend is transparent (e.g., made of glass), the air pockets can be seen. A beam of light, falling on the free surface of the glass and penetrating the glass plate at a suitable angle, is totally reflected by the air present on the opposite side of the plate. No total reflection occurs from the points in which an adhesive–glass contact exists, and these areas appear dark in the reflected light. The bubbles can also be "developed," in the photographic sense.[1] If a solid is immersed in a liquid supersaturated with a gas such as carbon dioxide, the bubbles present on the solid–liquid interface act as nuclei and grow to visible dimensions at the expense of the excess dissolved gas.

As water has a poor wetting ability, compared with that of typical organic liquids, weak boundary layers caused by incomplete wetting are particularly frequent when aqueous adhesives are used. A label coated with a starch or dextrin mucilage easily falls off an oily metal. Aqueous adhesives are not suitable for the majority of plastic adherends. On the other-hand, poly(tetrafluoroethylene) is difficult to wet with almost any liquid; this seems to be an important reason for the difficulty of attaching this polymer to another solid with any adhesive; for another opinion see §69.

An observation which indicates that the weak boundary layer occurring in poly(tetrafluoroethylene) is of the first rather than of the second class refers to adhints produced by melting the polymer on an adherend and cooling. Many commercial polyethylenes (whose weak boundary layers belong to the second class) give rise, in this manner, to adhints which are easily ruptured (see §69). On the contrary, adhints of the type "stainless steel–poly(tetrafluoro-ethylene)–stainless steel" needed[2] peeling tensions of over 1000 kilodynes/cm, and the breaking stress of the butt joints was, e.g., 140 bars (or 2000 psi), i.e., nearly equal to the tensile strength of the polymer. In unpublished experiments in the author's laboratory, copper was coated with a copolymer of tetrafluoroethylene and hexafluoropropylene, and the peeling strength was that to be expected from proper adhints not only immediately after preparation but also after storage in water.

If the adhesive cannot, unassisted, displace air from the adherend surface, this displacement may be aided by forming the adhint in a vacuum. Lap joints of "aluminum–an epoxy adhesive–oxidized polyethylene–the epoxy adhesive–aluminum" were prepared[3] in the usual manner in air; their breaking stress was 8–11 bars (or 120–160 psi). When they were made in a vacuum of 2.7 mbar (or 2 mm Hg), the breaking stress was 14–18 bars.

In some instances (see §67), a fluid different from air has to be displaced by the adhesive. Water, naturally, is the most common of these fluids. It is believed that the gravel which, after being mixed with molten asphalt, is used for making roads usually contains much moisture on its surface and that this moisture is not completely removed by the asphalt; after evaporation of the water, voids between the stone and the asphalt remain and facilitate loosen-ing of the sand particles. A strictly laboratory instance of a weak boundary layer consisting of water was observed[4] when mercury was used as the adhesive. If mercury and the adherend were cooled separately in air before being combined, a loose bloom of hoarfrost formed on their surfaces and precluded formation of strong adhints.

When adhints are assembled in a vacuum, the vapor of the pump oil is adsorbed or even condensed on the adherend. If it is soluble in the adhesive, as presumably was the case in the example above,[3] it does no harm, but it may form a weak stratum if the adhesive does not dissolve it. It is stated[5] that "the vapor pressure of most pump fluids in equilibrium with a baffle at 15° is such that the substrate surface would be covered with a monomolecular layer in a minute or so if every molecule striking the surface was sorbed." When a silica surface was exposed to the vapor (at room temperature) of a pump fluid (apparently, a dimethyl silicone of molecular weight 484) for a few minutes and then coated in a vacuum of about 0.13 barye (or 10^{-4} mm Hg) with zinc sulfide from its vapor, the coating obtained, about 0.25 μ thick, was not resistant to humidity; in a moist atmosphere it evolved hydrogen sulfide and flaked off. In the absence of silicone oil, the adherence was satisfactory. Strangely, glass was not adversely affected by the silicone oil vapor.

Contact angle (§22) is the quantitative measure of the displacement of air (or another medium) by the liquid adhesive. The air pockets illustrated in Fig. 60 are more likely to be present the greater the contact angle θ. As these defects lower the strength f_m of an adhint, a dependence of f_m on θ may be expected. Several studies of this dependence have been reported but some of them are not convincing.

It is clear that the contact angle referred to in the preceding paragraph is that between air, the adhesive, and the adherend. Unexpectedly, attempts were made to correlate θ at the boundary of air, *water,* and the adherend with the f_m of a system adherend–a nonaqueous adhesive–adherend. Polyethylene films were grafted[6] with various amounts of, e.g., methyl methacrylate, by means of irradiation with a ^{60}Co source. The θ of water drops on these films was approximately 94° as long as the content of the ester was below approximately 7%; between 7% and 15% of the ester, θ decreased to about 76°, and it maintained this value when the percentage rose from 15% to almost 50%. Two such films were glued together, as a lap joint, with a solution of a butadiene-acrylonitrile rubber, heated under pressure to remove the solvent and air, and then ruptured. The breaking stress was about 4.6 bars when the ester content was 0–8%, rose to about 6 bars when the ester percentage rose to 14%, and remained constant on further grafting. Thus, the effect of methyl methacrylate on f_m was similar but opposite to that on θ, as would be predicted. Unfortunately, the experimental data cannot be accepted as a confirmation of the theory. The adhesive was not aqueous. Its solvent (a mixture of acetone and toluene) presumably perfectly wetted every film tested; also the synthetic rubber, if liquid, would wet these films; thus, there was no ground to expect any air pockets. Moreover, the difference between $\theta = 94°$ and $\theta = 76°$ may not be significant as far as adhesion is concerned; numerous air pockets would be expected in either case. A third objection is that it was not tested whether the rupture really proceeded in a weak boundary layer; an increase in breaking stress from 4.6 to 6.0 bars could have been caused by an increase in the tensile strength of the polymer (see §61) on grafting. An example of the effect of grafting on both polymer strength and adhint strength can be found in reference 7; see also §110.

In a very similar investigation[8] the contact angles between air, aqueous butanol solutions, and papers of various degrees of sizing were compared with relative values of adhesion for polyethylene–paper adhints. The θ values for drops of aqueous solutions on Douglas-fir strips, as usually, decreased[9] with the surface tension γ of the solution but were still near 50° when γ was 70 gm/sec^2. When the wood was glued with, apparently, urea-formaldehyde adhesives containing variable amounts of a detergent, the greatest strength of a cross-lap adhint was observed for the adhesive whose γ was 50 rather than for one whose γ was 39 gm/sec^2 although the displacement of air by the latter would be expected to be more complete than by the former. The criticism formulated in the preceding paragraph applies, of course, to these publications also.

The poor design of the above experiments does not invalidate the truth, that no strong adhints are possible as long as air is still present along the adhesive–adherend interface. The reverse theorem is not valid; that complete displacement of air does not guarantee a proper joint is shown in the remaining sections of this chapter.

§69   If a material "does not stick to anything" and "nothing sticks to it," it is highly probable that this material is a carrier of a weak boundary layer, that is, it contains a soft or nearly liquid ingredient which tends to accumulate at the specimen surface and to form there a soft or a nearly liquid stratum. The locus of the least strength (see §56) will be in this layer and rupture will proceed in it.

Commercial polyethylene is probably the most thoroughly studied example of such a material; when polyethylene is employed as an adhesive, the adhint is an example of improper joints of the second class. When a grain of one of many (but not all) commercial polyethylenes is placed on a solid, however well cleaned, is heated until the grain melts and spreads, and then is permitted to cool again, the solidified drop is easily dislodged with a finger nail. When an ink, whose vehicle wets the polyethylene, is used to mark the latter, the mark usually becomes loose after a time. This behavior was believed to be a proof for the molecular theory of adhesion outlined in §60.2. Polyethylenes are, essentially, mixtures of long-chain hydrocarbons $-CH_2-CH_2-CH_2-$ with an occasional branching $-CH_2-CH(CH_3)-CH_2-$; the field of force around such chains is weaker than that around chains containing many $-OH$, $-COOH$, and similar highly polar radicals; consequently, also the molecular attraction between an adherend and a polyethylene must be weaker than that between an identical adherend and a "polar" adhesive (§60.2). This conclusion appeared to be confirmed by the experiment.

According to the concept on which this monograph is based, the intensity of the interfacial attraction cannot determine the breaking stress of an adhint as, at any rate, separation along the interface does not take place. Consequently, another hypothesis was formulated. The majority of polyethylenes on the market contain low-molecular-weight components which are perfectly miscible with the rest when the mixture is molten (i.e., those polyethylenes which can be melted without decomposition give clear melts), but then are rejected to the surface when the liquid freezes. This process, which is fully analogous to the crystallization of a solute from a supersaturated solution, is denoted as *syneresis* when the precipitate is not visibly crystalline. The above-mentioned low-molecular-weight ingredients are present either because the polymerization of ethylene always results in chains of different lengths and some of these chains may be rather short, or because foreign matter is deliberately introduced during the shaping of the resulting polymer; if, e.g., the polymer is extruded, a lubricant is invariably used, and antioxidants are added to polyethylenes whatever the method of shaping.

It might seem that the fact that some commercial polyethylenes adhere well to solids is sufficient to refute the molecular theory of adhesion: the field of force around every paraffin chain is weak. However, the strong adherence may be attributed to admixtures, just as well as, above, the weak adherence is; it could be claimed that those samples which stick well contain highly polar ingredients in a sufficient quantity to enhance molecular attraction.

A series of experiments decided in favor of the first alternative. Several polyethylene samples incapable of strong adherence were dissolved[10] in boiling hydrocarbons (e.g., xylene) and precipitated with acetone or butanone. The filtrate contained a greaselike matter, which usually accounted to about 1% of the original sample. The precipitate was outwardly quite similar to the original polymer; its modulus of elasticity and ultimate tensile strength were practically equal to that of the raw product. Also the contact angle between air, water, and polyethylene (102–105°) was not affected by the treatment. On the other hand, the infrared spectrum was different. The purified material had fewer methyl groups, i.e., less branching or a smaller percentage of short chains; and no oxygen-containing groups (—OH, :CO, etc.) could be detected in it even if the initial sample showed clear lines of these radicals. Thus, the purified polyethylene more nearly corresponded to the ideal composition represented by $(-CH_2-CH_2-)_n$; nevertheless, it gave strong (i.e., proper) adhints with every adherend which did not have a weak boundary layer of its own (see §70).

The effect of the treatment could be reversed by adding small amounts of suitable low-molecular-weight compounds to the "adhesionable" polyethylene prepared by reprecipitation. Oleic acid proved to be suitable. It is a typical polar compound, and the believers in the molecular theory of adhesion would expect it to raise the breaking stress of polyethylene adhints. In reality, it lowers the peeling tension as soon as its concentration c exceeds about 0.1%. This is shown in Fig. 61 which combines, slightly idealized, the data presented in Fig. 2 and Fig. 3 of reference 11. An aluminum ribbon was attached to glass with a molten mixture of "adhesionable" polyethylene and oleic acid, permitted to cool, and peeled off. The Γ was about 65 kilodynes/cm as long as c was below 0.1% and rapidly decreased to about 10 when c was greater; it was concluded that the solubility limit of oleic acid in the solid polymer used was near 0.1%.

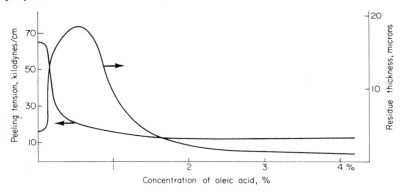

FIG. 61. Effect of oleic acid on the peeling tension (left-hand ordinate) and the thickness of the residue on the ribbon (right-hand ordinate) of polyethylene adhints. Abscissa: concentration of oleic acid, %. Data of reference 11.

Figure 61 demonstrates also the effect of oleic acid on the thickness τ of the polyethylene remaining on the ribbon after peeling. The τ of purified polyethylene was approximately 4 μ; this value is commented upon in §96. When oleic acid was gradually added, τ increased to about 19 μ at c equal to about 0.4% and decreased to below 1 μ when c was >1%. The total thickness of the adhesive film was 30–40 μ. The dependence of τ on c was accounted for[11] in the following manner. When the solubility limit of oleic acid in solid polymer is exceeded, the excess acid concentrates at the polyethylene–aluminum and the polyethylene–glass boundaries; according to which interface is particularly contaminated, the locus of rupture shifts from the one to the other phase boundary. If the probability of accumulation is equal for both, the average thickness τ on aluminum must be approximately equal to the thickness on the glass, that is, τ must be one-half the total thickness; this takes place near $c = 0.4\%$ when the amount of oleic acid present on 1 cm^2 of the interface is computed to be about 5×10^{-6} gm. When $c \geqslant 1\%$, the oleic acid layers on both surfaces are so thick (over $0.1\ \mu$) that the locus of rupture is determined by the position of the greatest stress; and this is found near the ribbon–polymer interface.

Another indication of the accumulation of oleic acid in the surface layer of polyethylene when $c > 0.1\%$ was found[12] by measuring electrical surface conductance. Flat polyethylene disks were melted between two aluminum plates. After cooling, the electric resistance between the plates, that is in the disks, was measured in the atmosphere containing water and ammonia vapors. Water, ammonia, and oleic acid formed an aqueous solution of ammonium oleate on the surface of the polymer "pancakes." As the electric conductivity of this solution was much greater than that of polyethylene, the current between the plates was carried practically completely in the solution; hence, the surface conductivity χ could be calculated from the resistance data. Figure 62 presents χ as a function of c. Evidently, the curve obtained is similar to that of Γ versus c in Fig. 61. When the bulk concentration of the acid is above, say, 0.1% or 0.2%, the excess covers the surface of the solid polymer and gives rise to a small Γ, a small τ, and a high χ.

Accumulation of oleic acid in the surface layer can be prevented if the dissolving power of polyethylene for the acid is enhanced by suitable additions. The principle may be illustrated by a familiar example. Water and benzene are little soluble in each other but their miscibility is greatly augmented by an addition of acetone

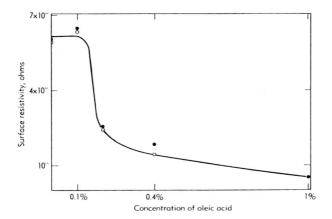

FIG. 62. Effect of oleic acid on the surface resistivity of polyethylene in humid ammonia vapor. Black and white circles: different methods of calculation. Abscissa: concentration of oleic acid, %. Ordinate: resistivity (ohms). From reference 12.

which is perfectly miscible with both these liquids. Thus, to render oleic acid soluble in solid polyethylene, to the latter a substance should be added which is readily miscible with it and with the acid. Ethyl palmitate is a suitable compound[13]; even 1:1 mixtures of this ester with polyethylene give rise to proper joints. When 94 parts of polyethylene were melted with 1 part oleic acid and 5 parts ethyl palmitate and the mixture was used as an adhesive between two steel cylinders, the breaking stress was 73 to 94 bars, i.e., almost as high as that of the "adhesionable" polyethylene alone (about 92 bars). The breaking stress of polyethylene 99, oleic acid 1 was below 1 bar; thus, a common solvent raised the strength by a factor of at least 100.

Two methods of avoiding weak boundary layers of the second class or, in other words, of making a material of this type "adhesionable," can be discerned in the preceding report: (1) the harmful impurities may be removed by purification and (2) they may be prevented from accumulating in the surface layer by adding a common solvent. In a third method, the low-molecular-weight impurities are polymerized or reacted with the main component and cease to be soft or oily.

Inert gases (e.g., argon) activated in an electrodeless discharge streamed around polymer films for a few seconds or a few minutes.[14] This caused a drastic increase in the surface hardness of the films which apparently was caused by cross-linking. The treated films were employed to make lap joints of the type "aluminum–epoxy adhesive–film–epoxy adhesive–aluminum." The breaking stress of these adhints was greater than when untreated films were used. This was true for a polyethylene and a poly(tetrafluoroethylene). The wettability of the latter is said to be unaffected by the reaction with excited noble gases.

To acquire an insight into the cause of the poor adherence of commercial polyethylenes, not only the breaking stress and the peeling tension of many adhints but also the main mechanical constants of the adhesives, the distribution of the latter among the two adherends, and the electric surface conductance were measured. It seems advisable to use measurements of these (and other) properties whenever a dependable understanding of an adhesion phenomenon is desired; testing the strength of adhesive joints alone is unlikely to result in a generally valid knowledge.

The mechanisms of the three above-mentioned methods for improving the adherence of polyethylenes are clear. Several recipies for achieving the same aim have been patented and successfully used in industry but the cause of the improvement was unknown or incorrectly guessed. The most popular treatments are, apparently, flaming, immersion in a chromic acid solution,[15] and exposure to a corona discharge.[16] Also irradiation of polyethylene powders or polyethylene coatings on aluminum with a ^{60}Co source or accelerated electrons gave satisfactory results.[17]

It was supposed that these operations caused an oxidation of the surface layer and thus enhanced the molecular attraction of the material. As is clear by now, molecular attraction was invoked in vain. Oxidation often occurs but in other instances no oxidized stratum can be detected by an examination of the infrared absorption spectrum.[18] In some instances, the peeling tension was smaller the greater the degree of oxidation.[19] Also, passing a stream of hot nitrogen over a polyethylene plate enhances its adhesive quality about as much as subjecting it to a flame of illuminating gas[20] although no significant oxidation is possible in nitrogen.

All three known mechanisms may be responsible for the improvement achieved by commercial methods. Superficial attack by acid or flame may destroy some of the low-molecular-weight ingredients present near the surface; these ingredients (especially if they are already oxygenated) may be expected to be more reactive than the long-chain polyethylene itself. Heating in nitrogen may volatilize these impurities. On the other hand, each of the above treatments may produce common solvents which render the harmful components innocuous in the same manner as ethyl palmitate disarms oleic acid. Finally, corona discharge (and perhaps not only corona discharge) may induce polymerization of the short molecules or their grafting on the polyethylene chains.

An increase in wettability of the polyethylene cannot be the reason for better adherence. As mentioned above, the contact angle (for water in air) on purified ("adhesionable") polyethylenes is practically identical with that on the starting material. Industrial treatments of polyethylene, which are approximately equivalent to each other as far as adhesion is concerned, result in very unequal contact angles. Thus[21] the θ in water at the boundary "water–a drop of hydrocarbon oil–polyethylene" was 161° when the polymer was untreated, about 138° when it was oxidized with chromic acid at 75°, and about 120° when it was subjected to a corona discharge or an irradiation with γ-rays.

Apparently, when one of the commercial treatments results in a far-reaching removal of the low-molecular-weight ingredients from the surface, these ingredients can migrate from the bulk and thus restore a weak boundary layer. It is well known in industry that a surface-treated polyethylene can be printed upon soon after the treatment but refuses to accept the ink a week or a month later. This effect was noticed also when measuring contact angles; a film which, at the above-mentioned three-phase line, gave immediately after a chromic acid rinse $\theta = 138°$ showed $\theta = 146°$ after a month's storage. Also, polyethylene coating on paper sometimes manifests a gradual decrease of adherence after the treatment.[22]

When an aluminum foil was coated[23] with an organic titanate ester and then with molten polyethylene, the peeling strength of the adhint appeared greater than when no primer was used. It is not known what happened to the weak boundary layer in the polyethylene surface when it was mixed with the titanate.

Four additional systems, less thoroughly studied, may be mentioned here. It was noticed[24] that the shear strength of several ice–metal, ice–quartz, and ice–polymer adhints was much smaller than their tensile strength (i.e., the breaking stress of the butt joints); and a hypothesis was advanced that a very thin layer of liquid water was present along the interface even when the temperature was as low as $-5°$. The presence of a liquid would account for the ease of shearing the adhint, and the relatively high tensile strength was attributed to capillary attraction (§37.1).

A coagulated latex of butadiene–styrene rubber adhered[25] to a tire cord better if a sodium salt was the coagulator, rather than a calcium salt. Samples made with a latex flocculated with NaCl ruptured after 1400 deformation cycles, while they lasted for only 700 cycles if $CaCl_2$ was the coagulating agent. It was surmised that the emulsifying agent (a dibutylnaphthalene sulfonic acid) formed a soluble salt with Na^+, and this salt was removed by washing after the flocculation. Calcium dibutylnaphthalene sulfonate was insoluble, was not fully removed by washing, and gave rise to a weak boundary layer between rubber and cord.

Coatings of poly(tetrafluoroethylene) on steel rollers used in paper making did not pick up any fibers in the early stages of their utilization. After a long working time, the coatings became sticky enough to extract some fibers from the paper. Apparently, the weak boundary layer was in some manner removed. To build it up again, a fresh piece of poly(tetrafluoroethylene) was rubbed against the aged coating.[26]

Ethyl cellulose coatings can be formulated in such a manner that they can be removed from the substrate in one piece.[27] Presumably, this formulation results in a weak boundary layer between the substrate and the coating.

§**70**   It may be said that weak boundary layers of the third class, i.e., those originating in the adherend, are the real subject matter of §§20–21. However, there it was not known what was to be removed. Here chiefly better investigated examples are mentioned. When the polymers discussed in §69 (polyethylenes, rubber, etc.) serve as adherends, the considerations of §69 are applicable.

Another instance of a weak boundary layer on rubber is mentioned in reference 28. When, in repairing tires, a new rubber mix is vulcanized in contact with an aged vulcanized rubber, the resistance to ply separation is, say, less than 500 kilodynes/cm. When the aged piece of rubber is first abraded and then brought in contact with the new mix, this resistance may be as high as 10^4 kilodynes/cm. This effect reminds one of the ancient admonition not to paint a wall over an old paint; this will crumble, fall off, and carry the new paint with it.

Commercial poly(caprolactam) (or Nylon 6) usually contains considerable amounts of the monomer which prevents elastomers, such as poly(isobutylene), from adhering to the polyamide. After removal of the monomer by extraction, strong joints could be made.[28a] Evidently, the treatment is similar to that recommended for polyethylene (§69).

Several observations have been published on injurious contaminations of metal surfaces.

Chromic acid treatment of magnesium alloys is mentioned in §21. When an alloy containing 4% Zn and 1% Ce was treated with a hot alkaline chromate solution and then glued with "Metlbond 4021" (composition unknown), adhints of a very low peel strength resulted and failure occurred cohesively in the chromate coating.[29]

As mentioned in §20, rubber is said better to adhere to brass than to many other metals. However, failures of the brass–rubber bond were common. Buchan[30] examined brass electrodeposits which gave rise to weak joints and found that they (a) either were mineralogically nonuniform (that is, consisted of α-brass in some and of β-brass in the other spots), (b) or contained cavities, (c) or were chemically impure (for instance, contaminated with zinc oxide or copper oxides). A particularly striking impurity consisted of the salt $[Zn(NH_3)_6][Zn_3(Fe(CN)_6)_2]$.[30,31] The bath contained no deliberately introduced iron, but the amounts of iron dissolved out of the tools used were sufficient to cause precipitation of this complex salt at the brass surface during electroplating. The difference between the adhesive properties of brass after electropolishing and after light abrasion was reported in §20.

The sensitivity of electrodeposited coating to impurities may also be illustrated by another example.[32] In the electroplating of nickel on some other metal, a brief interruption of current may ruin the adherence of the subsequent deposit. As soon as the electrostatic field near the cathode surface disappears, non-ionic ingredients of the solution become adsorbed on this surface and form a weak boundary layer.

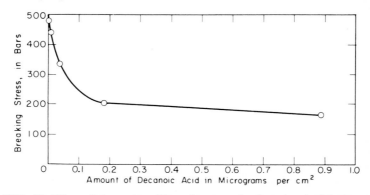

FIG. 63. Effect of decanoic acid on the strength of steel–poly (vinyl acetate) adhints. Abscissa: amount of decanoic acid per unit area ($\mu g/cm^2$). Ordinate: breaking stress (bars). Data of reference 33.

How small are the amounts of impurities sufficient to affect the strength of adhints is exemplified by Fig. 63 based on some published results.[33] Butt joints of steel–poly(vinyl acetate)–steel, at a glue line thickness of 0.0025 cm, had breaking stresses of approximately 486 bars. When decanoic acid was deposited on one of the steel surfaces before the application of the adhesive and the system "contaminated steel–poly(vinyl acetate)–steel" kept above the melting range of the adhesive for an hour, the breaking stress was smaller the greater the degree of contamination. As the numbers along the abscissa of the figure indicate, considerable changes are caused by amounts as small as 10^{-8} gm/cm^2; one touch of a finger may easily transfer greater quantities of finger grease. When the above system was maintained above the freezing temperature of poly(vinyl acetate) for a longer time, decanoic acid (or iron decanoate) apparently gradually dissolved in the liquid adhesive and, consequently, was losing its ability to form a weak boundary layer. Thus, at glue line thickness of 0.010 cm and total amount of $C_{10}H_{20}O_2$ equal to 8.9×10^{-7} gm/cm^2, the breaking stress was 207, 268, 321, and 471 bars when the heating time was 0, 1, 2 hr, or extrapolated to infinity. At a constant total amount of acid and a constant heating time, the effect of the acid was greater the thinner the adhesive film.

TABLE X

EFFECT OF STEARIC ACID ON THE ADHINT STRENGTH

Contaminant (gm/cm^2)	Alkyd paint				Vinyl resin lacquer			
	Before		After		Before		After	
	f_m	A_r	f_m	A_r	f_m	A_r	f_m	A_r
None	210	55%	120	95%	100	75%	120	100%
4×10^{-6}	150	90%	100	90%	60	95%	80	100%
4×10^{-5}	110	100%	60	100%	50	100%	70	100%

In a similar series of experiments[34] butt joints of "steel–epoxy adhesive–paint–steel sheet–epoxy adhesive–steel" were prepared using either cleaned steel sheets (§20), or steel sheets contaminated with stearic acid. Table X presents some selected data; f_m is the average breaking stress in bars, and A_r is the relative area (%) over which failure occurred in the weak boundary layer. The painted steel sheets served for adhint formation either before or after an accelerated weathering for 500 hr. The deleterious effect of stearic acid on the f_m values and the extension of the "interfacial" failure (§67) caused by the contaminant are clearly seen in the table. Equal amounts of petroleum jelly and lanolin spread on the sheets had no definite effect; perhaps these substances were soluble in the paints used.

When a little over 2×10^{-7} gm of stearic acid was deposited on 1 cm^2 of a stainless steel surface, the breaking stress of steel–

ice adhints at $-20°$ was lowered from about 28 to about 6 bars.[35]

Amounts as small as these presumably can remain on a metal even after a careful washing. When a metal (or a glass) surface is coated with a poly(methylhydroxysilane) or another suitable silicone oil, no usual adhesive "sticks to it"; and there is still no adherence when the solid is first extracted with ligroin at 80° (for how long?).[36]

In innumerable instances, weak boundary layers of the third class are necessary for the smooth flow of production and are intentionally introduced. Then they are known as parting agents. They cannot be reviewed here.

§71   Weak boundary layers of the fourth class, that is those formed in an interaction between the environment and the adhesive, apparently have not been systematically studied yet. They are observed, for instance, when polyethylenes (or some other polymers) are molten and spread over an adherend in air; oxidation of the polyolefins at a high temperature causes discoloration and splitting of long chains, and the resulting low-molecular-weight substances form a zone of weakness. To avoid this effect, the polyethylene adhints discussed in §69 were, as a rule, prepared in a nitrogen atmosphere.

The fifth class embraces weak boundary layers originating from the environment and the adherend together. All examples belonging here refer to heating (or at least aging) of metals in air.

Aluminum oxide is usually considered to be strong enough for any organic adhesive. Recent experiments[37] cast doubt on this belief. Lap joints of the type "aluminum–epoxy adhesive–aluminum" were prepared either in dry argon or in an atmosphere of argon 80, oxygen 20, and enough water vapor to make the relative humidity equal to 50%. Also the initial abrasion of the adherends with silicon carbide was performed in these two gas environments. After the abrasion, the adherends were left in the same medium for definite time intervals, and then the adhesive was applied and cured. Table XI compares the f_m values for the two atmospheres and the time intervals of 0 and 60 min. It is seen that the aging of freshly abraded metal in dry argon has almost no effect on the strength of the adhints, while an aging in the presence of oxygen and water lowers f_m to almost half the initial value. Water vapor seemed to be more deleterious than oxygen.

TABLE XI

EFFECT OF ATMOSPHERE ON ALUMINUM

	Aging in dry argon		Aging in humid Ar–O$_2$	
Aging time (min):	0	60	0	60
f_m (bars):	205	190	200	105

The adherence of copper oxide scale to copper may be hindered by a weak boundary layer. If a wire of particularly pure copper is oxidized in dry air at 900°, it becomes coated with a thin film consisting chiefly of cuprous oxide, with some cupric oxide at the interface with air. This wire can be twisted without losing any of its scale at all temperatures tested above 400°. When an analogous experiment is performed with a wire of copper containing 0.03% to 0.04% phosphorus, a twist causes the wire to shed its coating at both 400° and 500°. This coating contains some cuprous phosphate (Cu$_3$PO$_4$). The melt of the phosphate spreads around the grains of Cu$_2$O and thus, after solidification, produces weak interstitial films between them. The grains are smaller and, consequently, the relative importance of the intergranular weakness is greater, near the metal–oxide interface; hence, rupture may be expected to occur preferentially near this interface, and the flakes to be much greater than single oxide grains; unfortunately, the flake dimensions have not been ascertained by the experimenter.[38]

A weak boundary layer consisting of cuprous oxide between copper and a synthetic rubber was mentioned by Markin et al.[39] Phosphorus seems to lower the strength of oxide films not only on copper but on iron also.[40]

§**72**   Soldering and brazing sometimes result in a weak boundary layer of the sixth class (i.e., adhesive + adherend).

Iron is markedly soluble in molten copper but these metals are almost immiscible in the solid state. When copper was used as an adhesive ("brazing compound") between two bars of mild steel, some dissolution of iron in liquid copper took place. On cooling, iron dendrites precipitated in the adhesive film (of copper).[41] In this instance, crystal separation caused no weakening of the interfacial layer, but it is clear that an analogous crystallization may give rise to weak spots in another system. Metallographic examination of welded joints has been performed many times but its results are not reviewed in this book.

When metal A is heated in contact with metal B, the atoms of A may diffuse into the B phase more rapidly than B diffuses into A. Consequently, the layer of A next to B contains many vacancies in the lattice. Usually, the vacancies coalesce and thus form a microscopically porous stratum. The effect was noticed, for instance,[42,43] when a plate of copper coated with brass or with aluminum bronze (comprising Cu 93%, Al 7%) was kept for 25 days at 800° and the interface then examined. Numerous voids of e.g., 0.001 cm in diameter were visible in the brass or the bronze near its boundary with copper.

An analogous process occurs at the interface of gold and aluminum.[44] Gold wires were bonded by compression at a high temperature to an aluminum slab. When a tensile stress was applied to a wire, the adhint usually failed "at the interface." To see what actually happened, the joints were aged for 2 hr at 450°, and a bevelled cross section of the interfacial region was made. Eight distinct strata were visible after etching, namely aluminum, $AuAl_2$, $AuAl$, Au_2Al, $Au_5Al_2(?)$, an area of pores, Au_4Al, and finally gold. The voids were so numerous that the small breaking stress of the adhints was easy to account for.

Brittle intermetallic compounds can form a zone of weakness. Tin solders on copper or copper alloys form the two compounds Cu_3Sn and Cu_6Sn_5 (or $CuSn$). Usually, the amount of Cu_6Sn_5 is much greater than that of Cu_3Sn. The crystals of Cu_6Sn_5 are brittle and a brittle boundary layer results when their concentration in the interface is significant. Thus[45] the peeling strength of copper–tin–copper joints was about 9×10^6 dynes/cm width after heating for 1 sec at 400° and only 2×10^6 dynes/cm after 30 sec of heating; and the thickness of the Cu_6Sn_5 interlayer was about $1\ \mu$ after 1 sec and about $6\ \mu$ after 30 sec.

The joints between steel and brass are affected by the presence of silicon in the brass.[46] If the silicon concentration exceeds 0.17%, the iron silicides Fe_3Si and $FeSi$ are found in the boundary layer.

If the force needed to peel a tinned copper wire soldered to an alloy of platinum and gold is 100 (arbitrary units) in the instances when the rupture test is performed soon after the soldering, aging the adhint at 150° for 500 hr lowers this force to about 50. The authors[47] believe that this reduction in strength is caused by interdiffusion of tin, lead (from the solder), gold, and platinum to form a weak interlayer.

The adherence of enamel to iron is sensitive to the presence of water during the firing operation. At the high temperatures needed for firing, the reaction $Fe + H_2O \rightarrow FeO + H_2$ occurs, and hydrogen bubbles may afford a weak boundary layer between iron and glass. Water available for this reaction may originate from pickling, washing, and so on, but moisture occluded in the frit (i.e., in the future enamel) was shown[48] in one set of conditions to be more important than any other source. The molten enamel is a well conducting electrolyte, and there must be many local cells on the highly inhomogeneous iron surface. It is believed by some researchers that this electrochemical effect improves adherence. As a metal dissolves at the anodic areas and (probably another) metal is deposited on the cathodic areas, surface roughness of the iron increases; if the adhesion of enamel to iron is a purely mechanical (interlocking) effect (see §18), electrochemical corrosion would help adherence. On the other hand, it is easy to imagine conditions in which corrosion will result in weak boundary layers.

Corrosion may be responsible for the observation often made in industry, that aluminum alloys containing a significant percentage of zinc are more difficult to glue with many polymeric adhesives than aluminum free from zinc.

When a mixture of 80% molybdenum and 20% manganese was deposited on sintered alumina pellets and fired at 1550°, a spinel $MnAl_2O_4$ could be detected at the interface, and rupture apparently took place in this phase.[49]

Brass–rubber adhints are mentioned, for instance, in §70. In them, also weak boundary layers of the sixth class are encountered.

When rubber is vulcanized in contact with brass, the copper of the brass reacts with sulfur of the rubber, forming copper sulfides. The amount of sulfides and the strength of the brass–rubber bond depend on the brass quality and on the percentage of sulfur in the rubber. In one series of experiments,[30] a mixture of rubber, sulfur, and some other ingredients was dissolved in benzene, spread over a brass surface, and partially cured for 5 to 20 min; when the coating was then dissolved in benzene, measurable quantities of sulfur (detectable by chemical analysis) remained in the solid. The amount of this sulfur, its increase with duration of curing, and, above all, the form in which the sulfur compound was present were different for brasses suitable and those unsuitable for bonding. When the sulfur content of the mix was 10%, the sulfur compound on the brass surface appeared as a powdery deposit, whatever the properties of the brass. When only 5% S was present in the mix, the deposit on poorly bonding brasses was still powdery but was more coherent on good brass specimens; also the amounts of sulfur bound by the brass were different; thus, after a curing for 5 min, there was 0.05 mg S per cm^2 of poorly bonding metal and only 0.017 mg/cm^2 of suitable alloy. The surface concentration of sulfur on good brass was only 0.042 mg/cm^2 even after 15 min of curing. Bad brass gave rise to powdery sulfides also when the sulfur concentration in the mix was as low as 2%. The amount of sulfide increased with the duration of curing but the increase was relatively rapid and, apparently, limitless with unsuitable brasses, while with good brasses it was slow and seemed to tend to a limiting value. It appears that small amounts of sulfides are innocuous, perhaps because they do not form separate crystals, while amounts sufficient to give rise to a crystalline layer between brass and rubber ruin the adhesion because a layer of disconnected crystals has a negligible strength (see §48).

Weak boundary layers consisting of metal sulfide or spread between the metal sulfide and the metal were observed[50] in other adhints of α-brass (Cu 70, Zn 30%) and natural vulcanized rubber. As suggested in §21, the weakness of the interfacial stratum between brass and sulfide might have been caused by a rapid migration of copper ions into the sulfide phase with the consequent formation of vacancies near the phase boundary.

Apparently, a zone of weakness can form as a result of excessive vulcanization. A mixture of unvulcanized natural rubber and sulfur was spread on a plate of a vulcanized synthetic rubber, the system was heated for time t, and the film of (now vulcanized) natural rubber was peeled off with a tension Γ. This Γ had a maximum (over 5000 kilodynes/cm) at $t = 60$ min. When sulfur insoluble in rubber (the μ modification) was substituted for the common sulfur, Γ continued to increase with t past 60 min heating. It is believed[51] that the ordinary sulfur, which easily migrates in rubber, diffused into the vulcanizate plate during the heating and gave rise to a brittle overvulcanized zone near the boundary of the plate with the natural rubber.

It has been repeatedly noticed that wood glued with strongly alkaline adhesives broke near the interface at a stress lower than the breaking stress of the wood before glueing; and this effect was traced to hydrolysis of wood by the adhesive.

§**73**   Weak boundary layers which require collaboration of all three phases are also known.[52] If adhints are made between aluminum and aluminum with an experimental adhesive consisting mainly of a phenolic resin (8 parts) and an epoxy resin (1 part), their shear strength at room temperature is near 122 bars (or 1770 psi). Heating the adhints in air at 288° for 100 hr depressed the shear strength (at room temperature) to about 65 bars. If a stainless steel was joined rather than aluminum, the initial strength was not markedly different, but it was lowered to almost zero by the heating as above. Oxygen was needed for this deterioration of bonds; when heating was performed in nitrogen, only a moderate decrease in strength was noted. Apparently, an ingredient of the steel surface accelerated oxidation of the adhesive by air at 288°. In agreement with this view, the first sign of weakening appeared along the three-phase line, where the adhesive, the oxidizing agent, and the catalyst met. Presumably, the weak zone grew along the metal surface, where the catalyst concentration was highest, but this point was not recorded.

Table XII demonstrates[52] the catalytic effect of thin metal films deposited on an aluminum surface by displacement from an acid solution. Heating was again in air at 288°. It is seen that copper was the most powerful oxidation catalyst. The effect was not general as far as adhesives were concerned; apparently the epoxy resin was the substance susceptible to oxidation. Heating in air had only a moderate effect on adhints made with a nylon or with butadiene-acrylonitrile copolymers, whatever the metal.

TABLE XII

EFFECT OF HEATING IN AIR ON ADHINTS BETWEEN DIFFERENT METALS

Metal	Shear strength (bars)	
	Before heating	After heating
Aluminum	122	65
Manganese	118	72
Chromium	112	63
Iron	99	38
Nickel	111	47
Zinc	127	78
Copper	96	0
Silver	146	80
Cerium	130	82

Observations analogous to those summarized in Table XII, 2nd column, have been made earlier but remained unexplained.[53] Phenol-formaldehyde adhesives were used to glue two pieces of metal together (as butt joints). The breaking stresses for aluminum adhints and cast iron adhints were similar (e.g., 189 and 179 bars, respectively) but brass gave distinctly lower values (e.g., 39 bars).

§74　　Weak boundary layers and their elimination are of great importance in the modern industry of reinforced plastics. These composite materials usually comprise glass filaments (such as rovings, yarns, or fabrics) embedded in a polymer matrix. Commercial glass fibers almost always are coated with a lubricant whose function is to prevent one fiber from scratching its neighbors. This lubricant would constitute a feeble region between the glass and the matrix. However, even if the lubricant is removed, the adherence of the polymer to glass often is not satisfactory. This is attributed by many technologists to the presence of water on the filaments. The "bond" between the glass and epoxy adhesives generally is less sensitive to the moisture present before the bond formation than the "bond" between glass and polyesters. This may be due to those components of the epoxy mix which dissolve, or react with, water and to the retardation by water of the polymerization reaction (§50) on which the curing of polyesters is based.

Heating the glass filaments long enough to destroy the residue of the organic lubricants and to drive water away, as a rule, makes it possible to obtain reinforced plastics in which no separation at the interface occurs, that is, no weak boundary layer can be detected. However, composite materials thus prepared are easily degraded by water. Water seems to migrate along the filament–matrix interface and to form a zone of weakness there.

To render reinforced plastics more water-resistant, the filaments are treated with a "finish" or "coupling agent" before the embedding. Vinyltrichlorosilane $CH_2:CHSiCl_3$ is one of the substances suitable as such an agent. When glass fibers are treated with it, then embedded in a plastic mix, and the system is cured (i.e., heated to complete polymerization), the laminates obtained do not separate along the interface either when dry or when immersed in water for several years. A chemical explanation was given to this effect. Vinyltrichlorosilane was supposed to react with the hydroxyl groups on the glass surface, as the scheme below exemplifies:

$$\begin{array}{c}\text{—Si—OH}\\ \text{O}\diagdown \\ \quad\text{Si}\diagup\text{OH} \quad + \quad CH_2:CHSiCl_3 = 3\,HCl \quad + \\ \text{O}\diagup \quad\diagdown\text{OH}\end{array} \qquad \begin{array}{c}\text{≥Si—O}\\ \text{O}\diagdown \diagup\text{O—SiCH:CH}_2 \\ \quad\text{Si}\diagup \\ \text{O}\diagup\diagdown\text{O}\\ \text{(I)}\end{array}$$

and the vinyl group of (I) was said to take part in the subsequent polymerization, so that finally a chain of primary valencies connected the bulk of the glass with the bulk of the polymer, thus making the "bond" extremely strong.

This explanation is defective on many counts. (1) A chain of primary valencies does not need to be strong. The silicon is bound to the chlorine in vinyltrichlorosilane by primary valencies but hydrolysis of this compound is easy. The bonds

$$\diagdown\text{Si}\diagup\overset{\textstyle O}{\underset{\textstyle O}{\diagdown\diagup}}\text{Si}\diagdown$$

presumably present in the surface of dry glass are readily broken to afford silanol groups

and the resulting compound occludes (i.e., swells in) water thus creating a weak region. An effect of this kind could easily take place also in the hypothetical structure (I) shown above.

(2) The second objection is not crucial. Silane agents usually are applied in water. Thus, the reacting species would be $CH_2{:}CHSi(OH)_3$ rather than $CH_2{:}CHSiCl_3$, and the above reaction would be impossible. However, polymerization of silica chains, so familiar in water glass, occurs in water also, and compound (I) could be generated by vinyltrihydroxysilane almost as readily as by vinyltrichlorosilane.

While a chemical reaction of the "finish" with the glass surface often is probable, it is very unlikely that a "coupling agent" really reacts with the organic polymer and, if it does, that this reaction contributes anything to the strength of the adhint. Three types of experiment lead the observer to this conclusion.

(3) Ethyltrichlorosilane $CH_3CH_2SiCl_3$ was shown in some tests to be about as active as vinyltrichlorosilane. As ethyl group cannot take part in a polymerization reaction, the adherence between glass coated with ethyltrichlorosilane and a polymer ought to be zero, if primary valencies were essential for strength.

(4) In some experiments it was demonstrated that, even when vinyl groups were present, they did not participate in the curing reaction.

(5) If the curing involves no polymerization at all, customary "finishes" are still as useful as in polyester and epoxy polymers. No polymerization is involved whenever the glass filaments are embedded in a melt, and setting is accomplished by cooling (see §48).

As the chemical explanation of the action of the "finishes" cannot be correct, alternative mechanisms must be considered. In several series of tests, the polymer matrix wetted the fibers better when they were coated with a "coupling agent" than when they were bare.

If this is the cause of the better adherence in the dry state, then the weak boundary layer which facilitates separation of untreated glass from matrix belongs to the first class (§68). The enhanced resistance to water of composites made with a treated glass may also be connected with wetting. The treated glass is more hydrophobic than the bare glass; its surface layer does not swell in water easily; consequently, water from outside cannot rapidly advance along the fiber–matrix interface (see §121).

The above outline is a digest of many publications and a conclusion from many discussions. A more detailed report would occupy more space than can be afforded in a book on adhesive joints. Perhaps, if and when a third edition of this book is called for, our knowledge of the adhesion in reinforced plastics will be more trustworthy and a more definite summary will be possible.

REFERENCES

1. DeBruyne, N. A., *Plastics Inst. (London), Trans. J.* **27**, 140 (1959).
2. Korolev, A. Ya., Bek, V. L., and Grishin, N. A., *Vysokomolekul. Soedin.* **4**, 1411 (1962); *Chem. Abstr.* **59**, 803 (1963).
3. DeBruyne, N. A., *Aero Res. Tech. Notes, Bull. No.* **168** (1956).
4. Kobeko, P. P., and Marei, F. I., *Zh. Tekhn. Fiz.* **16**, 277 (1946).
5. Holland, L., and Bateman, S. K., *Brit. J. Appl. Phys.* **11**, 382 (1960).
6. Friese, K., *Plaste Kautschuk* **12**, 478 (1965).
7. Lewis, A. F., and Forrestal, L. J., *Am. Soc. Testing Mater., Spec. Tech. Publ.* **360**, 59 (1964).
8. Swanson, J. W., and Becher, J. J., *Tappi* **49**, 198 (1966).
9. Herczeg, A., *Forest Prod. J.* **15**, 499 (1965).
10. Bikerman, J. J., *Adhesives Age* **2**, No. 2, 23 (1959).
11. Bikerman, J. J., *J. Appl. Chem.* **11**, 81 (1961).
12. Bikerman, J. J., *SPE Trans.* **2**, 213 (1962).
13. Bikerman, J. J., and Marshall, D. W., *J. Appl. Polymer Sci.* **7**, 1031 (1963).
14. Hansen, R. H., and Schonhorn, H., *J. Polymer Sci.* **B4**, 203 (1966).
15. Schrader, W. H., and Bodnar, M. J., *Plastics Technol.* **3**, 988 (1957).
16. Rossmann, K., *J. Polymer Sci.* **19**, 141 (1956).
17. Spitsyn, V. I., Zubov, P. I., Kabanov, V. Ya., and Grozinskaya, Z. P., *Vysokomolekul. Soedin.* **8**, 604 (1966); *Chem. Abstr.* **65**, 2421 (1966).
18. Kreidl, W. H., *Kunststoffe* **49**, 71 (1959).
19. Nakao, K., and Nishiuchi, M., *J. Adhesion Soc. Japan* **2**, 239 (1966).
20. Peukert, H., *Kunststoffe* **48**, 3 (1958).
21. Sinegub-Lavrenko, A. A., *Dokl. Akad. Nauk SSSR* **143**, 925 (1962).

22. Leeds, S., *Tappi* **44**, 244 (1961).
23. Crolius, V. G., Ebeling, W. E., and Parsons, R. C., *Tappi* **45**, 351 (1962).
24. Jellinek, H. H. G., *J. Appl. Phys.* **32**, 1793 (1961).
25. Buiko, G. N., and Zinchenko, N. P., *Soviet Rubber Technol. (English Transl.)* **19**, No. 4, 25 (1960).
26. Foster, R. E., and Winn, E. B., *Adhaesion* **6**, 614 (1962); *Chem. Abstr.* **59**, 8977 (1963).
27. Parker, D. H., "Principles of Surface Coating Technology," p. 762. Wiley (Interscience), New York, 1965.
28. Kamenskii, B. Z., Vostroknutov, E. G., and Reznikovskii, M. M., *Kauchuk i Rezina* **23**, No. 8, 35 (1964).
28a. Raevskii, V. G., Voyutskii, S. S., Gul', V. E., Kamenskii, A. N., and Moneva, I., *Izv. Vysshikh Uchebn. Zavedenii, Khim. i Khim. Tekhnol.* **1965**, 305.
29. Hunter, R. J. E., *Can. Aeron. J.* **3**, 161 (1957).
30. Buchan, S., "Rubber to Metal Bonding," 2nd ed. Crosby Lockwood, London, 1959.
31. Malden, J. W., *Trans. Inst. Rubber Ind.* **27**, 175 (1951).
32. Vagramyan, A. T., and Tsareva, Yu. S., *Dokl. Akad. Nauk SSSR* **74**, 303 (1950).
33. Lasoski, S. W., and Kraus, G., *J. Polymer Sci.* **18**, 359 (1955).
34. Bullett, T. R., and Prosser, J. L., *Trans. Inst. Metal Finishing* **41**, 112 (1964).
35. Raraty, L. E., and Tabor, D., *Proc. Roy. Soc.* **A245**, 184 (1958).
36. Vinogradova, L. M., Korolev, A. Ya., Davydov, P. V., and Kuchenkova, R. V., *Plasticheskie Massy* **1964**, No. 9, 18; *Chem. Abstr.* **61**, 16235 (1964).
37. Wegman, R. F., *Adhesives Age* **10**, No. 1, 20 (1967).
38. Tylecote, R. F., *J. Inst. Metals* **78**, 301 (1950).
39. Markin, Yu. I., Gorchakova, V. M., Gul, V. E., and Voyutskii, S. S., *Izv. Vysshikh Uchebn. Zavedenii, Khim. i Khim. Tekhnol.* **5**, 810 (1962); *Chem. Abstr.* **58**, 12693 (1962).
40. Vodopivec, F., *Rudarsko-Met. Zbornik* **1963**, No. 1, 15; *Chem. Abstr.* **60**, 256 (1964).
41. Bredzs, N., and Schwartzbart, H., *Welding J. (N.Y.)* **37**, 493-s (1958).
42. Bueckle, H., and Blin, J., *J. Inst. Metals* **80**, 385 (1952).
43. Arkharov, V. I., and Mardeshev, S., *Dokl. Akad. Nauk SSSR* **103**, 273 (1955).
44. Blech, I. A., and Sello, H., *J. Electrochem. Soc.* **113**, 1052 (1966).
45. Chadwick, R., *J. Inst. Metals* **62**, 277 (1938).
46. Francke, K. P., *Baender, Bleche, Rohre* **6**, No. 1, 24 (1965); *Chem. Abstr.* **63**, 17577 (1965).
47. Hoffman, L. C., Bachetta, V. L., and Frederick, K. W., *IEEE., Trans. Parts, Mater. Packaging* **1**, 381 (1965).
48. Moore, D. G., Mason, M. A., and Harrison, W. N., *J. Am. Ceram. Soc.* **37**, 1 (1954).
49. Floyd, J. R., *Am. Ceram. Soc. Bull.* **42**, 65 (1963).

50. Stuart, N., *Proc. 4th Rubber Technol. Conf., London, 1962*. Inst. Rubber Ind.,
     London, 1962.
51. Kamenskii, B. Z., Reznikovskii, M. M., and Vostroknutov, E. G., *Kauchuk i
     Rezina* **25,** No. 1, 35 (1966).
52. Black, J. M., and Blomquist, R. F., *Ind. Eng. Chem.* **50,** 918 (1958).
53. Ehlers, J. F., *Kunststoffe* **40,** 151 (1950).

CHAPTER VIII / **STRESSES IN PROPER ADHINTS**

Frozen Stresses

§75   In Chapter VII, the idiosyncrasies of adhesive joints are reviewed; the weak boundary layers are specific for each individual adhint. This chapter deals with very general properties of composite systems. Deformation and rupture of a proper adhint is not basically different from the deformation and rupture of a homogeneous solid specimen; however, an effort is made here to restrict the treatment, as far as possible, to adhint-like composites.

The factor β in the approximate equation (see §61)

$$f_m = \frac{1}{\alpha} \left(\frac{\xi}{\beta} - s \right) , \tag{76}$$

was discussed in §§63–66. Here attention is directed to the frozen stress s.

The values for shrinkage recorded in §52 are valid only as long as the solid in its final state is stress-free, that is as long as the contraction was not restrained by external forces. Consider an adhesive filling the clearance, of constant thickness h_0, between two parallel plates. If the adhesive were permitted to set in the absence of external restraints, its thickness would have been, say, h_1. As long as $(h_0 - h_1)/h_0$ is smaller than the total relative elongation of the adhesive, this will not break (except, perhaps, near the three-phase line defined in §25). Far from the edge of the adhint, i.e., in the region where the strain is normal to the adherend plates, the stress "frozen" in the adhesive film is $E_2(h_0 - h_1)/h_0$, assuming that the adhesive follows Hooke's law with a modulus of elasticity E_2.

No void will form as long as this quantity is less than the ultimate tensile strength of the adhesive, but the external stress required to break the adhint (in the adhesive film) will be correspondingly smaller. Let the tensile strength of the stress-free adhesive (still treated as a Hookean solid) be f_M: the only a tensile stress

$$f_m = f_M - \frac{E_2 (h_0 - h_1)}{h_0} \tag{77}$$

would be needed for rupturing the prestressed material.

If, as is common in real solids, the stress is not constant in time but, on the contrary, decays because of relaxation, more complicated equations[1] are required. Apparently, an attempt[2] to test them was made. "Steel–poly(vinyl acetate)–steel" and "steel–poly(vinyl butyral)–steel" butt joints were made at 100–120° (with molten adhesives), the temperature was rapidly lowered by about 70°, and the breaking stress f_m of the adhints kept at the lower temperature was measured from time to time. A connection between these tests and Eq. (77) exists only if the distance between the steel adherends is kept rigorously constant during formation and aging of the adhint; and this point is not made clear in the paper. At any rate, f_m usually slightly increased during the aging when the polymers were not plasticized, and increased more rapidly when the adhesives contained a plasticizer; this effect presumably was due to a gradual stress relaxation, that is a decrease of s.

§76 Let the adhesive be present as a plate, $a \times b \times h$ cm^3, h being much smaller than either a or b. The stresses caused by heating or cooling a system, in which this plate is attached to a rigid adherend by one[3] of the faces $a \times h$, or by the two[4] opposite faces $a \times h$, have been calculated but the results are not in agreement with each other.

The system resulting when the adhesive plate is bonded to the adherend along one of its large faces (i.e., $a \times b$) has been studied better; heat expansion of bimetal thermometers, shrinkage of coatings generally and of electrodeposits[5] in particular, and many other effects belong here. If the two adherend–adhesive interfaces are

sufficiently far from each other, the following treatment of one interface will be valid for both of them.

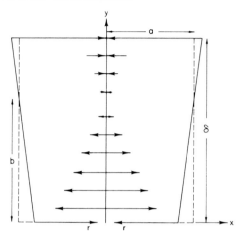

FIG. 64. Stresses caused by a shrinking coating.

Mathematically, the simplest model consists of an adherend
plate, δ cm thick, in which a uniform compressive force acts over
one of the two large faces. In other words, the coating is supposed
to be infinitely thin and the effect of shrinkage stresses in it is
equivalent to that of a concentrated force. If the system is free to
deform, it will be bent to a part of a sphere. In Fig. 64 a short piece
of a narrow strip along one of the meridians is shown, and the
deformation perpendicular to the plane of the drawing is disregarded. The top and the bottom surfaces of the strip are, of course,
curved but are shown straight in the figure to facilitate calculation.
The forces directed toward the plane of $x = 0$ act along the bottom
surface which represents the extremely thin coating which tends to
contract. The arrows in the body of the adherend represent, and
their length is proportional to, the stresses caused by these forces.

In equilibrium, the sum of all moments and the sum of all forces
must be zero. The moments are calculated here for the points of
$x = 0$ and $y = 0$ as, for this choice, the moment of the compressive
forces F also is zero. If the width of the strip (normal to the plane

of the drawing) is w, the tension produced by F is $F/w = \Gamma$. The reaction forces (per unit width) in the adherend are of the form $k(y - b)dy$, if b is the distance from the plane of $y = 0$ to the plane not distorted by the curling; k is a proportionality constant whose dimension is $gm/cm^2 sec^2$. The moments are $k(y - b)y\,dy$. Thus

$$\int_0^\delta k(y - b)y\,dy = k\delta^2 \left(\frac{\delta}{3} - \frac{b}{2}\right) = 0 . \tag{78}$$

that is $b = \frac{2}{3}\delta$, as drawn in Fig. 64. Summation of forces affords the equation

$$\Gamma + \int_0^\delta k(y - b)\,dy = 0 , \tag{79}$$

that is, $\Gamma + 0.5k\delta^2 - kb\,\delta = 0$. Introducing $b = \frac{2}{3}\delta$ into this equation, the relation[6]

$$\Gamma = \frac{1}{6} k\delta^2 \quad \text{or} \quad k = 6\Gamma/\delta^2 \tag{80}$$

is obtained. Thus, the reaction stress at any y is equal to $(6\Gamma/\delta^2)$ $(y - \frac{2\delta}{3})$.

The value of Γ usually is calculated[5-7] from the radius of curvature of the strip bent by shrinkage stresses. Let r be the distance from the center of curvature to the plane of zero deformation, i.e., to the plane of $y = b$. Then the distance from this center to the top surface is $r + \frac{1}{3}\delta$ (because $b = \frac{2}{3}\delta$). The ratio of $(r + \frac{1}{3}\delta)/r$ is equal to the ratio l_m/l_0 if l_m is the length of the upper arc represented in Fig. 64 and l_0 is the corresponding length in the plane of zero deformation. The stress along the upper arc, where $y = \delta$, is $2\Gamma/\delta$ [see above]. From Hooke's law, the strain, i.e., $(l_m - l_0)/l_0$, is $2\Gamma/E_1\delta$, E_1 being the modulus of elasticity of the adherend. Hence, $l_m/l_0 = 1 + (2\Gamma/E_1\delta)$; but this ratio is equal also to $1 + (\delta/3r)$; thus

$$r = \frac{\delta^2 E_1}{6\Gamma} . \tag{81}$$

If the thickness of the coating is not infinitely small but rather is equal to h (h being much smaller than δ), then the average stress σ in the coating is $\sigma = \Gamma/h$ and[6] $\sigma = \delta^2 E_1/6hr$. A somewhat better approximation is

$$\sigma = \frac{E_1(\delta + h)^3}{6\delta hr} . \tag{82}$$

If $h \ll \delta$, Eq. (82) becomes identical with the preceding equation.

These relations are approximately valid for the stress as it exists *after* the curling of the strip. Before the curling the length of the bottom of the section shown in Fig. 64 was l_0, and it was $l_0 [1 - (2\delta/3r)]$ after the deformation; hence, the tension Γ_0 before the deformation would be, if Hooke's law is applicable,

$$\Gamma_0 = \frac{3\Gamma r + 2\delta E_2 h}{3r - 2\delta} ; \tag{83}$$

E_2 is the modulus of elasticity of the coating.

More elaborate equations have been suggested[7-10] and many experimental data (which use new methods of study) have been presented[9] on the stresses in electrolytic deposits but they cannot be reviewed here.

The above equations have been tested by photoelasticity measurements in, e.g., references 4 and 11. It is seen in Fig. 64 that the stresses are compressive in the two-thirds of the strip nearer to the coating, and tensile in the remaining third. This change of sign was detected[12] in glass on which a gelatin film was formed by depositing an aqueous gelatin solution and permitting water to evaporate. The results are exemplified by Fig. 65. Its ordinate represents the stress in glass determined from the birefringence, and the abscissa is the distance from the glass–gelatin interface. The distance b was about 0.3 cm in this instance.

Extrapolation of the curve of Fig. 65 to zero distance leads to a value of about 180 bars for the stress along the interface. This

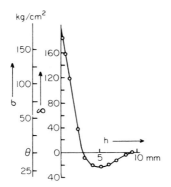

FIG. 65. Shrinkage stress in glass on which a gelatin film has dried. Abscissa: distance from glass–gelatin surface, in millimeters. Ordinate: stress (kg wt./cm²). (δ is optical path difference.) From reference 12.

maximum value σ' of the residual stress was independent of the initial concentration of the gelatin solution. The explanation advanced was[13] that, as long as water content of the gel exceeded, say, 20%, the mobility of the chains was so great that no stress became "frozen"; hence, it did not matter how long it took the excess water to evaporate before its concentration sank to 20%. On the other hand, the final thickness τ of the film was expected to affect σ' because, for the water content to sink from, say, 20% to 15%, more time was needed when τ was greater; thus, there was more time for stress relaxation the greater was the τ. This decrease of σ' when the drying period was longer, i.e., τ was greater, was found for plasticized gelatin; when τ was 0.04, 0.05, 0.20, and 0.26 mm, the σ' was 80, 60, 40, and 30 bars.

However, without a plasticizer, σ' of a gelatin coating was independent of τ, namely 270–280 bars at τ 0.04 to 0.20 mm. Also in a polyester lacquer, τ (varying from 0.10 to 0.75 mm) had no effect on σ' (about 3 bars); this was expected as polyester solidified because of a chemical reaction (§50) whose rate would be little affected by small changes in the film thickness. When a gelatin membrane spanning a rigid ring was permitted to dry, the maximum stress in it appeared to be[14] 300 bars, i.e., almost equal to the σ' of reference 13.

Some idea of the value of frozen stresses in the absence of relaxation can be obtained by permitting an unattached gelatin film to dry and, simultaneously, to contract, and then determining the force needed to extend it to its initial area. The σ' measured on coatings is a small fraction of this magnitude.[13] In an adhesive film which was attached to two adherends, σ' was greater than in an identical film present as a coating, i.e., attached to one solid only.[15] The difference between the stress as it would be without any chain mobility and the experimental σ' may be significant[16] even for materials as viscous as silicate glass at 425°.

The rate of relaxation may depend on the environment. Glass was coated[17] with a mixture of an epoxy resin and a hardener (such as m-phenylenediamine), heated at 130°, and cooled to room temperature. The σ' in the glass was determined during curing and during the subsequent aging at room temperature. Depending on the composition of the coating, the maximum value of σ' varied between 20 and 100 bars. The relaxation, when a polyamide was the hardener, was slow (say, 5% in 10 days) as long as the system was kept in dry air (over concentrated sulfuric acid) and rapid (say, 50% in 10 days) when the air had a relative humidity between 60% and 70%. Apparently, at least for this polymer, occluded water acted as a plasticizer.

An unexplained observation was made[18] on polyester coatings on glass, aluminum, steel, and wood. When these systems were stored at room temperature and, after different storage intervals, some specimens were broken by a thermal treatment, the maximum σ' at which this treatment still did not cause flaking off was smaller the longer the preceding storage.

An equation was given for the case of two very long plates, of width w, glued together and subjected to a medium in which the upper plate does, and the lower does not swell.[19] The mathematics ought to be identical also when the adhint cools and the contraction of the lower plate is greater than that of the upper member. If after cooling the width of the latter (see Fig. 66) is $w + \epsilon_0 w$, the maximum shear stress along the x axis near point m is approximately

$$\tau = 0.7\epsilon_0 (E_x G_{xy})^{0.5} , \tag{84}$$

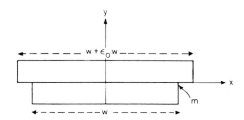

FIG. 66. Shrinkage stress in two plates glued together.

E_x being the common modulus of elasticity of the two members in the x direction and G_{xy} being the modulus of shear in the xy plane.

Apparently, unwanted stresses can form not only because of the setting of the adhesive but also as a result of incorrect handling of the adhint. When two pieces of glass with a liquid adhesive between them were cured at 149°C under a strong pressure, the final strength of the joint showed a maximum when this pressure was 200 psi (14 bars); for the four adhesives studied the strength after heating at 14 bars was by about 10%, 10%, 10%, and 150% greater than when the pressure was 7 bars and about 20% greater than when the pressure was 21 bars.[20] The improvement caused by an increase in pressure might be attributed to the more complete squeezing out of the bubble-containing polymer (see §34), but the decrease in strength observed when pressure rose from 14 to 21 bars must have another explanation. It seems possible that high pressure caused elastic deformation of the glass plates and, in particular, of the microscopic or submicroscopic hills on the glass surfaces in contact with the adhesive; when pressure was released, the plates and the hills tended to regain their initial shape and thus caused stresses unsuspected by the experimenter.

§**77**   The total relative elongation is so small for silicate glasses (near 0.5%) that shrinkage stresses in glass-to-metal seals are more dangerous than in any other of the usual adhints.[21] Consequently, considerable attention was paid to these stresses. In this section, butt joints are reviewed; see references 22, 23, and 24. The derivation has been carried out for two thin-walled hollow cylinders[25, 26] stuck together with their annular ends in contact. If R is the external and $R - \delta$ is the internal radius of the hollow cylinder, the equations contain the product $R\,\delta$; apparently, when two plates $l \times w \times h_1$ and $l \times w \times h_2$ are in contact along the area $l \times w$, these equations are approximately valid also for the central parts of the lengths l and w, far from the corners, if $0.5w$ and $0.5l$, respectively, are substituted for $(R\,\delta)^{0.5}$.

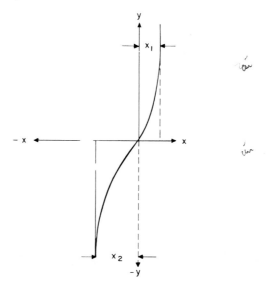

FIG. 67. Shrinkage stress at the boundary of two hollow cylinders.

In Fig. 67 the upper half represents the adherend and the lower, the adhesive, both as hollow cylinders. Air is at the right of the sketch. If the two bodies did not deform each other, their outlines would be straight right to the x axis. In reality, the transition from the external radius $R + x_1$ of the adherend to the external radius $R - x_2$ of the adhesive is gradual as shown by the continuous line; x_1 and x_2 exist because the cylinders were joined at a high temperature and had, at this temperature, identical radii; during cooling they contracted to different extents. R is the radius of the three-phase line. Let the intercept of this line with the plane of the drawing be the origin of the coordinate system. Thus, at $y > 0$, the value of $x_1 - x$ is the deviation of the adherend–air surface from the unstressed position; analogously, $x - x_2$ is the deformation suffered by the adhesive (at $y < 0$).

The equation of the adherend–air boundary is

$$x_1 - x = (e^{-\beta_1 y}/2\beta_1^3 D_1)[P \cos \beta_1 y - \beta_1 M (\cos \beta_1 y - \sin \beta_1 y)] \tag{85}$$

and of the adhesive–air boundary

$$x_2 - x = (e^{-\beta_2 y}/2\beta_2^3 D_2)[P \cos \beta_2 y + \beta_2 M (\cos \beta_2 y - \sin \beta_2 y)]. \tag{86}$$

In these equations,

$$\beta_1 = [3(1 - v_1^2)/R^2\delta^2]^{0.25}$$
$$\beta_2 = [3(1 - v_2^2)/R^2\delta^2]^{0.25}$$
$$D_1 = E_1\delta^3/12(1 - v_1^2)$$
$$D_2 = E_2\delta^3/12(1 - v_2^2).$$

P is the tension (gm/sec^2) acting along the three-phase line toward the axis of the cylinder in the adherend and away from this axis in the adhesive, and M is the bending moment at the three-phase line. E_1 and E_2 are the moduli of elasticity, and v_1 and v_2 the Poisson ratios of the two materials.

The value of $R + x_1$ may be considered to be unaffected by the shrinkage of the adhesive. If the relative linear contraction (which is about one-third of the volume shrinkage for which numerical data were listed in §52) of the adhesive is λ (or $100\lambda\%$), then $R - x_2 = (1 - \lambda)(R + x_1)$ and $x_1 + x_2 = \lambda R + \lambda x_1$ or, approximately,

$$x_1 + x_2 = \lambda R . \tag{87}$$

Also, because no discontinuity is expected when the sign of y values changes from positive to negative, dy/dx must be identical at $y = 0$ for both adherend–air and adhesive–air boundaries. These two conditions are sufficient to calculate P and M as functions of λR, β_1, β_2, D_1, and D_2; thus,

$$P = \frac{4\beta_1^3\beta_2^3 D_1 D_2(\beta_1 D_1 + \beta_2 D_2)\lambda R}{\beta_1^4 D_1^2 + 2\beta_1\beta_2(\beta_1^2 + \beta_1\beta_2 + \beta_2^2)D_1 D_2 + \beta_2^4 D_2^2} \qquad (88)$$

and

$$M = \frac{2\beta_1\beta_2 D_1 D_2(\beta_1^2 D_1 - \beta_2^2 D_2)\lambda R}{\beta_1^4 D_1^2 + 2\beta_1\beta_2(\beta_1^2 + \beta_1\beta_2 + \beta_2^2)D_1 D_2 + \beta_2^4 D_2^2}. \qquad (89)$$

As β_1 and β_2 usually will be very similar, we may set each of them equal to a quantity β; thus

$$P = \frac{4\beta^3 D_1 D_2(D_1 + D_2)\lambda R}{D_1^2 + 6D_1 D_2 + D_2^2} \qquad (90)$$

is obtained. Often, D_2 will be small compared with D_1; in these instances

$$P = \frac{4\beta^3 D_1 D_2 \lambda R}{D_1 + 6D_2} \qquad (91)$$

and

$$M = \frac{2D_1 D_2 \lambda R}{D_1 + 6D_2}. \qquad (92)$$

Theoretically, P acts on the three-phase line which, like any other geometrical line, is infinitely thin; thus the stress caused by P is infinitely large. Actually, the "line" will have a thickness determined by surface roughness (see §§3 and 80.2). The stress concentrations caused by surface roughness have been approximately calculated[27] but the results do not seem applicable to the present problem.

§78   The case of tubular lap joints has been discussed many years before that of butt joints. Let an adhesive sleeve of thickness $b - a$

set around a solid adherend cylinder of radius a (see Fig. 68). If the adhesive contracts more than does the adherend, three types of stress will be established in the sleeve, namely p_r along the radius r (r is a variable), p_θ parallel to the circumference of adherend, and p_z parallel to the z axis. If it is assumed that p_z is independent of r and z, that is, if the stress concentrations near the three-phase boundary are disregarded, the three stress systems can be calculated,[28, 29] namely

$$p_r = \frac{E_2\lambda}{1 + \alpha + \alpha\beta(E_2/E_1)}\left(\frac{a^2}{r^2} - \frac{a^2}{b^2}\right), \tag{93}$$

$$p_\theta = -\frac{E_2\lambda}{1 + \alpha + \alpha\beta(E_2/E_1)}\left(\frac{a^2}{b^2} + \frac{a^2}{r^2}\right), \tag{94}$$

and

$$p_z = -\frac{E_2\lambda}{1 + \alpha + \alpha\beta(E_2/E_1)}$$
$$\times \left[2\nu\frac{a^2}{b^2} + \frac{1 + \alpha + \alpha\beta(E_2/E_1)}{1 + \beta(E_2/E_1)}\right]. \tag{95}$$

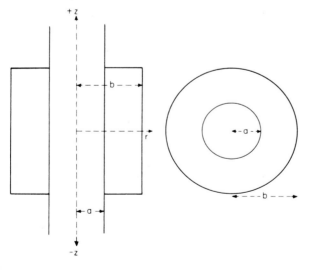

FIG. 68. Shrinkage stress in a cylindrical coating.

Here $\alpha = (a^2/b^2)(2\nu - 1)$, $\beta = (b^2/a^2) - 1$, E_1 and E_2 are the moduli of elasticity of adherend and adhesive, respectively, and λ has the meaning defined in §77. The Poisson ratio ν is assumed to be equal for the two substances.

It is seen that radial stress p_r, as it should, disappears at the adhesive–air interface (that is, at $r = b$); no calculation apparently has been done for real adhints in which the adhesive sleeve is in its turn surrounded with a cylinder of the second adherend. In any case, the greatest p_r occurs at the inner boundary of the adhesive, i.e., at $r = a$. The absolute value of p_θ also is greatest at $r = a$. The three stresses have somewhat similar magnitudes. If we write h for $b - a$ and if h is small compared with a, the greatest radial stress p_r is approximately $2E_2\lambda h/a$. The p_z under these circumstances would not be greatly different from $2E_2\lambda\nu$ or from $E_2\lambda$. A Hookean solid breaks when tensile stress of ϵE_2 is applied to it, ϵ being the total relative elongation. Thus, p_z caused by setting will approximately reach the value of the breaking stress when $\lambda = \epsilon$ and will be nearer the breaking stress the smaller the difference $\epsilon - \lambda$.

The equations in this section, in common with those of the preceding section, are inexact because they assume all the materials involved to be Hookean solids and neglect the relaxation phenomena whose importance was indicated in §76.

Butt Joints

§**79**   Stress concentration at flaws as discussed in §§63–66 exists in every solid and thus is not characteristic for adhesive joints as such. In the rest of this chapter stress concentrations near the adherend–adhesive boundary are considered. The corresponding stress concentration factors are denoted by the letter α in §61; as mentioned there, α generally would be unity if the adherend and adhesive had identical mechanical properties.

Unfortunately, calculation of α has not yet been carried out in a fully satisfactory manner for any type of adhint or any type of fracture. Thus the following review is a crude approximation only. It is believed, however, that even a crude approximation might be helpful in understanding the behavior of real adhints.

The subject can be systematized either according to the type of adhint and of the external action, or according to the rheological class of the adhesive (Hookean solids, perfectly plastic solids, and so on). The first-named arrangement has been selected for this book; thus we start with butt joints stressed in tension and complete the list with peeling.

§80   1. If the adhint consists of two cylinders joined basis to basis, external pull applied along the common axis of the two cylinders would cause a "geometrical" concentration of stress.

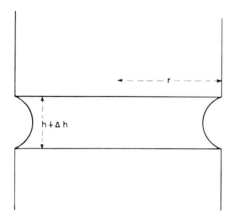

FIG. 69. Geometrical stress concentration in a butt joint.

Let r be the radius of the cylinders and of the adhesive "pancake" before straining (see Fig. 69). Let the thickness of the adhesive film be h before and $h + \Delta h$ after straining, and suppose that the adhint was annealed, keeping the distance $h + \Delta h$ constant, until the stresses induced by the external force relaxed to become insignificant. In the absence of stresses, the volume of the adhesive will be nearly equal to that before the stretch, i.e., to $\pi r^2 h$. The new volume between the two cylinders is $\pi r^2 (h + \Delta h)$. The difference is the volume of the circumferential groove visible in Fig. 69. If the profile of this groove is approximated as a half-ellipse with half-axes $\frac{1}{2}(h + \Delta h)$ (vertical) and a (horizontal), the equation

$$\pi r^2 \, \Delta h = 0.5 \, \pi^2 ar \, (h + \Delta h) \qquad (96)$$

results. Thus

$$a = \frac{2r}{\pi} \frac{\Delta h}{h + \Delta h} \qquad (97)$$

and Eq. (75) becomes writing

$$\alpha = 1 + \frac{8}{\pi} \frac{r}{h + \Delta h} \frac{\Delta h}{h + \Delta h} \qquad (98)$$

If $r/(h + \Delta h)$ is about 100 and $\Delta h(h + \Delta h)$ is about 0.03, α is equal to about 9.

2. Usually, however, deformation such as depicted in Fig. 69 will be associated with stresses resisting deformation. Apparently these stresses can be approximately calculated by the methods explained in §77. If the initial external radius of the cylinders and of the adhesive disc was r (see Fig. 70), and stress f was applied parallel to their axis, the radius of an unattached cylinder would decrease to $r[1 - (\nu_1 f/E_1)]$, ν_1 and E_1 being the Poisson ratio and the modulus of elasticity of the adherend. Analogously, the radius of the unattached adhesive would be $r[1 - (\nu_2 f/E_2)]$, ν_2 and E_2 standing for

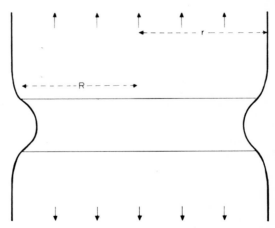

FIG. 70. Stresses caused by Poisson contraction in a butt joint.

Poisson's ratio and Young's modulus of the adhesive material. The actual radius of the circle where the adherend and the adhesive meet is R. Thus, the adherend at the interface is contracted from $r[1 - (\nu_1 f/E_1)]$ to R, while the adhesive is extended from $r[1 - (\nu_2 f/E_2)]$ to R; we assume that ν_2/E_2 is greater than ν_1/E_1. Hence, x_1 of §77 is equal to $r - (r\nu_1 f/E_1) - R$ and $x_2 = R - r + (r\nu_2 f/E_2)$; consequently λ of Eq. (87) is

$$\lambda = \frac{rf}{R}\left(\frac{\nu_2}{E_2} - \frac{\nu_1}{E_1}\right). \tag{99}$$

If this λ is introduced in Eq. (88) to (92), the values of tension P and moment M acting along the three-phase line are obtained.

A numerical example will show the order of magnitude which may be expected for P and the stress caused by this tension. First we approximate (99) as

$$\lambda \approx \frac{f}{2E_2}, \tag{100}$$

i.e., we assume the Young modulus of the adherend to be much greater than that of the adhesive, $r \approx R$ and $\nu_2 \approx 0.5$. With this assumption we may also write

$$P \approx 4\beta^3 D_2 \lambda R \tag{101}$$

instead of (91). Introducing the expressions for β and D_2 from §77 and that for λ from (100), we arrive at the expression

$$P = \frac{\delta^{1.5} f}{2[3(1 - \nu^2)]^{0.25} R^{0.5}}, \tag{102}$$

which may be simplified to

$$P \approx \frac{\delta^{1.5} f}{2R^{0.5}}. \tag{103}$$

Let $r\,(\approx R)$ be equal to 100δ; then $P \approx f\delta/20$. If $\delta = 0.1$ cm, $P \approx$

$0.005f$ gm/sec^2. This tension must be distributed over an interfacial layer whose thickness will be determined by the roughness of the adherend. Let this thickness be 10^{-4} cm (see §7). In this particular instance, radial stress which causes contraction $r[1 - (\nu_1 f/E_1)] - R$ and expansion $R - r[1 - (\nu_2 f/E_2)]$ in adherend and adhesive, respectively, would be $\sigma_r = 50f$ gm/cm sec^2. Thus, radial stress may considerably exceed the axial stress caused by the external force. In other words, α of Eq. (68) may reach the value of 50.

It is true that the above calculation is very crude, first of all because the theory of beams on elastic foundation is only a first approximation. Nevertheless the existence of considerable radial stresses along the three-phase boundary cannot be doubted. These stresses are dangerous not only because of their magnitude but also because of their direction. Suppose that the worst cracks in the adhesive are oriented normally to the adherend–adhesive boundary; in this case their presence would not markedly affect the strength of the adhesive disc (see §64). But these cracks will greatly lower the strength in the radial direction. If factor β of §64 is, say, 1.4 for axial stresses and 11 for radial stresses [i.e., if a/b in Eq. (75) is 0.2 in the axial and consequently is 5 in the radial direction], radial stress will start fracture even if σ_r is only a fraction (one-seventh) of the axial stress.

A more elaborate calculation[30] (see also reference 31), permits calculation of the stress concentration factor at the center of the adhint, at the middle of the adhesive–air boundary, and at the three-phase line. Experimental analysis of the stress distribution in butt joints in tension is in at least qualitative agreement with the predictions of the theory. Figure 71 shows a typical photoelastic fringe pattern of a stressed butt joint.[32] Two metal plates were glued together with a commercial epoxy adhesive, the width of the plates (from left to right in the figure) being 20 times the thickness of the adhesive film (downward from the top of the figure), and the fringes produced by compressing the sandwich (see the arrows) were photographed. The pattern produced by compression ought to be analogous to that produced by tension as long as both compression and tension are small. The left-hand end of the figure represents an edge of the adhesive, while the center of the adhesive

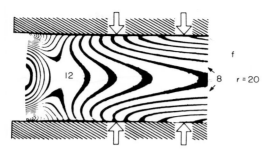

FIG. 71. Photoelastic fringe pattern of a stressed butt joint. From reference 32.

film is far to the right of the picture. The stress gradient, i.e., the rate of change of stress with distance, is greater the more crowded the fringes. As number 8 at the right end of the figure indicates, there are only seven fringes between the center of the film and the part photographed; thus, the stress near the center is almost independent of the distance from the center. However, stress rapidly varies with distance near the middle of the adhesive–air boundary and, particularly, at the three-phase line. The stress concentration factor at this line is approximately equal to 3.

3. The deformations considered in §§80.1 and 2 are purely elastic. The opposite extreme is afforded by rigid-plastic bodies. These fictitious materials show no deformation whatsoever as long as the local shearing stress is below a value which here is denoted by k; and as soon as k is reached, the material starts plastic flow. When there is flow, transformation of mechanical work into heat must occur, that is, viscosity effects should be taken into account. However, in the approximate theory, due chiefly to Prandtl (1923), time effects are disregarded; in other words, only an extremely slow motion is considered. With this restriction also the inertia terms are excluded.

If two flat plates (see Fig. 72) very long in the direction perpendicular to the plane of the page and having width w much greater than the distance h_0 between the plates, are glued together and an average pull f is applied parallel to the y axis, the tensile stress σ_y in the adhesive (parallel to y) may be taken to be independent of y. However, tensile stress σ_x acting parallel to x will depend on both

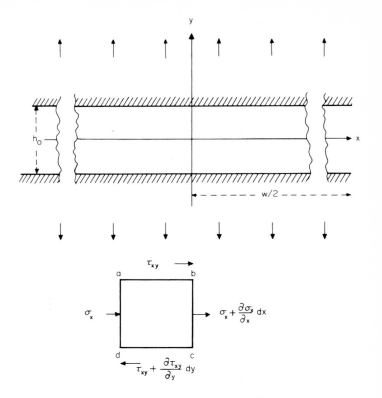

FIG. 72. Stresses in a rigid-plastic adhesive film.

x and y; this stress causes flow of the adhesive toward the plane of $x = 0$ when the plates are pulled apart, analogously to the pressure gradient causing the centripetal flow of a Newtonian liquid in Stefan's experiments (§38). In addition, there are shearing stresses. If $abcd$ in Fig. 72 is a rectangle in the xy plane in the adhesive, and if $\overline{ab} = \overline{cd} = dx$ and $\overline{ad} = \overline{cb} = dy$, the tension originating from the gradient of σ_x along x and pushing the rectangle to the right is $(\partial \sigma_x / \partial x) \, dx \, dy$. If the shearing stress along ab is τ_{xy} (meaning a stress acting parallel to axis x on a plane whose normal is parallel to axis y) and that along cd is $\tau_{xy} + (\partial \tau_{xy} / \partial y) \, dy$, the tension (gm/sec^2) originating from these stresses and pushing the rectangle to the left is $(\partial \tau_{xy} / \partial y) \, dy \, dx$. In equilibrium,

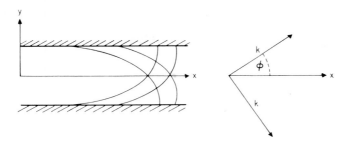

FIG. 73. Slip lines in a rigid-plastic film.

$$\frac{\partial \sigma_x}{\partial x} + \frac{\partial \tau_{xy}}{\partial y} = 0 . \tag{104}$$

There is, of course, no such equilibrium when accelerated flow takes place; thus we really determine the force which is just insufficient to cause plastic deformation. Analogously to (104),

$$\frac{\partial \sigma_y}{\partial y} + \frac{\partial \tau_{yx}}{\partial x} = 0$$

or, as $\partial \sigma_y / \partial y = 0$,

$$\frac{\partial \tau_{yx}}{\partial x} = \frac{\partial \tau_{xy}}{\partial x} = 0 . \tag{105}$$

The local shearing stress, that first reaches the value k at which motion starts, in general is not parallel to either y or x axis. Its directions are those of *slip lines*. A few slip lines are indicated in Fig. 73; they cross each other at right angles. If a slip line at a point makes an angle ϕ with the x direction, then the other slip line at the same point makes, with the same direction, an angle $\phi - (\pi/2)$. If stress k acts along 1 cm of the first slip line (see Fig. 73) the projection of the tension on the x axis is $k \cos^2 \phi$ (because the length along the x axis is $\cos \phi$) and the projection of the corresponding tension acting along the second slip line is $-k \sin^2 \phi$. Thus, shearing stress τ_{xy} along the x direction is

$$\tau_{xy} = k(\cos^2 \phi - \sin^2 \phi) = k \cos 2\phi . \tag{106}$$

It can be shown in an analogous manner that

$$\sigma_x = -p - k \sin 2\phi \qquad (107)$$

and

$$\sigma_y = -p + k \sin 2\phi , \qquad (108)$$

p being the hydrostatic pressure (acting equally in all directions) caused by external stress f. From (106) to (108) we conclude that

$$\sigma_x = \sigma_y - 2\,k \sin 2\phi = \sigma_y - 2k\left(1 - \frac{\tau_{xy}^2}{k^2}\right)^{0.5} . \qquad (109)$$

As neither k nor τ depend on x [see Eq. (105)], Eq. (104) affords

$$\frac{\partial \sigma_y}{\partial x} + \frac{\partial \tau_{xy}}{\partial y} = 0 , \qquad (110)$$

an equation in which σ_y is independent of y and τ_{xy} is independent of x. If τ_{xy} is expressed as $aky + b$, a and b being constants to be determined from the boundary conditions, $\partial \tau_{xy}/\partial y = ak$ and, consequently, $\partial \sigma_y/\partial x = - ak$ and

$$\sigma_y = -akx + kc ,$$

kc being the integration constant. As Fig. 73 indicates, slip lines are tangential to the plates; thus at the plates, i.e., at $y = h_0/2$, the angle $\phi = 0$ and $\tau_{xy} = k$ [see Eq. (106)]. At $y = 0$, $\tau_{xy} = 0$ because of symmetry. Thus, $a = 2/h_0$ and $b = 0$, i.e.,

$$\tau_{xy} = 2ky/h_0 \qquad (111)$$

and

$$\sigma_y = -\frac{2kx}{h_0} + kc . \qquad (112)$$

From the conditions near the adhesive–air boundary it can be shown[33] that constant c is approximately $-\pi/2$. Thus, except near the plane of $x = 0$, x/h_0 is greater than $-c$ whenever $w/2$ is much greater than h_0, i.e., in practically all joints. Thus we may write

$$\sigma_y = -2kx/h_0 .$$

The force on a plate l cm deep (normally to the plane of the drawing) and w cm wide is

$$-\int_0^w l\frac{2k}{h_0} x \, dx = -\frac{w^2 lk}{h_0}$$

and the average stress is $-wk/h_0$. It is balanced by the external stress f which, consequently, is equal to

$$f = wk/h_0 . \tag{113}$$

An analogous calculation for the case of two circular discs of radius a gives

$$f = \frac{2ka}{3h_0} ; \tag{114}$$

see, e.g., references 34 and 35.

It is instructive to compare Eqs. (113) and (114) with Eqs. (33) and (36). Evidently, there is an analogy between k and η/t, which have identical dimensions (gm/cm sec^2). However, f for Newtonian flow is proportional to $(w/h)^2$ or $(a/h)^2$ while f for plastic flow is proportional to w/h or a/h; here h stands for h_2 in (33) and (36), h_1 in (50), and h_0 in (113) and (114).

In both instances the calculated f would increase without limit as long as a/h increases, i.e., ever thinner adhints are tested. At large a/h values, adherends may break before a plastic adhesive starts flowing. Experiments concerning this conclusion are referred to in §104.

Block Joints

81   Adhints used in the block shear test, also known as test in shear by compression loading (Am. Soc. Testing and Materials D 905-49) are of the type illustrated in Fig. 74(a). The rigid frame of the instrument (shaded) is marked with numbers 1 and 1'; 2 is the plunger which causes the rupture of the adhint; and 3, 3' are the two adherends (many fine dots); white spaces are air. It is clear that, in the absence of support 1', the specimen would turn clockwise as soon as 2 starts moving down; and this rotation would cause the upper part of adherend 3' to press against 2, and the lower part of 3 to press against 1; and when 1' is provided, the upper part of 3 presses against 1'.

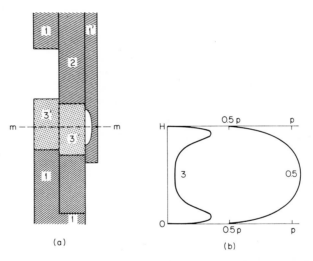

(a)   (b)

FIG. 74. (a) Block shear test. 1 and 1', rigid frame; 2, plunger; 3 and 3', the adhint. (b) Shear stress in the adhesive film in a block shear test. Abscissa: shear stress; *p*: external pressure. Ordinate: distance from an end of the overlap. Right hand curve is for *H*:*b* = 0.5, left hand curve for *H*:*b* = 3; *b* is the breadth of the adherend. Data of reference 36.

In the specimen of Fig. 74, the adhesive covers the whole area of contact between 3 and 3'. For calculating the stress pattern, the adhesive was neglected and the system treated[36] as if the two adherends were one homogenous solid body. The main qualitative result of the computation is that the principal stresses in the boundary between 3 and 3' are not in the plane of this boundary and that the shear stress τ acting in this plane (this is the stress that tends to slide one adherend relatively to the other) is not uniform over it. Figure 74(b) shows the dependence of τ on the distance from the horizontal central plane mm, if there is no overlapping of the two adherends (that is, the upper surfaces of 3 and 3' are in one plane and so are their bottom surfaces). The length (in the vertical direction) of each adherend is H, and the breadth is b; the width w in the direction perpendicular to the plane of the drawing is irrelevant.

It is seen that the variation of τ along the interface between 3 and 3' in the direction of the plunger motion strongly depends on the ratio $H:b$. When this is 0.5 (see the right-hand curve), the highest stress is found at the center plane (mm). When $H:b = 3$ (the left-hand curve), the stress has two maxima near the upper and the lower end of the block. The pressure on the plunger is p, i.e., the force is pbw. When the adherend is stout (i.e., $H:b = 0.5$), the maximum τ exceeds p; but for slender adherends (i.e., for $H:b = 3$) the τ never exceeds $0.4p$. Thus, judgement of the strength of a block adhint from compression loading tests is likely to be misleading unless, at least, the ratio $H:b$ is taken into consideration.

Lap Joints

§**82**   Lap joints are similar to block joints but a tensile, rather than a compressive, force is applied to cause fracture. Stress distribution in lap joints, as long as the deformation is elastic, is influenced by at least three factors. The first is active also when the adherends are absolutely rigid; the second exists because they are extensible; and the third when they are not only extensible but also flexible.

1. To understand the first factor, supplement a lap joint with its mirror image, as in Fig. 75 in which the real adhint is outlined with a continuous, and the image with an interrupted line. It is clear that the empty rectangle above M_2 must cause a stress concentration analogous to that observed at the corners of a quadratic hole punched in a sheet (§65). As the adhesive, if it perfectly wets the two adherends, will have a boundary with air of the shape of a

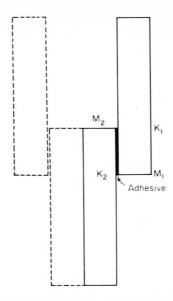

FIG. 75. Geometrical stress concentration in a lap joint.

quarter of a circular cylinder (Fig. 76), the radius of curvature of this boundary will be approximately h_0, if h_0 is the thickness of the adhesive film, while twice the thickness of the adherend, i.e., 2δ would correspond to length l of §65. Thus, if $h_0 : 2\delta = 0.014$, the factor of stress concentration at a corner would be about 6, assuming that the deformation of the adherends may be neglected.

2. This deformation, as long as the adherends are not flexible, will tend to lower the above stress concentration but will cause another nonuniformity of stress.[37-39] To make clear that bending is disregarded, we consider the middle member of a *double lap* joint (see Fig. 77). If pull F_0 is applied to this member, force F_0 acts on all cross sections of it above level ab, while evidently tensile force acting on the member at the cd level (i.e., at $z = 0$) is zero. Thus, force F along the axis of z decreases from F_0 to 0 when z decreases from L to 0, L being the length of the overlap. This decrease of F occurs because F is gradually balanced by shearing forces along the adherend–adhesive boundary. Consider a horizontal slice of the

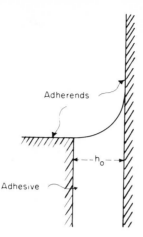

FIG. 76. The adhesive–air boundary in a lap joint.

middle member, dz cm thick. The tensile force on its lower bound-ary is $-F$ and on its upper boundary, $F + (\partial F/\partial z)\,dz$; hence the re-sultant force is $(\partial F/\partial z)\,dz$. This force is balanced by the two shear-ing forces along the lines ad and bc; if the shear stress at the given z is τ, each of these forces is $\tau w\,dz$, w being the width of the ad-herend (i.e., normal to the plane of the drawing). Thus, $\partial F/\partial z = 2\tau w$

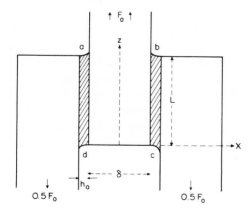

FIG. 77. Differential strain in a double lap joint.

or, substituting stress f for force F according to the equation $F = fw\delta$,

$$\frac{\partial f}{\partial z} = \frac{2\tau}{\delta}, \qquad (115)$$

δ being the thickness of the middle adherend.

Both $\partial f/\partial z$ and τ can be expressed as functions of the elongation of the middle adherend (and of the adhesive which is supposed to follow all deformations of the bar). If an atom, which was situated z cm above the cd level before the application of force, is now l cm above this level, an atom which initially was at $z + dz$ now is at $l + dl$. From Hooke's law (E is Young's modulus of the bar)

$$\frac{\partial(l - z)}{\partial z} = \frac{f}{E} \qquad (116)$$

or

$$\frac{\partial^2 l_1}{\partial z^2} = \frac{1}{E}\frac{\partial f}{\partial z} \qquad (117)$$

if l_1 is written for $l - z$.

The correlation between τ and l_1 depends on the geometry of the system. If, as in Fig. 77, the two side bars are about as thick as the middle adherend, the stress τ must have high values at the two ends of the overlap and a minimum somewhere near the middle of it, i.e., near $z = 0.5L$. The mathematics is simpler when the two side adherends are much thicker (or have much greater moduli of elasticity, or both) than the middle member; in other words, when a strip is pulled out of a slit to whose walls it is glued. In this case, the line cd retains its position as long as the adhint is not broken, and the three quantities l_1, τ, and f must be equal to zero at $z = 0$. For this instance, it is reasonable to assume that

$$\tau = G_1 l_1/h_0, \qquad (118)$$

G_1 being the modulus of shear of the adhesive and h_0 the thickness of the adhesive film. From (115), (117), and (118), the equation

$$\frac{\partial^2 l_1}{\partial z^2} = \frac{2G_1 l_1}{E\delta h_0} \qquad (119)$$

follows. No solution of this differential equation which would satisfy all three boundary conditions (i.e., at $z=0$, $l_1 = \tau = f = 0$) came to the attention of the author. Let f_0 denote the ratio $F_0/w\delta$. Then a formula for l_1 which satisfies the first and the second conditions is

$$l_1 = \frac{f_0}{E}\left(\frac{Eh_0\delta}{2G_1}\right)^{0.5} \frac{e^{\lambda z} - e^{-\lambda z}}{e^{\lambda L} + e^{-\lambda L}}; \lambda = \left(\frac{2G_1}{E\delta h_0}\right)^{0.5}. \qquad (120)$$

When $z = 0$, also $l_1 = 0$. From (118), $\tau = 0$ as well but f has a finite magnitude. To make $f = 0$ at $z = 0$, instead of (120), the equation

$$l_1 = \frac{f_0}{E}\left(\frac{Eh_0\delta}{2G_1}\right)^{0.5} \frac{e^{\lambda z} + e^{-\lambda z}}{e^{\lambda L} + e^{-\lambda L}} \qquad (121)$$

may be considered. This relation makes l_1 and τ finite at $z = 0$ but f, which according to Eq. (116) is equal to $E(\partial l_1/\partial z)$, becomes zero at $z = 0$; see §123.

For those interested in the final strength of adhints the situation at $z = L$ is more important than that at $z = 0$ because the most dangerous stress τ occurs at the upper end of the overlap. If λ is not too small and L not too short, the two rival equations (120) and (121) give almost identical results for the value of l_1 at $z = L$ because near this point $e^{-\lambda z}$ may be neglected as compared with $e^{\lambda z}$. Thus, in both variants, at $z = L$

$$l_1 \approx \frac{f_0}{E}\left(\frac{E\delta h_0}{2G_1}\right)^{0.5} \frac{e^{\lambda L}}{e^{\lambda L}} = \frac{f_0}{E}\left(\frac{E\delta h_0}{2G_1}\right)^{0.5}. \qquad (122)$$

Consequently the greatest τ, from Eq. (118), is

$$\tau_{\max} = \left(\frac{G_1\delta}{2Eh_0}\right)^{0.5} f_0. \qquad (123)$$

The average shear stress in the adhesive is

$$\tau_{av} = \frac{F_0}{wL} = \frac{f_0 \delta}{L}.$$

(124)

Hence the greatest stress concentration factor

$$\frac{\tau_{max}}{\tau_{av}} = \left(\frac{G_1}{2E \delta h_0}\right)^{0.5} L.$$

(125)

It is present at points a and b of Fig. 77.

If rupture occurs when a definite value of τ_{max} is reached, Eq. (123) shows that the external tensile stress f_0 needed to break the adhint is independent of the length L of overlap. Experimentally, breaking stress increases with L; sometimes it is approximately proportional to $L^{0.5}$. This discrepancy manifests another weakness of the theory. The stress concentration described in §82.1 increases with the ratio δ/h_0, while stress concentration factor due to the extensibility of the adherends [see Eq. (125)] is inversely proportional to the root $(\delta h_0)^{0.5}$. When considering these conclusions, the crudeness of the underlying theories should be borne in mind.

The preceding treatment and the final equation (125) can, if at all, be correct only if the adherends and the adhesive are Hookean solids, if contraction normal to the external stress (as in §§80.1 and 80.2) may be neglected, and if no bending of the adherends occurs, This bending is treated in §83.

§83   Figure 78 illustrates the shape change of a lap joint caused by an external pull; the adhesive is shaded. If the adhint does not break before, it acquires the shape, in Fig. 78 b, such that the centroid lines of the two adherends far from the overlap are parts of one straight line, and the central point of the adhesive film lies on this line. The overlapping parts of the adherends are each doubly bent, the concave side being away from the adhesive between the center of the latter and the unattached lengths of each adherend and toward the adhesive near the overlap–air boundaries.

Of the two bends, the second usually will be more dangerous for

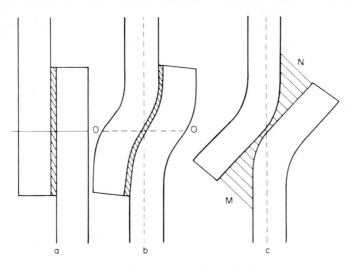

FIG. 78. Deformation of a flexible lap joint.

the joint than the first. When the two adherends meet with their convex sides in contact, the elastic forces in the adherends cause compression of the adhesive film between them, and compressive stresses usually are less destructive for adhesives than are tensile stresses. Strong tensile stresses must be present where the adhesive is situated between a convex surface of one and a concave surface of the other adherend. If the adhesive had no tensile strength, the shape would have been as indicated in Fig. 78 c. It is the adhesive that prevents parting of the two solids as shown in the sketch. Thus, near points M and N a tendency to peel is present, and peeling stresses usually cause fracture of lap joints whose adherends are flexible.

A theory in which this flexibility has been accounted for exists.[38] When tensile force F_0 is applied to a lap joint of width w and overlap L, not only tension F_0/w but also a moment M_0 and a tension V perpendicular to the plane of the adhesive film act in the adhint. Let σ_f be tensile stress (i.e., in the direction of F_0) in the adherend at the adherend–adhesive boundary, σ_0 be stress in the adhesive perpendicular to the plane of the joint (i.e., the peeling stress as indicated in Fig. 78 c), and τ_0 be the shear stress in the adhesive. We are interested in the relations between the greatest values of these stresses and the value of F_0 which, in usual rupture experiments, is increased until the adhint breaks down. These relations depend on the nondimensional ratio $k = 2M_0/F_0\delta$, δ being the thickness of each adherend. This k is equal to 1.00, 0.61, 0.45, and 0.37 when the nondimensional ratio $(L/\delta)(F_0/w\,\delta E)^{0.5}$ is 0.0, 0.2, 0.4, or 0.6, respectively; E is the modulus of elasticity of the adherend material. Thus, in a given adhint, k decreases when F_0 increases; in fact, as a coarse approximation, we may put $k \approx 1 - k_0F_0^{0.25}$, k_0 being a constant.

The dependence of σ_f, σ_0, and τ_0 on k and, consequently, on F_0 is quite different according to whether the flexibility of the adhint is determined mainly by the adherends or mainly by the adhesive. The first case is observed when $h_0/\delta \ll E_1/E$ and $h_0/\delta \ll G_1/G$, h_0 being the thickness of the cement layer, E_1 its modulus of elasticity, and G and G_1 the shear moduli of adherend and cement, respectively. For the second case, h_0/δ must be much greater than E_1/E or G_1/G. No approximation is available for the intermediate range in which h_0/δ, E_1/E, and G_1/G have comparable magnitudes; if, for instance, $E = 100E_1$, the theory gives no information on lap joints in which ratio δ/h_0 is confined between 10 and 1000. However, some calculations for the intermediate range of $h_0E/\delta E_1$ have been published more recently.[40]

Figure 79 represents stress distribution in the first case. The values of k are plotted along the abscissa from right to left; thus F_0 increases from left to right. The maximum values of σ_f/f_0, σ_0/f_0, and τ_0/f_0 are indicated along the ordinate. Thus, for instance, the greatest value of σ_f occurring in a lap joint (for which $h_0/\delta \ll E_1/E$) is 4.0 f_0, i.e., 4.0 times as great as the external stress. When k decreases, i.e., F_0 increases, stress concentration factors σ_f/f_0, etc., decrease because the system is deformed and "adjusts itself" to the external force; as pointed out in §66 also stress concentration factors caused by holes are smaller at greater stresses. The maximum values of the stresses themselves increase with F_0; e.g., F_0 increases fourfold between $k = 0.61$ and $k = 0.45$ while σ_0/f_0 in this range decreases from 2.9 to 2.3 only; thus σ_0 increases in the ratio 9.2:2.9.

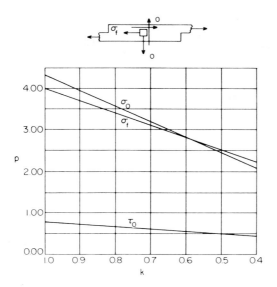

FIG. 79. Stress concentrations in adhints whose flexibility is determined by the adherends. Abscissa: ratio $2M_0/F_0\delta$ plotted from right to left. Ordinate: maximum values of stress concentration factors σ_f/f_0, σ_0/f_0, and τ_0/f_0. From reference 38.

If E, δ, and F_0 are kept constant, the abscissa of Fig. 79 increases with L (in the direction from left to right). Thus stress concentration factors σ_f/f_0 and so on are smaller the greater L. This is so because the adjustment of the glued part is easier the longer this part.

The maximum values of σ_0 and σ_f occur at the two ends of the overlap, i.e., near points M and N of Fig. 78 c. When starting from these points we approach plane 00 of the adhint, Fig. 78 b, σ_f continues to be a tension stress but σ_0 changes sign and becomes a compression stress, as mentioned in the second paragraph of this section. In some joints, as calculation [40] shows, the cement is slightly compressed for 75% of the length of the overlap and extended only near the overlap ends, but the greatest degree of extension may be ten times the greatest degree of compression.

§84 When $h_0/\delta \gg E_1/E$ and $h_0/\delta \gg G_1/G$, stress concentrations depend on the dimensions of the adhint and on the properties of the adhesive, while none of these factors is of importance in the first case (of $h_0/\delta \ll E_1/E$) except insofar as they affect the value of k. Therefore, instead of σ_0/f_0 as function of k, in Fig. 80 the maximum value of $(\sigma_0/f_0)(L/2\delta)^2$ is plotted along the ordinate as function of $0.5L(6E_1/E\delta^3 h_0)^{0.25}$ for four different values of parameter k. Consider a system in which L/δ is about 64; then $\sigma_0/f_0 = 0.001$ the ordinate of Fig. 80 and the highest value of σ_0/f_0 indicated is only 0.07.

The maximum shear stress in the adhesive (still at $h_0/\delta \gg G_1/G$) for small external forces is

$$\tau_{max} = \frac{f_0\delta}{L}\left[\left(\frac{2G_1L^2}{Eh_0\delta}\right)^{0.5} \coth\left(\frac{2G_1L^2}{Eh_0\delta}\right)^{0.5}\right].$$

In a typical adhint, $(2G_1L^2/Eh_0\delta)^{0.5}$ may be equal to unity; as $\coth 1 = 1.31$, the maximum shearing stress is $1.31(f_0\delta/L)$. The average shearing stress [see Eq. (124)] is $f_0\delta/L$; thus the maximum stress concentration factor in this example would be 1.31. The maximum ratio of $\sigma_0 L/f_0\delta$ for the example computed in the preceding paragraph would be near 4.4. When $2G_1L^2/Eh_0\delta$ is considerably greater than unity, maximum shear stress can be expressed as

$$\tau_{max} = \left(\frac{2G_1\delta}{Eh_0}\right)^{0.5} f_0, \tag{126}$$

i.e., is twice that given in Eq. (123). If in addition $h_0 = \delta$, then it is $f_0(2G_1/E)^{0.5}$.

If joints of different overlaps L but otherwise of identical dimensions are compared, Fig. 80 becomes one of $\sigma_0 L^2/f_0$ versus L. The effect of L on σ_0/f_0 is difficult to discern from this graph because k itself depends on L but it appears that σ_0/f_0 is less at longer overlaps, as would be expected from a nonmathematical inspection. When rupture occurs in shear, as an increase in L renders Eq. (126) more nearly valid, the maximum shear stress becomes independent of L; consequently, the maximum concentration of shear stress becomes proportional to L. However, this conclusion must be modified if the external force is not small.

A procedure for predicting the strength of lap joints by combining

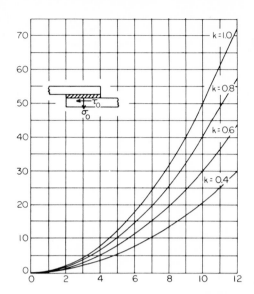

FIG. 80. Stress concentrations in adhints whose flexibility is determined by the adhesive. Abscissa: ratio 0.5 $L(6E_1/E\delta^3h_0)^{0.25}$. Ordinate maximum values of (δ_0/f_0) $(L/2\delta)^2$. From reference 38.

some theoretical deductions with typical experimental results has been worked out.[41]

§**85**   The predictions of the theories of §§82–84 were compared[42,43] with the experiment. Two plates of an aluminum alloy, 25 mm wide and 1.5 mm thick, were overlapped over, for instance, 20 mm and glued with Redux 775 (composition unknown). They were marked along the sides (20 × 1.5 mm), the displacement of the marks during a tensile pull was measured in a microscope, and the shear stress τ calculated. Figure 81 illustrates the main results. The abscissa is the distance along the overlap; the numbers mean the distance from the ends of the overlap in millimeters. The ordinate is τ in kg wt./mm²; multiply by 98.1 to obtain τ in bars. The three sets of curves refer to the overlap lengths (5, 10, and 20 mm from top to bottom). Each set consists of three curves; the flattest represent the experimental results; the middle, the theory of §82; and the steepest,

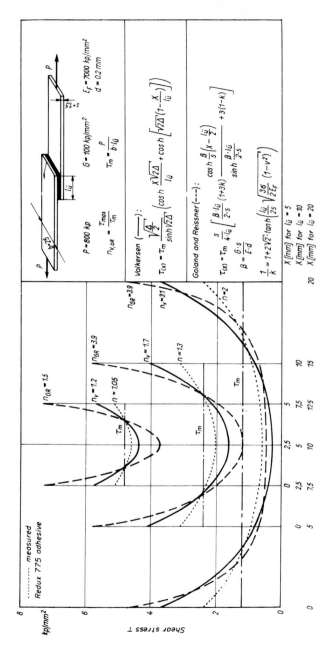

FIG. 81. Stresses in lap joints. Abscissa: distance from one end of the overlap. Ordinate: shear stress. Dots: experimental; dashes: theory of § 82; solid line: theory of § 83. From reference 43.

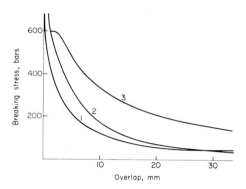

FIG. 82. Dependence of breaking stress on overlap length. Abscissa: overlap, in millimeters. Ordinate: breaking stress, in bars. Curve 1: theory of § 83. Curve 2: theory of § 82. Curve 3: experimental. Data of reference 43.

the theory of §§83–84. The numbers n (1.5, 1.2, 1.05, etc.) mean the ratios $\tau_{max} : \tau_{av}$ [see Eq. (125)].

It is seen that the increase of τ from the middle to the ends of the overlap is less rapid than predicted and, consequently, the ratio $\tau_{max} : \tau_{av}$ is not as great as expected. On the other hand, the qualitative predictions are correct: τ has a minimum in the middle, is greatest at the ends, and the ratio $\tau_{max} : \tau_{av}$ increases with L.

Another test[42, 43] of the theories is shown in Fig. 82. Its abscissa is the overlap length L (in millimeters) of adhints similar to those of Fig. 81, and the ordinate is the breaking stress defined, apparently, as F_m/wL (see §61). The upper curve is based on the experimental data; it is significantly different from the two theoretical curves of which the middle is for the theory of §82 and the lowest for §§83–84. The actual stress concentrations are not as dangerous as they would have been for Hookean solids.

§86   A further comparison between the theory and the experiment can be made by means of some test data obtained when the strength of lap joints was measured as a function of the geometrical parameters. An example is shown in Fig. 83 from reference 44. The ordinate of the figure represents the breaking stress $f_m = F_m/w\delta$, F_m being the breaking force of lap joints, in pounds per square inch (multiply

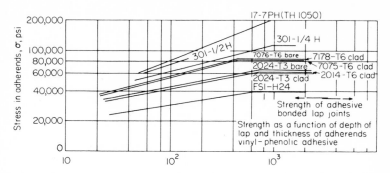

FIG. 83. Experimental rupture stress and dimensions of lap joints. Abscissa: $(L/\delta)^2$. Ordinate: breaking stress, $F_m/w\delta$ psi. One adhesive and seven different metallic adherends. From reference 44.

by 0.06895 to obtain stresses in bars) and the abscissa shows $(L/\delta)^2$ on a logarithmic scale. Note that f_m here is not defined as F_m/wL (see §61). One adhesive (a "vinyl-phenolic resin") was used for all adhints. The adherends were a magnesium alloy (FSI-H24), six aluminum alloys (2014, 2024, 7075, 7178, and their variations), and three steels (301-¼ H, 301-½ H, and 17-7PH). It is seen that f_m is independent of L/δ at great overlaps; in this region the adherends break and f_m is the tensile strength of the adherend material; this is, for instance, 180,000 psi for 17-7 steel and 39,000 psi for FSI magnesium. At smaller L/δ values, f_m increases nearly linearly with log (L/δ), that is, an increase in L is less effective the greater the ratio L/δ, as it should be according to the theory (see §§83 and 91). Thus, for magnesium, an increase of L/δ from 40 to 100 raises f_m from 28,200 to 30,500 psi, while an increase from 200 to 260 causes a rise of f_m from 34,000 to only 35,800 psi.

The f_m of Fig. 83 is greater the greater the tensile strength and the modulus of elasticity of the metal. This also is in agreement with the theory. It is clear from Eq. (125) and §84 that products $E\delta$ rather than the values of δ itself should be compared when different adherends are studied. Thus f_m should be represented as a function of $(L/\delta E)^2$ rather than of $(L/\delta)^2$. The E of steel 17-7 is about 4.4 times that of magnesium FSI. As $4.4^2 \approx 19$, ratio $(L/\delta)^2 = 20$ for steel is equivalent to ratio $(L/\delta)^2 = 20 \times 19 = 380$ for magnesium;

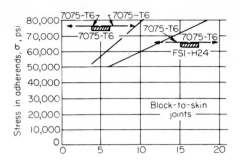

FIG. 84. Rupture stress of stiffened lap joints. Abscissa: L/δ. Ordinate: breaking stress, $F_m/w\delta$ psi. From reference 44.

and indeed extrapolation of the uppermost line to $(L/\delta)^2 = 20$ leads to a f_m of about 40,000 psi, i.e., only a few percent greater than f_m of FSI at $(L/\delta)^2 = 380$.

Peeling (see §83), which so markedly lowers f_m, can be reduced not only by making both adherends stiff but also by combining a thin plate with a thick block, as indicated in Figs. 84 and 85. Breaking stress again is the ordinate, but this time L/δ is plotted on the abscissa; δ is the thickness of the plate, not of the block. In the experiments of Fig. 84, upper line, two thin plates of aluminum alloy 7075 were glued to a block of an identical alloy, and pull was applied to the plates. The lower line is for two aluminum alloy

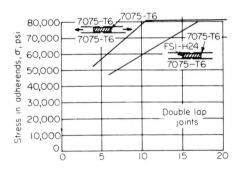

FIG. 85. Rupture stress of double lap joints. Abscissa: L/δ. Ordinate: breaking stress, $F_m/w\delta$ psi. From reference 44.

plates glued to a magnesium block. Figure 85 refers to double lap joints, the medium adherend being a block; the composition of the adherends is marked as in Fig. 84. Naturally, the highest breaking stress attained in all instances was equal to the tensile strength of the 7075 alloy. However, the ratio L/δ at which the greatest stress was reached was different for different blocks and, above all, different from the L/δ value at which tensile strength is reached in ordinary lap joints (see Fig. 83). As this figure shows, for the 7075 alloy $(L/\delta)^2$ was about 420, i.e., L/Δ was about 20 when f_m became independent of L/δ. For lap joints supported by thick blocks (see Figs. 84 and 85) the kink was observed at L/δ values as low as 10 or 11. In other words, the joint ceased to be the weakest region of the system at overlaps which for supported lap joints were only half as long as for unsupported adhints.

Additional experimental data[45] on the relative strength of single and double lap joints are shown in Fig. 86. The adherends were 99.5% aluminum (left), an Al-Mg-Mn alloy, and an Al-Cu-Mg alloy (right). Their yield stresses (in kg wt./mm², multiply by 98.1 to obtain them in bars) are plotted along the abscissa, and f_m (kg wt./mm²) along the ordinate. The lower shaded strip is for single, and the upper, for double lap joints. The f_m is defined as force F_m divided by the glued area, but it is not clear whether the glued area of the double lap system was taken as equal to, or twice as great as, that of the single lap assembly; the overlap L was 1.0 or 0.5 cm, and the width w was 2.5 cm.

§87   The importance of the stress concentration near the two ends of the overlap in a single lap joint could be demonstrated in a striking manner.[46] Lap joints with an overlap length of 2.5 cm failed at loads near 3000 lb (i.e., 1.335×10^9 dynes). When adhints were made in which the 2.5 cm long overlap was only half-filled with the adhesive, namely 0.625 cm band of adhesive–1.25 cm unfilled center of the overlap–0.625 cm long band of adhesive, breaking force was 2500 lb (1.11×10^9 dynes). Thus removal of the middle half of the adhesive film lowered the resistance of the adhint by only 20%.

Similar results are shown in Fig. 87 redrawn from reference 47. Two plates of an aluminum alloy, 25 mm wide and 1.5 mm thick,

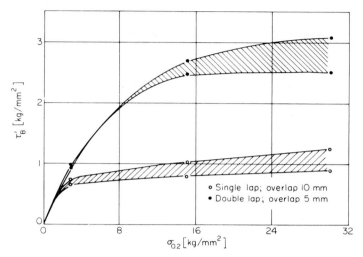

FIG. 86. Rupture stress of single (lower shaded strip) and double (upper shaded strip) lap joints. Abscissa: yield stress of the adherend metal (kg wt./mm²). Ordinate: breaking stress (kg wt./mm²). From reference 45.

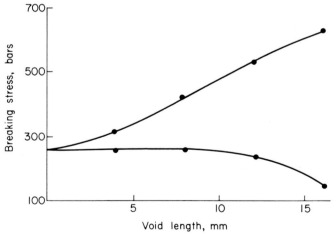

FIG. 87. Breaking stress of an interrupted adhesive film. Abscissa: length of the void (millimeters) in a 20 mm overlap. Ordinate: breaking stress, in bars. Lower curve: calculated for the total length. Upper curve: calculated for the actual length of the adhesive. Data of reference 43.

were overlapped along 20 mm but the adhesive was applied only to the two ends of the overlap, leaving in the center a void that was 4, 8, 12, or 16 mm long. The abscissa of Fig. 87 means this empty length. The ordinate means $f_m = F_m/wL$ in bars. For the lower curve, L was taken as the total overlap, i.e., 20 mm. It is seen that this f_m is almost unaffected by the presence of the voids as long as this is less than, say, 12 mm or 60% of the total length L. For the upper curve, L was taken as the actual length of the adhesive film (i.e., $20 - 4 = 16$ mm, etc.). Obviously, the adhesive can stand higher stresses than it would seem from the strength of an ordinary lap joint. The apparent failure stress of the adhint free of voids was (see the left-hand end of the curves) approximately 250 bars, but the real stress was over 600 bars (the upper end of the upper curve); the lower value was obtained because the load was, incorrectly, assumed to be distributed uniformly.

§88   A lap joint can be subjected to bending rather than to pull. Stresses occurring in this operation have been calculated and also measured by the photoelasticity technique.[48] Figure 88 indicates the system. "Tab" is a thin plate (of thickness h_1) glued or brazed to a thicker "base bar" (of thickness h_2), and the thickness of the adhesive film ("braze") is h_b. Stress σ_{max} is that stress which would exist in the uppermost fibers of the base if its free end (to the right) was bent down in the absence of braze and tab; because braze and tab are there, the actual maximum stress at the boundary between base, braze, and air is $k\sigma_{max}$. Letter p indicates the major principal stress in the braze, and ratio p/σ_{max} is a measure of the stress concentration achieved in the joint. Figure 89 presents calculated and experimental values of this ratio (along the ordinate) as functions of the adhesive thickness h_b (along the abscissa). The upper two curves are valid for relatively thick tabs ($h_1 = 0.20$ cm, $h_2 = 0.63$ cm, i.e., $h_1{:}h_2 \approx 0.32$); for the middle two curves ratio $h_1{:}h_2$ is 0.16, and for the lower pair, $h_1{:}h_2 = 0.08$. Thus, a stress concentration factor of almost five is reached when $h_1{:}h_2$ is not too small and when $h_b{:}h_2$ is very small (in our instance, 0.004). When h_b is infinitely small compared with h_1 and h_2, stress concentration is analogous to that referred to in §82.1 and the stress concentration factor is

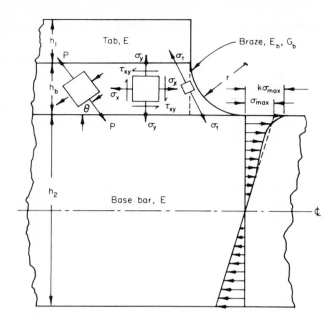

FIG. 88. A lap joint for which bending stresses have been calculated. From reference 48.

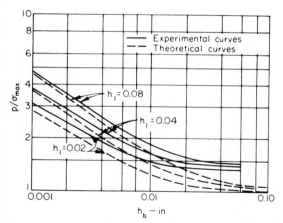

FIG. 89. Stress concentration in a bent lap joint. Abscissa: thickness of the adhesive film, in inches. Ordinate: ratio $P/\sigma_{\max}$. From reference 48.

infinitely great if the tab and the base bar form an exact right angle, i.e., if the radius of curvature (r in Fig. 88) is zero.

The values of σ_x, σ_y, and τ_{xy} decrease when the distance from the "fillet" (whose radius of curvature is r) increases, i.e., when we move to the left in the braze layer of Fig. 88. Figure 90 demonstrates this behavior of σ_y/σ_{max} for the interface of base bar and braze. In these tests, h_1 was 0.10, $h_2 = 0.63$, and $h_b = 0.025$ cm. It is seen that the effect of the edge is small when the distance from the edge exceeds 0.05 cm, i.e., $2\,h_b$.

§89   The strength of a lap joint can be raised by making the angle between the plane of the adhesive film and the axis of the adherends less than 90°, that is by using scarf joints. Figure 91 represents such an adhint; φ is the "scarf angle," δ the thickness of the adherend bar, and F_0 is the external force; the adhesive film is shaded.

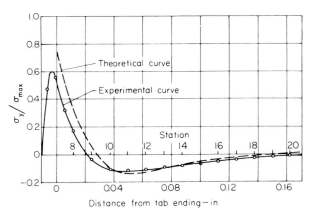

FIG. 90. Stress concentrations at the interface between adherend and adhesive. Abscissa: distance from the air–adhesive–adherend line. Ordinate: σ_y/σ_{max}. From reference 48.

The main results of a theory[49] of scarved joints are shown in Figs. 92 and 93.

In calculating the data on which Fig. 92 is based it was assumed that rupture occurred as soon as tensile stress at any point in the adhesive exceeded a value σ_m. The ordinate of the figure represents ratio $f_m \sin \varphi / \sigma_m$, if f_m is the breaking stress, i.e., the maximum value of F_m divided by $w\delta$; w is again the width of the adherend bar.

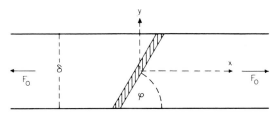

FIG. 91. A scarf joint; φ is the scarf angle.

The scarf angle is plotted along the abscissa. Note that all lines reach the value of unity at $\varphi = 90°$, i.e., for a butt joint. This observation characterizes the range of validity of the theory; evidently, the theory neglects the stress concentrations discussed in §82. Thus it may be argued that it deals only with the difference between butt and scarf joints without delving into the absolute values of strength in either system; in other words, if σ_m is the fracture stress of a butt joint (rather than the maximum local stress), the breaking stress f_m of an analogous scarf joint would be given by Fig. 92.

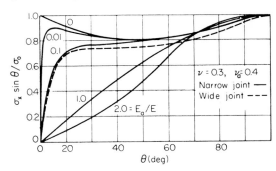

FIG. 92. Breaking stress in scarf joints, rupture occurring in tension. Abscissa: scarf angle. Ordinate: $f_m \sin \varphi / \sigma_m$. From reference 49.

The numerical data of Fig. 92 are valid if Poisson's ratio is 0.3 for the adherend and 0.4 for the adhesive. The numbers marked at the curves signify the ratio E_1/E, E_1 and E being the moduli of elasticity of adhesive and adherend, respectively. The discontinuous curve is computed for a wide joint having $E_1/E = 0.1$, while the continuous curves are for narrow joints. Since usual values of E_1/E are confined between 0.01 and 0.1 and the usual scarf angles are greater than 10° and smaller than 80°, Fig. 92 demonstrates that the effect of φ on $f_m \sin \varphi$ is not very great. The f_m itself is, for $E_1/E = 0.1$, about four times as great at $\varphi = 10°$ as at 80°.

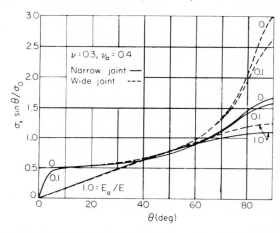

FIG. 93. Breaking stress in scarf joints, rupture occurring in shear. Abscissa: scarf angle. Ordinate: $f_m \sin \varphi/2\tau_{max}$. From reference 49.

When the adhesive ruptures in shear rather than in tension, Fig. 93 rather than Fig. 92 should be consulted. A crack is assumed to appear as soon as shear stress anywhere in the adhesive exceeds a value equal to τ_{max}. The ordinate of Fig. 93 is $f_m \sin \varphi/2\tau_{max}$, and the abscissa again is φ. The continuous curves are for narrow, and the discontinuous for wide adhints. The value of $f_m \sin \varphi$ in the most important range of angles φ, i.e., between $\varphi = 20°$ and $\varphi = 70°$, evidently little depends on E_1/E and almost linearly increases with φ. If f_m were simply proportional to the area of the adhesive film, $f_m \sin \varphi$ were independent of φ.

Because the dependence of f_m on φ is different in Fig. 92 and Fig. 93, it is possible to decide whether tensile or shear failure caused the breakdown of a scarf joint by comparing the experimental curve of "f_m versus φ" with the two theoretical curves. In Fig. 94 such an experimental curve is shown. The experiments have been performed by Hartman[50] but the data are taken from reference 49. The five vertical lines indicate the ranges of the experimental breaking stresses f_m of adhints made of duraluminum plates and a commercial poly(vinyl acetate) adhesive at different scarf angles plotted along the abscissa. The circles are the mean values of $f_m \sin \varphi$. As the curve connecting these is more similar to those of Fig. 92 than to those of Fig. 93, we conclude that the adhesive probably failed in tension, not in shear.

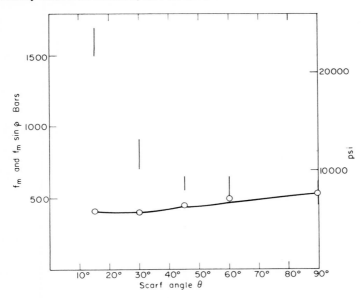

FIG. 94. Experimental dependence of breaking stress on scarf angle. Abscissa: scarf angle. Ordinate: breaking stress f_m (vertical lines) and $f_m \sin \varphi$ (circles) in bars and pounds per square inch. Data of reference 50.

§**90**   A type intermediate between an ordinary lap joint and a scarf joint has been suggested and studied by the photoelasticity method.[51] It is indicated in Fig. 95. When pull is applied in the direction of the

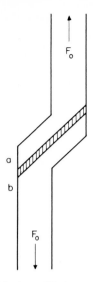

FIG. 95. A modified scarf joint.

arrows, point a of the upper adherend is pressed toward point b of the lower adherend; thus the peeling effect depicted in Fig. 78 c

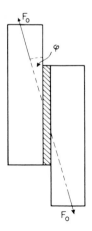

FIG. 96. A lap joint stressed at an acute angle.

should not occur. Photoelastic observations confirmed this conclusion. It is still unknown how the strength of these scarf-lap joints
compares with that of ordinary lap and ordinary scarf adhints. The
fringe pattern of an ordinary lap joint greatly depended on the direction of the external force (see Fig. 96), but the dependence of the
breaking stress on angle φ has not been determined.

§**91**   A cylindrical lap joint is a simpler system than the flat lap joints
discussed in §§82 to 87. Figure 97 shows the notations used. The
annular space between two hollow circular cylinders, each of thickness δ, is filled with an adhesive (of thickness h_0) along overlap L.
The outside diameter of the inner tube is $2a - h_0$, and the inside
diameter of the outer tube is $2a + h_0$. Pull F_0 is applied in the
direction of the black arrows; thus the mean shear stress in the
adhesive is $F_0/2\pi a L$.

The greatest shear stress τ_{max} and the greatest normal stress σ_{max}
in the adhesive occur along the three-phase line in which the inner

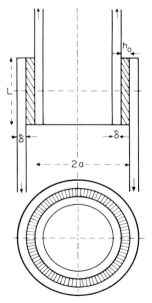

FIG. 97. A cylindrical lap joint.

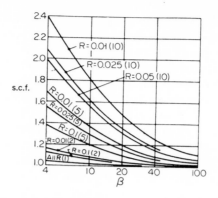

FIG. 98. Shear stress concentration in tubular lap joints. Abscissa: rigidity parameter $h_0E/E_1\delta$. Ordinate: stress concentration factor $2\pi aL\tau_{max}/F_0$. From reference 52.

tube, the cement, and air meet.[52] Thus, contrary to flat lap joints, the two adherends are not interchangeable even if their thicknesses are equal. Because the cross-sectional area (normal to the cylinder axis) of the inner tube $[\pi(2a\delta - \delta^2 - h_0\delta)]$ is smaller than that of the outer tube $[\pi(2a\delta + \delta^2 + h_0\delta)]$, the stress in the former is greater, its deformation also is greater, and finally the stress concentration at its surface is greater than at the end of the wider tube.

Figure 98 shows the dependence of $2\pi aL\tau_{max}/F_0$ (i.e., of the stress concentration factor) plotted along the ordinate as a function of the "rigidity parameter" $h_0E/E_1\delta$ along the abscissa; E and E_1 are the moduli of elasticity of adherend and adhesive, respectively. At each curve the ratio $R = \delta/2a$ and (in parentheses) the ratio L/δ are marked; thus the top curve is calculated for $2a = 100\delta$ and $L = 10\delta$. In the calculations it is assumed that Poisson's ratios are 0.3 for all materials and that $E_1 = (8/3)G_1$, G_1 being the shear modulus of the adhesive. It is seen that the stress concentration factor for shear rarely exceeds 2, i.e., as a rule is smaller than those observed in flat lap joints; greater factors would be attained at smaller "rigidity parameters" but the theory is not likely to be even approximately correct when $h_0/\delta < 4E_1/E$.

Figure 99 represents analogous calculations for the tensile stress; ratio $2\pi aL\sigma_{max}/F_0$ is plotted along the ordinate while the abscissa

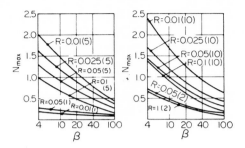

FIG. 99. Tensile stress concentration in tubular lap joints. Abscissa: rigidity parameter $h_0E/E_1\delta$. Ordinate: stress concentration factor $2\pi aL\sigma_{max}/F_0$. From reference 52.

again is $h_0E/E_1\delta$. The two graphs for τ_{max} and σ_{max} obviously are very similar.

In Fig. 100 the ratio of "external stress at failure" (equal to $F_m/2\pi a\delta$, if F_m is the load causing rupture) to the largest value (σ_0) of the principal tensile stress is shown; it is postulated that rupture starts as soon as σ_0 exceeds a minimum value characteristic for the adhesive material. The abscissa represents the ratio of overlap length to adherend thickness, i.e., L/δ. Figure 100a is calculated for a relatively stiff adhesive film (having $h_0E/E_1\delta$ equal to 4) while Fig. 100b is valid for a more flexible adhint (with $h_0E/E_1\delta$ equal to 100). If no stress concentration took place in the joint, F_m and $F_m/2\pi a\delta\sigma_0$ would increase linearly with the length L of the over-

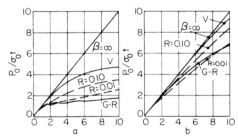

FIG. 100. Theoretical relation between breaking stress and adhint dimensions in flat and tubular lap joints. Abscissa: L/δ. Ordinate: $F_m/2\pi a\delta\sigma_0$. Ratio $h_0E/E_1\delta$ is 4 for Fig. 100a and 100 for Fig. 100b. From reference 52.

lap; this hypothetical condition is shown by the straight lines marked $\beta = \infty$. The lines marked $R = 0.10$ and $R = 0.01$ are calculated for tubular joints whose ratios $\delta/2a$ are 0.10 and 0.01, respectively; it is manifest that the strength of the adhint is not proportional to L; when $h_0 E/E_1 \delta = 4$, F_m increases roughly as $L^{0.5}$ and when $h_0 E/E_1 \delta = 100$, F_m is approximately proportional to $L^{0.8}$ to $L^{0.9}$. For comparison, two other curves, both for flat lap joints, are drawn. That marked V indicates the dependence of F_m on L according to Eq. (123) and that marked $G - R$ is drawn in agreement with the theory of §83. Figure 100 is a particularly clear summary of present theoretical predictions for the relation between strength and overlap in lap joints.

Peeling

§92   Peeling has been mentioned as taking place in the rupture of lap joints by a tensile force, §83. However, usual peeling tests are different and can be typified by Fig. 101. A flexible ribbon of width w is attached to a rigid plate by a cement; when a sufficiently great force F_m is applied to the free end of the ribbon, the adhesive film rips at the bend of the ribbon, and the "knee" gradually travels to the right.

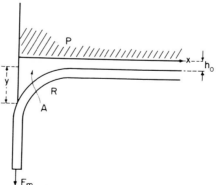

FIG. 101. A peeling test. P: rigid plate. R: flexible ribbon. A: adhesive film.

In the simplest theory,[53] which is presented first, the external force acts along the adhesive–air boundary as is shown in Fig. 101. It is postulated moreover that both ribbon and adhesive are Hookean solids and that shear stresses in the adhesive are negligible, that is, each fiber or column of the adhesive reaching from the plate to the ribbon is extended (when the ribbon curves) in the direction of the applied force without any interference by the neighboring fibers or columns. Tearing occurs when the extension of the column nearest to the load (i.e., at the left-hand end of the adhesive film in Fig. 101) reaches the greatest value possible in the adhesive. Thus, if the total relative elongation of the adhesive substance is ϵ_m and the initial thickness of the adhesive film is h_0, the film starts ripping when the fiber nearest to the load acquires the length of $(1 + \epsilon_m)h_0$.

For a Hookean solid

$$\epsilon_m = \frac{\sigma_m}{E_1}, \tag{127}$$

σ_m being the tensile strength and E_1 the modulus of elasticity of the cement.

To find the value of F_m at which the strain (or relative elongation) ϵ attains, at any point of the adhesive film, its maximum value equal to ϵ_m, we consider the forces acting on any cross section of the ribbon. If, at any value of x, Fig. 101, the thickness of the adhesive is $h_0 + y$, and if (as for Hookean solids) extension y implies stress $(y/h_0)E_1$, then a strip of the ribbon, dx cm long and w cm deep (w is perpendicular to the plane of the sketch) is pulled up with the force $(y/h_0)E_1 w\, dx$. Hence[26]

$$\frac{d^4y}{dx^4} = -\frac{12E_1 y}{E\delta^3 h_0}; \tag{128}$$

E and δ are again the modulus of elasticity and the thickness of the ribbon. If we abbreviate $3E_1/E\delta^3 h_0$ as n^4, we obtain

$$\frac{d^4y}{dx^4} = -4n^4 y, \tag{129}$$

which is satisfied, for instance, by setting

$$y = Ae^{-nx} \cos nx. \tag{130}$$

This equation contains only one adjustable constant, namely A. Therefore it can be valid only if either a force or a moment, not both a force and a moment, is applied to the free end of the ribbon. We consider here the instance of a force.

This force (F_0) is compensated by the sum of the forces $(y/h_0)E_1w$ dx (see preceding paragraph). Thus,

$$F_0 = \frac{E_1wA}{h_0} \int_0^l e^{-nx} \cos nx \, dx = \frac{E_1wA}{2nh_0} \\ \times (e^{-nl} \sin nl - e^{-nl} \cos nl + 1) \tag{131}$$

if l is the length of the glued part of the ribbon. For this equation to be valid, l must be long, i.e., nl must be considerably greater than unity; then the term $e^{-nl} (\sin nl - \cos nl)$ may be neglected in comparison with unity. Thus

$$F_0 = \frac{E_1wA}{2nh_0} \quad \text{and} \quad A = \frac{2nh_0F_0}{E_1w}. \tag{132}$$

At $x = 0$, from (130) and (132), $y = 2 nh_0F_0/E_1w$. Rupture starts when this y reaches the value of ϵ_mh_0. Thus [see Eq. (127)], $F_m = w\sigma_m/2n$ or

$$F_m = \frac{1}{2 \times 3^{0.25}} w\sigma_m \left(\frac{E\delta^3h_0}{E_1}\right)^{0.25} \\ = 0.3799 \, w\sigma_m \left(\frac{E}{E_1}\right)^{0.25} \delta^{0.75}h_0^{0.25}. \tag{133}$$

Comparison of Eq. (133) with the zero-order approximation for butt joints, namely

$$F_m = wl\sigma_m \tag{134}$$

is instructive. The numerical value of $0.3799(E/E_1)^{0.25}$ usually is of the order of unity. Thus, in peeling, $F_m \approx w\delta^{0.75}h_0^{0.25}\sigma_m$. If $\delta = h_0$, we have simply

$$F_m \approx wh_0\sigma_m . \tag{135}$$

Thus in tensile tests the external force is equal to σ_m multiplied with the greatest cross section of the adhesive film (namely length × width), while in peeling F_m is equal to σ_m multiplied with the smallest cross section (i.e., width × thickness); it is clear that peeling must be much easier than pulling, as it indeed is.

§93   Take now the case such that the adherend still is a Hookean solid while the stress–strain curve of the adhesive may be approximated as

$$\sigma = e_1\epsilon^m \tag{136}$$

(ϵ^m should not be confused with ϵ_m !), where σ is stress; ϵ, strain; e_1 is a material constant, and m is an exponent (another material constant) which may have any value less than unity. Then, instead of (128), the equation

$$\frac{d^4y}{dx^4} = -\frac{12e_1y^m}{E\delta^3h_0^m} \tag{137}$$

results. It can be satisfied, for instance, by setting

$$y = Ax^J ; \tag{138}$$

contrary to Fig. 101, $x = 0$ here at the point where the adhesive just starts to elongate rather than at the point where it breaks; and the constants A and J have to be derived from the boundary conditions. If the reasoning of the preceding section is repeated for this case, the following expression[54] for the stripping force F_m is arrived at

$$F_m = \left[\frac{(3+m)(2+2m)}{3(1+3m)^3}\right]^{0.25}\frac{w\sigma_m^{(3m+1)/4m}E^{0.25}\delta^{0.75}h_0^{0.25}}{e_1^{1/4m}} . \tag{139}$$

Perhaps the most striking peculiarity of this expression is that F_m is not proportional to σ_m, as in Eq. (133), but rises with σ_m more rapidly than σ_m itself. For instance, when $m = 0.5$,

$$F_m = 0.688w\,\sigma_m^{1.25}E^{0.25}\delta^{0.75}h_0^{0.25}/e_1^{0.5} \qquad (140)$$

and increases in the ratio $2.38:1$ when σ_m increases twofold. If two adhesives having identical values of σ_m are compared, that material whose ϵ_m is smaller usually will be easier to strip off than the cement of a higher ϵ_m; this is understandable because the area of the adhesive film in which this is significantly stretched by the external force is greater the greater ϵ_m.

§**94**   The equations of §§92–93 were derived for a system corresponding to Fig. 101, in which the adhesive breaks in the plane of the external force F_m (this plane is perpendicular to that of the drawing). Such a break can happen only in the limit of extremely flexible ribbons and extremely strong adhesives. A more common profile of a system being subjected to peeling is illustrated in Fig. 102. The coordinates x and y are analogous to those of Fig. 101 but the external force does not act along the negative axis of y; it is applied at some other point whose abscissa is $x = -\zeta$. Consequently, force F_m gives rise to a bending moment $F_m\zeta$ acting in the rupture plane of the adhesive. This more complex system was considered both before[55] and after[56] the publication of the theories of §§92–93.
    Equations (128) and (129) remain unaffected but, instead of (130), the relation

$$y = e^{-nx}(A\,\cos\,nx + B\,\sin\,nx) \qquad (141)$$

is obtained. B is not zero because ζ is not zero. Analogously to (131),

$$F_0 = \frac{E_1 wA}{h_0}\int_0^l e^{-nx}\cos\,nx\,dx + \frac{E_1 wB}{h_0}\int_0^l e^{-nx}\sin\,nx\,dx. \qquad (142)$$

As in §92, l may be set[56, 57] equal to infinity, but this still leaves two

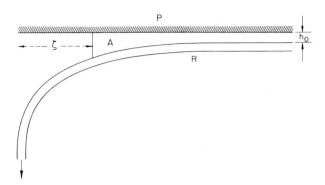

FIG. 102. A peeling test. P: rigid plate. R: ribbon. A: adhesive. ζ: distance between the plane of the external force and the locus of fracture. h_0: initial thickness of the adhesive.

unknown magnitudes (A and B) in Eq. (142). An additional equation can be obtained in two ways. (a) The bending moment (caused by all stretched fibers in the adhesive) relative to the plane of $x = -\zeta$ must be equal to zero because the moment of the external force F_0 also is zero there. Consequently,

$$\frac{E_1 w A}{h_0} \int_0^\infty (x + \zeta) \, e^{-nx} \cos nx \, dx$$

$$+ \frac{E_1 w B}{h_0} \int_0^\infty (x + \zeta) \, e^{-nx} \sin nx \, dx = 0 \, ;$$

here the sign of infinity is used instead of l. (b) As the curvature of the ribbon is supposed to be small — otherwise Eq. (128) cannot be derived — the second derivative of y at $x = 0$ must be

$$\frac{d^2 y}{dx^2} = \frac{12 F_0 \zeta}{E \delta^3 w} \, .$$

With the aid of either of these equations it is possible to express B as a function of ζ but the value of ζ still is needed to compare experiment and theory.

The distance ζ can simply be measured for each adhint[55,56,58] or a function of ζ can be calculated from the experimental data.[59] It may also be assumed[57,60] that the adhesive fails when the ribbon is still almost parallel to the rigid plate, that is, that the adhesive has a very small ϵ_m and the ribbon is very stiff; these assumptions are opposite to those of §92. Physically, the length ζ ought to be determined by the geometry of the system and the mechanical constants of the materials employed but no such calculation came to the author's attention.

For some particular systems in which the ribbons (various aluminum alloys) behaved as almost ideal rigid-plastic bodies (see §80.3), it appeared permissible[60] to treat the bending moment M as independent of ζ. Experimentally, M was approximately equal to $0.25\,\delta^2\sigma_p$; δ is still the thickness of the ribbon and σ_p is the stress at which plastic flow in it seems to start; thus σ_p is the real equivalent of the theoretical stress k of §80.3. For these systems, the theoretical equation analogous to (133) is

$$F_m = 0.707w\,\sigma_m\,(E/E_1)^{0.25}\,\delta^{0.75}h_0^{0.25}$$
$$- 0.177w\,\sigma_p\,(E_1/E)^{0.25}\,\delta^{1.25}h_0^{-0.25} \tag{143}$$

The first right-hand term differs from the right-hand term of Eq. (133) only in its numerical factor. This difference exists because the Poisson ratio ν was disregarded (or treated as if $\nu = 0$) in the derivation of (133) while each value of ν (for adhesive and adherend) was set equal to 0.33 when deriving (143). A disadvantage of the latter relation is that F_m is obtained as a difference between two terms of similar magnitudes. As a matter of fact, if σ_p is much greater than σ_m, F_m may acquire negative values. However, Eq. (143) is not supposed to be generally valid. It was in poor agreement with test data also for the special combinations in which M seemed to be constant.

§95   Equations (133) and (139) disregard not only the moment $F_m\zeta$ (§94) but also the local stress concentrations analogous to those reviewed in §§80 to 91 for butt and lap joints; the equations of §94 are equally deficient in this respect. These omissions make themselves felt when the theoretical predictions are tested by experiment.

Such a test was carried out[54] with glass as the plate material, aluminum and nickel as ribbon materials, and various polyethylenes (purified, §69) and a poly(vinyl acetate) as the adhesive. The discrepancy between theory and experiment is illustrated in Table XIII.

TABLE XIII

STRIPPING FORCE (FOR 1 CM WIDTH) OF ALUMINUM–POLYETHYLENE–GLASS ADHINTS

		F_m calc. (kilodynes)	
Polyethylene	F_m exptl. (kilodynes)	From Eq. (133)	From Eq. (140)
Epolene	100	579	—
Epolene 1 + Marlex 0.67	250	749	—
Epolene 1 + Marlex 1.5	420	732	1430
Epolene 1 + Marlex 3.0	740	—	2720

Equation (133) was used to calculate F_m for the low-molecular-weight polyethylene known as Epolene and for a mixture of this substance with 0.67 part of Marlex (a high-molecular-weight polyethylene) because these hydrocarbons behaved as near-Hookean solids. The other two mixtures approximately satisfied Eq. (136) with $m = 0.5$; the F_m of one of them was calculated also from Eq. (133) to illustrate the numerical difference between the two approximations.

The ratio of calculated to experimental F_m varied between 3 and almost 6 and, apparently, little depended on the rigidity or flexibility of the cement. However, the dependence of F_m on ribbon width w was different according to whether the adhesive was a near-Hookean solid or had $m \approx 0.5$. Figure 103 summarizes the experimental results; its ordinate is stripping force F_m (in kilodynes) and its abscissa is w (in centimeters). The F_m of brittle solids (the two lower lines) is proportional to w, as was predicted by Eq. (133) and (139), observed elsewhere,[61] and often is assumed without any proof. But F_m for the elastoplastic mixture of Epolene 1 + Marlex 3 is not proportional to w; for this polymer an equation

$$F_m = 1.4 \times 10^5 + 3.5 \times 10^5 \, w \text{ dynes} \qquad (144)$$

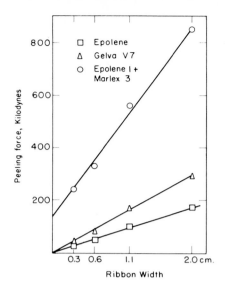

FIG. 103. Experimental dependence of peeling force F_m on ribbon width w. Abscissa: w, in centimeters. Ordinate: F_m, in kilodynes. Upper line: an elasto-plastic adhesive. Lower lines: brittle adhesives. Data of reference 54.

(if w is in centimeters) seems to emerge. The author accounts for this strange relation in the following manner.

When the adhesive is extended parallel to the y coordinate (see Fig. 101), it must contract (because Poisson's ratio is not zero) in the direction perpendicular to x and y, which may be designated as z (see Fig. 104). Thus, at the two extremities of the width of the adhesive film (this width is parallel to z) stress concentrations must appear, analogous to those depicted in Fig. 69. Let that part of the width which is subjected to concentrated stresses be w_1 and the average tension in it be ζ_1; and let ζ_0 be the average (nearly constant) tension acting on the rest of the width, that is on $w - w_1$. Evidently, $\zeta_1 > \zeta_0$ and $w \gg w_1$. The total force F_m can thus be written as a sum: $F_m = \zeta_1 w_1 + \zeta_0(w - w_1)$ or

$$F_m = \zeta_0 w + (\zeta_1 - \zeta_0)w_1. \tag{145}$$

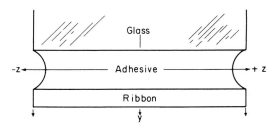

FIG. 104. Lateral contraction of the adhesive during peeling.

Comparing (145) with (144), we conclude that $(\zeta_1 - \zeta_0)w_1$ was 1.4×10^5 dynes and ζ_0 was 3.5×10^5 dynes/cm. The length w_1 must be, according to Saint-Vénant's principle (see also §88), for both ends of the width together, about twice the thickness of the adhesive film. This was 0.024 cm. Assume $w_1 = 0.05$ cm. Then $\zeta_1 - \zeta_0 = 28 \times 10^5$ dynes/cm and $\zeta_1 = 31.5 \times 10^5$ dynes/cm. The force on 1 cm thus would be 3150 kilodynes, i.e., nearly equal to the theoretical value listed in Table XIII.

That F_m sometimes is not proportional to w, was observed also in other experiments.[62]

§**96**   Since the F_m of brittle cements is proportional to w (see the two lower lines of Fig. 103), the most dangerous stress concentration in these adhints is not likely to be situated at the extremities of the width. Its location seems to be, instead, at the "knee' of the ribbon. If the ribbon material were a Hookean solid, the longitudinal stress in its external fibers (i.e., at the boundary with the adhesive) would be $\delta E/2R$, R being the radius of curvature of the ribbon at the bend. This R usually was near 0.1 cm. The stress calculated in this manner was markedly greater than the yield stress of the metal. Thus, the ribbon was plastically deformed at the "knee"; this was confirmed also by the fact that the ribbon did not straighten itself on removal of the external load. If the ribbon length at the knee increased, say, by $100\epsilon\%$ of its original length, the adhesive in contact with the ribbon also should have extended in the ratio $(1 + \epsilon):1$; if, however, the total relative elongation of the brittle adhesive was less than ϵ, the adhesive must have cracked.

This conclusion was substantiated by two observations.

(a) While in the adhints containing flexible cements comparable amounts of adhesive remained on both the rigid plate and the ribbon, the separation in the brittle cements took place much nearer to the ribbon than to the rigid member; for instance, the thickness of the polyethylene residue on aluminum was about 4 μ while that on glass was near 35 μ.[63] It could be shown by special experiments that this was not due to the presence of a weak boundary layer.

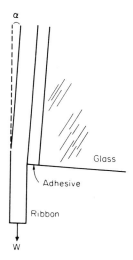

FIG. 105. Stretching a ribbon without peeling.

(b) If failure of the adhesive in contact with the ribbon really was due to the excessive stretching of the latter, it ought to be possible to reproduce this effect by stretching the ribbon without peeling and then applying stripping force. Figure 105 illustrates the technique used. Adhints of the usual shape were prepared and weights W were applied to the ribbons so as to extend them past the yield point without increasing the distance between plate and ribbon; the angle α was between 1° and 5°. Then the weights were removed, the plates placed in horizontal position, and the ribbons were stripped off with a force equal to about 25% of the force needed to peel an undamaged adhint. It was found that 0.2 to 0.7 cm could be stripped off in this manner; thus, stretching the ribbon parallel to itself must have caused cracking of the cement along 0.2–0.7 cm length. Similar stretching of ribbons glued to glass with a flexible adhesive had no effect on the minimum peeling force as determined in a subsequent experiment.

It may be worth pointing out here, in reference to §60.2, that in a group of three materials of which one was nonpolar and flexible, another nonpolar and brittle, and the third polar and brittle, the two last named, not the two first-named behaved in similar manner (see Fig. 103). The degree of brittleness, not the degree of polarity was important.

§97   Two predictions of the theory of peeling were tested in separate experiments. The theory expects the value of the peeling force F_m or the peeling tension Γ to remain constant during the peeling process, except the first stage when the "fillet" is being ruptured. In reality, Γ sometimes shows abnormally high values followed by abnormally easy peeling. A mechanism of this effect was visible[54] in one series of tests. The adhesive continued to stretch without breaking past the usual value of ϵ_m, then suddenly ruptured, and the fissure advanced for a few millimeters almost instantaneously. Oscillations of Γ in another investigation[61] were recorded; however, in it double peeling joints (or "T-peel") were employed (Fig. 106), and the vibrations of the freely hanging tail were not prevented. A similar effect apparently was observed[64] in splitting experiments (§99). These observations have not been well explained yet; see also §99.

The other prediction refers to the stress distribution along the adhesive "pancake." According to Eqs. (130) and (141), the extension y and, consequently, the stress $(y/h_0)E_1$ (§92) change in a sinusoidal fashion when the distance of the point considered from the point of application of force increases. In the plane of rupture, i.e., at $x = 0$ (§§92 and 94) the stress in the adhesive has the highest value and is contractile, that is, resists extension. When x increases, then y gradually decreases and [see Eq. (130)], is lowered to zero when $nx = 0.5\pi$. If n is 50 cm^{-1}, the stress is nil at $x = 0.03$ cm. When x increases past the value $x = \pi/2n$, the stress in the adhesive is tensile, that is the material is compressed, and this compressed region covers the distance until $x = 3\pi/2n$; then y becomes positive again. Because of the factor e^{-nx} the "waves" rapidly die out; e.g., the greatest decrease in thickness (i.e., $y = Ae^{-nx} \cos \pi$) is to the greatest extension (i.e., A) as $e^{-\pi} : 1$. A numerical evaluation of these stresses was published.[65]

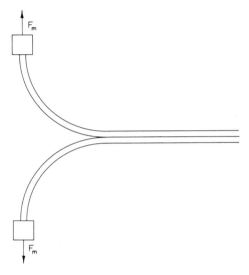

FIG. 106. Double peeling or T-peel test.

Stresses at small x values can, and have been,[66] measured. Figure 107 makes clear the principle of the experiment. The ribbon R is glued (but the adhesive is not shown) to a split adherend; part N is rigidly connected to the frame of the instrument but part M is movable without friction and is supported by a load-measuring device so that only the tension or pressure acting on M is recorded. When R is pulled up by force F_m and the plane of failure of the adhesive moves to the left, M experiences first a very weak pull upward, then a stronger pressure downward, an even stronger upward pull and, finally, a rapid drop of the pull to zero. At least parts of the predicted stress–distance curve were far enough from the zero stress line to be measurable.

§98 The discussion of §§92–97 deals with peeling at a right angle; the direction of the external force F_m was perpendicular to the adhesive–plate interface. Stripping can be achieved also at any other angle greater than 0° and equal to, or smaller than, 180°.

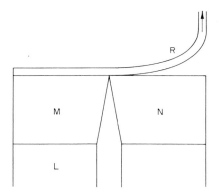

FIG. 107. Measurement of tensile and compressive stresses during peeling. R: ribbon. M: movable, and N: immobile half of the adherend. L: load measuring device.

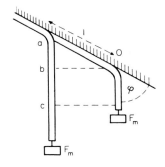

FIG. 108. Peeling at an acute angle φ.

When peeling angle φ (see Fig. 108) is small, the cement is sheared in addition to being extended normally to the above interface. If stripping starts when force F_m acts at angle φ, then the work $\mathfrak{M}$ of stripping is[67]

$$\mathfrak{W} = F_m l(1 - \cos \varphi) \tag{146}$$

if l is the length of the stripped area. Equation (146) is readily proved by means of Fig. 108. A material particle which initially was at the three-phase line, after length l has been stripped off, now is in position c. Thus, $\overline{ac} = l$. But the load descended only by the distance $\overline{bc} = \overline{ac} - \overline{ab} = l - l \cos \varphi$. Thus, the work done by the load is given by Eq. (146). When $\varphi = 90°$ as assumed in §92,

$$\mathfrak{W} = F_m l . \tag{147}$$

Earlier experimental results concerning the relation between peeling tension Γ and φ were in a reasonable agreement with this expectation. Figure 109 is based on the data[68] obtained by peeling a poly(vinyl acetate) film reinforced with a silk fabric from a glass plate. Peeling tension Γ in kilodynes/cm is plotted along the ordinate.

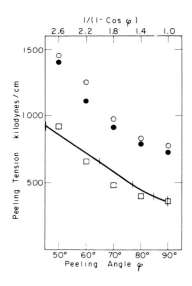

FIG. 109. Experimental relation between peeling tension F_m/w and peeling angle φ. Abscissa (bottom) is φ; abscissa (top) is $1/(1 - \cos \varphi)$. Ordinate: F_m/w (kilodynes/cm). A poly(vinyl acetate) adhesive. Data of reference 68.

The lower scale of the abscissa represents peeling angle φ, and the upper scale is $1/(1 - \cos \varphi)$. For white circles, black circles, and squares the bottom scale is valid; the amount of plasticizer (tricresyl phosphate) in the film was 20, 40, and 60 gm for 100 gm of resin, respectively, for these three sets of data. The vertical lines and the curve connecting them refer to the upper scale and the 60:100 mixture; the curves for the other two mixtures would be almost parallel to that shown. The deviation of the curve from a straight line is not very serious; thus in the instance of plasticized poly(vinyl acetate) the work of peeling was almost independent of peeling angle.

The stripping tension at $\varphi = 45°$ was always greater than that at $\varphi = 90°$ also when an epoxy resin cross-linked with phthalic anhydride or a diamine was the adhesive and an aluminum alloy the adherend (see Fig. 131 in §117). Stripping tension at $\varphi = 180°$ was, with different adhesives, either greater or smaller than, or indistinguishable from, that at $\varphi = 90°$. The effects were complicated by the buckling of the metal ribbon caused by the shrinkage of the adhesive.[69]

The situation is more complicated according to later measurement.[59] When the rate of stripping of an adhesive tape from a sheet of cellophane is high (e.g., 0.8 cm/sec), the dependence of Γ on φ is similar to that of $1/(1 - \cos \varphi)$ on φ at all angles between 40° and 160°. Contrary to the expectation, the minimum of Γ occurs near $\varphi = 160°$ rather than at $\varphi = 180°$. When stripping was slow (e.g., 0.0008 cm/sec), Γ increased (rather than decreased) between 20° and 50°; for instance, for a glass cloth tape Γ was 0.7 and 1.1 arbitrary units at these peel angles, and the change was even greater for a tape with an aluminum foil backing: 0.5 to 3. The Γ of the former tape at 10° was 1.5, i.e., greater than at 20°. The meaning of the minima and the maximum manifested in the "Γ versus φ" curves is still debated.

Contrary to the data of the preceding paragraph, the product $F_m (1 - \cos \varphi)$ was constant at low rates of peeling in the most recent study,[70] in which films of polyisobutylene and poly(vinyl acetate) were stripped from glass plates. The authors tested also the equation $\mathfrak{W} = F_m l (1 - \cos \varphi) + F_m^2/2h_0 E_1$ (see §99), and found that the apparent modulus of elasticity of the adhesive (E_1) varied with the rate of peeling.

Work of Fracture

§99   In the theoretical treatment of the fracture of solids, use is made of the idea that a work "γ" $= d\mathfrak{W}/dA$ is needed to extend the area A of a crack (both surfaces) by dA. This "γ" was identified[71,72] with the surface energy of the solid but is more likely caused[73] by the necessity of stretching the solid ahead of the crack to its highest possible strain, ϵ_m. Whatever the physical meaning of the "γ", it is supposed to be a property of the solid and thus not to depend on the mode of rupture (by peeling, by shear, etc.). As rupture of the adhesive layer in proper adhints is not basically different from that of any other solid, it was natural to extend the above concepts to adhesive joints.

Whether the specimen is one solid bar or two solids with an adhesive interlayer, the main difficulty confronting the experimenter is that of determining that part of the total work (done by the breaking load) which belongs to the crack propagation. The total work, such as $F_m l$ of §98, includes that spent on the deformation of the adherends. It is easy to believe, for instance, that if the lap joint has to be doubly bent as in Fig. 78c, §83, before the adhesive fails, the work of bending the adherends may be far greater than that of rupturing the adhesive.

Unfortunately, it is impossible to predict without drastic simplifications what fraction of $\mathfrak{W}$ should be considered as "γ." In peeling, it may be argued that "γ" is the work required to extend 1 cm² of the adhesive layer from its initial thickness h_0 to the final thickness $h_0(1 + \epsilon_m)$ (§92). In this instance, for a Hookean solid, "γ" $= h_0 \sigma_m^2/ 2E_1$, i.e., depends on h_0 instead of being a property of the material. When a polymer bar, 1 cm thick and 0.6 cm wide, was glued with an epoxy adhesive to a similar bar and then peeled off by a force concentrated at one end of the former bar,[74] the force F_m needed for peeling gradually decreased when the length l of the crack increased but the ratio $3F_m y/2wl$ remained nearly constant (about 4×10^4

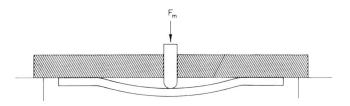

FIG. 110. Separation of a flexible disc glued to a rigid plate by force F_m acting on a plunger.

ergs/cm^2) when the distance y between the point of application of the force and the second bar increased; w is again the width (0.6 cm) of the bars. The above ratio is equal to "γ" if the adhesive layer is disregarded and if it is assumed that no heat is evolved during the peeling operation. As it was not ascertained where the rupture proceeded, it is not known to what material the "γ" thus determined is supposed to refer (to the unnamed polymer or to the epoxy binder). The most common values of "γ" calculated from splitting polymer bars are about 10 times as great.

A determination of "γ" was performed also for another system.[74] Figure 110 represents a rigid plate (shaded), supported along two edges, to whose bottom a thin flexible disk has been glued. The plate is perforated, and a plunger is pushed through the hole with a force F_m which causes bulging and delaminating of the disk. If again the rupture of the adhesive is disregarded and only the deformation of the disk is considered, then

$$\text{``}\gamma\text{''} = \frac{3F_m^2\,(1-\nu^2)}{8\pi E\delta^3}; \tag{148}$$

ν and E are the Poisson ratio and the Young modulus of the disk, and δ is its thickness. When the plate was of steel, the disk of an organic polymer, and the adhesive was of the epoxy type, the "γ" was near 1.7×10^4 ergs/cm^2.

Values of "γ" in the range of 1.4 to 3.0×10^5 ergs/cm^2 were observed[64, 75] in the majority of experiments with adhints of the kind illustrated in Fig. 111. Two aluminum bars were provided with

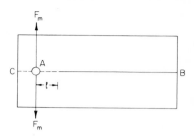

FIG. 111. Splitting of two rigid adherends glued together along AB.

grooves which formed a cylindrical pore (A) when the two bars were placed in contact. They were glued together with an epoxy adhesive along the area AB, leaving the stretch AC unattached. The force F_m was applied, and its dependence on the length l of the crack was measured. An empirical equation for calculating "γ" from these data was found by using bars (without any adhesive) provided with cracks of different lengths. The "γ" was almost independent of the thickness of the adhesive layer, which was varied between 0.005 and 1.2 cm, and was practically equal to the "γ" derived from splitting a bar of an identical epoxy resin.

The "γ" of an epoxy adhesive *in situ* was consistently smaller (0.5 to 1.0×10^5) than that in bulk (0.7 to 1.8×10^5 ergs/cm^2) but the difference was not striking, when the aluminum adherends were of a tapered shape such that the ratio l^2/δ^3 was constant along the bar.[76] As before, l is the length of the crack; δ is the thickness of each bar at a given l. The unusual shape facilitated the calculation of "γ" from the observed values of the force F_m.

In the rupture experiments of references 64 and 74 the rupture surfaces were found striated, showing that the delamination process was more or less rhythmical. The mechanism of this effect apparently is unknown, see also §97.

REFERENCES

1. Kanamaru, K., *Kolloid-Z. Z. Polym.* **192,** 51 (1963).
2. Kanamaru, K., *Kolloid-Z. Z. Polym.* **209,** 151 (1966).
3. Aleck, B. J., *J. Appl. Mech.* **16,** 118 (1949).

4. Kobatake, Y., and Inoue, Y., *Appl. Sci. Res.* **A7,** 53 (1958).
5. Popereka, M. Ya., *Zh. Fiz. Khim.* **40,** 1347 (1966).
6. Stoney, G. G., *Proc. Roy. Soc. (London)* **A82,** 172 (1909).
7. Brenner, A., and Senderoff, S., *J. Res. Natl. Bur. Std.* **42,** 105 (1949).
8. Hill, A. E., and Hoffman, G. R., *Brit. J. Appl. Phys.* **18,** 13 (1967).
9. Popereka, M. Ya., "Internal Stresses in Electrolytically Deposited Metals." West-Siberian Publ., Novosibirsk, 1966 (in Russian).
10. Sanzharovskii, A. T., *Zh. Fiz. Khim.* **34,** 466 and 668 (1960).
11. Inoue, Y., and Kobatake, Y., *Appl. Sci. Res.* **A7,** 314 (1958).
12. Shreiner, S. A., and Zubov, P. I., *Dokl. Akad. Nauk SSSR* **124,** 1102 (1959).
13. Sanzharvoskii, A. T., and Epifanov, G. I., *Dokl. Akad. Nauk SSSR* **142,** 403 (1962).
14. Weatherwax, R. C., Coleman, B., and Tarkov, H., *J. Polymer Sci.* **27,** 59 (1958).
15. Zubov, P. I., Sukhareva, L. A., Kiselev, M. R., and Chistyakov, A. M., *Vysokomolekul. Soedin.* **6,** 803 (1964).
16. Turnbull, J. C., *J. Am. Ceram. Soc.* **41,** 372 (1958).
17. Shreiner, S. A., Zubov, P. I., and Volkova, T. A., *Vysokomolekul. Soedin., Adgeziya Polimerov, Sb. Statei* **1963,** 28.
18. Zubov, P. I., Sukhareva, L. A., and Smirnova, Yu. P., *Dokl. Akad. Nauk SSSR* **150,** 359 (1963).
19. Dietz, A. G. H., Grinsfelder, H., and Reissner, E., *Trans. ASME* **68,** 329 (1946).
20. Moser, F., *in* "Adhesion and Adhesives, Fundamentals and Practice," p. 84. Wiley, New York, 1954.
21. Partridge, J. H., "Glass-to-Metal Seals." Soc. Glass Technol., Sheffield, England, 1949.
22. Rawson, H., *Brit. J. Appl. Phys.* **2,** 151 (1951).
23. Svenson, N. L., *Brit. J. Appl. Phys.* **3,** 30 (1952).
24. Zaid, M., *Brit. J. Appl. Phys.* **3,** 31 (1952).
25. Timoshenko, S., "Strength of Materials," 3rd ed., Part II. Van Nostrand, Princeton, New Jersey, 1956.
26. Hetényi, M., "Beams on Elastic Foundation." Univ. of Michigan Press, Ann Arbor, Michigan, 1946.
27. Palmov, V. A., *Izv. Akad. Nauk SSSR, Otd. Tekhn. Nauk, Mekhan. i Machinostr.* **1963,** No. 3, 104; No. 5, 60; *J. Appl. Math. Mech.* **27,** 1479 (1963).
28. Poritsky, H., *Physics* **5,** 406 (1934).
29. Redston, G. D., and Stanworth, J. E., *J. Soc. Glass Technol.* **29,** 48 (1945).
30. Timoshenko, S., *Phil. Mag.* [6] **47,** 1095 (1924).
31. Kobatake, Y., and Inoue, Y., *Appl. Sci. Res.* **A7,** 100 (1958).
32. Mylonas, C., *Proc. Soc. Exptl. Stress Anal.* **12,** No. 2, 129 (1955).
33. Hill, R., "The Mathematical Theory of Plasticity," p. 233. Oxford Univ. Press, London and New York, 1950.
34. Shield, R. T., *Quart. Appl. Math.* **15,** 139 (1957).
35. Meyerhof, G. G., and Chaplin, T. K., *Brit. J. Appl. Phys.* **4,** 20 (1953).
36. Niskanen, E., "On the Distribution of Shear Stress in a Glued Single Shear

Test Specimen on Finnish Birch Timber." Valtion Teknillinen Tutkimuslaitos, Helsinki, 1957.
37. Volkersen, O., *Luftfahrt-Forsch.* **15,** 41 (1938).
38. Goland, M., and Reissner, E., *J. Appl. Mech.* **11,** 17 (1944).
39. Hahn, K. F., and Fouser, D. F., *J. Appl. Polymer Sci.* **6,** 145 (1962).
40. Sherrer, R. E., *U.S. Dept. Agr., Forest Serv., Forest Prod. Lab., Rept.* **1864** (1957).
41. Tombach, H., *Machine Design* **29,** No. 7, 113 (1957).
42. Matting, A., and Draugelates, U., *Stahl Eisen* **84,** 947 (1964).
43. Henning, G., *Plaste Kautschuk* **12,** 459 (1965).
44. Sheridan, M. L., and Merriman, H. R., *Am. Soc. Testing Mater., Spec. Tech. Bull.* No. **201,** 33 (1957).
45. Kaliske, G., *Aluminum* **31,** 275 (1955).
46. Koehn, G. W., *in* "Adhesion and Adhesives. Fundamentals and Practice," p. 120. Wiley, New York, 1954.
47. Matting, A., and Ulmer, K., *Kautschuk Gummi* **16,** 213, 280, 334, and 387 (1963) (quoted in Henning[43]).
48. Cornell, R. W., *J. Appl. Mech.* **20,** 355 (1953).
49. Lubkin, J. L., *J. Appl. Mech.* **24,** 255 (1957).
50. Hartman, A., *Neth. Luchtvaardlabor., Rept.* No. **M1275** (1948).
51. McLaren, A. S., and McInnes, I., *Brit. J. Appl. Phys.* **9,** 72 (1958).
52. Lubkin, J. L., and Reissner, E., *Trans. ASME* **78,** 1213 (1956).
53. Bikerman, J. J., *J. Appl. Phys.* **28,** 1484 (1957).
54. Bikerman, J. J., *J. Appl. Polymer Sci.* **2,** 216 (1959).
55. Spies, J., *Aircraft Eng.* **25,** No. 289, 64 (1953).
56. Jouwersma, C., *J. Polymer Sci.* **45,** 253 (1960).
57. Gardon, J. L., *J. Appl. Polymer Sci.* **7,** 643 (1963).
58. Kaelble, D. H., *Trans. Soc. Rheol.* **3,** 161 (1959).
59. Kaelble, D. H., *Trans. Soc. Rheol.* **4,** 45 (1960).
60. Mylonas, C., *Proc. 4th Intern. Congr. Rheol., Providence, 1963,* Part 2, p. 423. Wiley (Interscience), 1965.
61. Gardon, J. L., *J. Appl. Polymer Sci.* **7,** 625 (1963).
62. Hammond, G. L., and Moakes, R. C. W., *Trans. Inst. Rubber Ind.* **25,** 172 (1949).
63. Bikerman, J. J., *J. Appl. Chem.* **11,** 81 (1961).
64. Ripling, E. J., Mostovoy, S., and Patrick, R. L., *Am. Soc. Testing Mater., Spec. Tech. Publ.* **360,** 5 (1964).
65. Nonaka, Y., *J. Adhesion Soc. Japan* **2,** 153 (1966).
66. Kaelble, D. H., *Trans. Soc. Rheol.* **9,** Part II, 135 (1965).
67. Deryagin, B. V., and Krotova, N. A., "Adgeziya," p. 55. Acad. Sci. U.S.S.R., Moscow, 1949.
68. Inoue, Y., and Kobatake, Y., *Bull. Tokyo Inst. Technol. Ser. B* p. 199 (1958).
69. Snoddon, W. J., *Am. Soc. Testing Mater., Spec. Tech. Publ.* **201,** 73 (1957).

70. Hata, T., Gamo, M., and Doi, Y., *Kobunshi Kagaku* **22,** 152 (1965); *Chem. Abstr.* **64,** 6833 (1966).
71. Dupré, A., *Ann. Chim. Phys.* [4] **7,** 245 (1866).
72. Griffith, A. A., *Phil. Trans. Roy. Soc. London* **A221,** 180 (1920).
73. Bikerman, J. J., *SPE Trans.* **4,** 290 (1964); *Phys. Status Solidi* **10,** 3 (1965).
74. Malyshev, B. M., and Salganik, R. L., *Zh. Prikl. Mekhan. i Tekhn. Fiz.* **1964,** No. 5, 91; *Dokl. Akad. Nauk SSSR* **160,** 91 (1965).
75. Ripling, E. J., Mostovoy, S., and Patrick, R. L., *Mater. Res. & Std.* **4,** 129 (1964).
76. Mostovoy, S., and Ripling, E. J., *J. Appl. Polymer Sci.* **10,** 1351 (1966).

CHAPTER IX / **EXPERIMENTAL STRENGTH OF ADHINTS**

§100 The strength of adhints has been measured very many times; even that fraction of the results which has found its way into journals and books could fill several volumes of the size of this monograph. Unfortunately, only a small part of the published data has a validity general enough to justify their inclusion here. A common cause of the unsuitability of these findings was the belief of the investigator that he measured molecular adhesion, a primary quantity independent of the dimensions of the adhint and other external parameters; consequently, no attention was paid to the magnitudes of α, β, and s in Eq. 68, §61. Another cause acted perhaps even more often. The adhints were tested rather than studied. The tester had to formulate an adhesive for a definite application. He mixed the contents of several bottles in several ratios and found the most satisfactory mixture. Obviously, the results of his efforts are almost valueless if the application envisaged is a little different from his, if, for instance, the dimensions of the adhints, the thickness of the adhesive film, etc., have to be changed. (See also §113.)

In an attempt to extract as much usefulness from published data as possible, these data are grouped so as to supply answers to the following problems:

1. Is there any correlation between the breaking stresses of adhints of different types (butt, lap, etc.)?
2. What is the effect of adhint dimensions?

3. What is the relation between the properties of the adhesive material in bulk and *in situ?*

4. How close is the correlation between the breaking stresses of adhints and adhesives?

5. How does the composition of an adhesive affect its strength in adhints?

6. What is the effect of the rate of loading and separation?

7. What is the effect of temperature?

8. What is the effect of environment?

In this discussion it will be convenient to refer to Eq. (68), which may be rewritten as

$$f_m = \frac{1}{\alpha} \left(\frac{\xi}{\beta} - s \right) . \tag{149}$$

In principle, an analogous expression ought to be valid for the strength f_M of the adhesive itself, assuming that the rupture of the adhint proceeds in the adhesive layer:

$$f_M = \frac{\xi_o}{\beta_o} - s_o ; \tag{150}$$

suffix 0 means that values for the bulk adhesives are used. The coefficient α is equal to 1 if there is no interphase boundary. From (149) and (150), the relation

$$\frac{f_m}{f_M} = \frac{\beta_o(\xi - \beta s)}{\alpha \beta (\xi_o - \beta_o s_o)} \tag{151}$$

results.

Adhints of Different Types

§101   Consider the adhints depicted in Fig. 112. On the left, a system ready for stripping is shown (see Fig. 101); the adhesive film, not

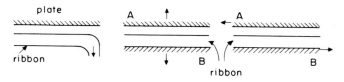

FIG. 112. Three different types of rupturing an adhint.

marked, is between the ribbon and the plate. In Fig. 112, in the middle, the lower face of the ribbon is attached to a rigid plate, and plates A and B are pulled apart by a tensile force. Finally, on the right, the same plates are sheared as in a single lap joint. If the adhesive films in the three systems are identical, comparison of the forces needed for their rupture would show the effect of the straining procedure, that is, whether by peeling, tensile pull, or shear. Since the residual stresses s and the microscopic stress concentration factors β, Eq. (149), are supposed to be identical, the contemplated comparison would give us information on the relative magnitude of factor α. If also the values of α were identical, the ratios of the peeling to the tensile force and of the tensile to the shear force would have been obtainable from the equations of Chapter VIII. For instance, if peeling proceeds in such a manner that ζ remains very near to zero, i.e., Eq. (133) is valid, then the first ratio would have been $0.3799(E/E_1)^{0.25}\delta^{0.75}h_o^{0.25}/l$. The second ratio would be equal simply to $\sigma_m/\tau_{\max}$ [see Eqs. (123) and (134)].

Apparently, of the three types sketched in Fig. 112, small values of $\alpha - 1$ are most readily achieved in butt joints. A butt joint, in which the stress concentration depicted in Fig. 70 is believed to have been eliminated, is illustrated in Fig. 113 from reference 1. An amount of adhesive insufficient to fill the clearance between two cylinders is applied to their bases. When molten, it wets the two solids and forms an "hourglass-like" body. Because the waist of the hourglass has a smaller cross section than the area of the adherend–adhesive boundary, the adhesive breaks across this waist; consequently, stress concentrations along the three-phase boundary line are of no importance. Evidently, the stress concentration indicated in Fig. 69 must exist in adhints of Fig. 113 but the central part of the hourglass seemingly was more like a cylindrical column

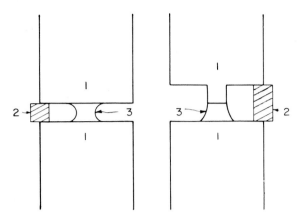

FIG. 113. Butt joints in which stress concentrations are relatively unimportant. 1: adherends; 2: spacers; 3: adhesive. From reference 1.

so that the magnitude of $\alpha - 1$ was moderate. The rupture stress f_m in this arragement should be computed from $f_m = F_m/A_{min}$, A_{min} being the smallest cross section (i.e., through the waist) of the adhesive column; F_m is again the external force just causing fracture.

The value of $\alpha - 1$ seems to be small in many butt joints produced in the customary manner because the adhesive–air interface has a shape different from that postulated in §80. Since liquid adhesives, as a rule, wet the adherends (§31), a film of the adhesive remains, after setting, on the surfaces perpendicular to the adherend–adhesive interface (see Fig. 113 right and 114). Stress distribution in systems of this kind is unknown but it is highly probable that factor α is smaller in these adhints than in those of Figs. 69 and 70.

It is a common observation that adhesives having a high modulus (E_1) of elasticity and a small total relative elongation appear stronger in tensile (butt) than in peeling tests. The general explanation of this effect is that the stress in the adhesive film being peeled is more concentrated the higher E_1. This is seen quantitatively in Eqs. (130) and (141). The length of the layer stressed by the external force is $\pi/2n$ (§97); it is shorter the greater n, i.e., when E_1 increases. Also Eq. (143) predicts the peeling tension to increase when E_1 rises. In

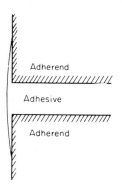

FIG. 114. A butt joint in which stress concentrations presumably are unimportant.

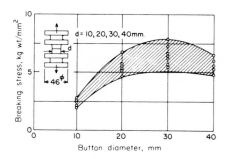

FIG. 115. Rupture stress in butt joints. Abscissa: diameter of the adherend buttons (mm). Ordinate: breaking stress (kg wt./mm^2). From reference 3.

addition to this effect associated with peeling, the change in the breaking stress of butt joints, caused by a change in E_1, should be taken into account. When E_1 is large, it is less different from the modulus E of the adherend. Consequently, the magnitude λ in Eq. (99), §80, is small and, hence, the stress concentration illustrated in Fig. 70 also is small. Thus, an increase in E_1 affects peeling and pulling in the opposite directions.

§102   It would be tempting to conclude that the inherent strength of an adhesive is better utilized in butt joints than in peeling joints by comparing data[1,2] on aluminum–polyethylene adhints. The breaking stress f_m of the butt adhints (designed to achieve a low magnitude of $\alpha - 1$) was greater than the tensile strength of the polymer in bulk; for additional analogous results see §103. On the other hand (see Table XIII, §95), the peeling tension Γ was only a fraction of that expected from Eq. (133). This comparison is not convincing because it is questionable whether the conditions needed for this equation to be valid were satisfied.

A comparison of butt, lap, and torque joints was performed[3] on adhints consisting of aluminum alloy adherends (the alloy contained copper and magnesium, had designation F44, and a very high value of Young's modulus) and "Metallon 130" (apparently, a cured epoxy resin) as the adhesive. Figure 115 presents f_m of butt joints (in kg. wt./mm.[2]; multiply by 98.1 to express it in bars) as a function of the diameter (in mm.) of the buttons glued together. It is seen that the average breaking stress for the most favorable button diameter ($= 3$ cm) was about 6.3 kg wt/mm^2 (or 620 bars). The tensile strength of the adhesive in bulk covered the range between 490 and 760 bars, that is, was almost identical with the f_m of the better joints. Lap joints between 0.1 cm thick strips of the same alloy, with an overlap of 1 cm, gave f_m values near 250 bars. The difference between butt and lap joints could have been due to the ratio $\sigma_m/\tau_{\max}$ being about 2 to 3 (see §101), but the results of torque tests refute this hypothesis.

For torque tests, two short lengths of a tube (of the above aluminum alloy) were glued as illustrated in Fig. 116 and then one of them was rotated around the common axis. The details of calculating f_m from the force F_m needed to twist the adhint to rupture are not given; it is clear that the stress near the external boundary of adhesive and air was greater than that near the internal boundary (see §91). Figure 117 exhibits the f_m values (again in kg wt./mm^2) as a function of the thickness h_0 (in mm) of the adhesive film. The upper shaded region is for torque, and the lower, for lap tests. In twisting also $\tau_{\max}$, theoretically, is measured. Thus the values of 470 to 660 bars calculated for $\tau_{\max}$ from the upper range of Fig. 117 are not in accord with the much lower values computed from the lower range;

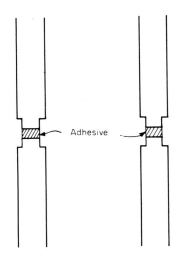

FIG. 116. A specimen for torque test.

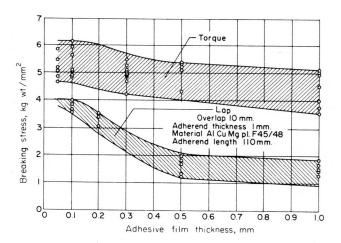

FIG. 117. Rupture stress and adhesive film thickness. Abscissa: film thickness, in millimeters. Ordinate: breaking stress (kg wt./mm²). Upper region for torque; lower region for lap tests. From reference 3.

hence, the stress concentration factor α must have been larger in the lap joints.

The f_m of butt joints made of aluminum adherends and various nylons (Nylon 6, Nylon 66, and so on) or a high-density polyethylene was 1.7–2.7 times as great as f_m of lap shear adhints prepared from identical materials.[4] It would be expected that the ratio of the two breaking stresses would be greater for brittle than for ductile polymers but no such regularity was observed.

Extremely different adhints required very different breaking stresses.[5] A glass fiber was embedded in a polyester film so that the area of contact was approximately 10^{-4} cm^2; and the stress needed to pull it out was 78 bars. An identical polyester was employed as the adhesive in a cross-lap joint in which the contact area was 1 cm^2, and this time the f_m was between 20 and 24 bars.

Peeling tension Γ for 180° peel (see §98) was compared[6] with the lap shear strength of graft polymers of commercial polyethylene (100 parts) and acrylic acid (5 parts). For the peeling tests, a ribbon of about 0.02 cm was deposited on an aluminum foil strip, 0.005 cm thick, and the aluminum was bent back. The lap joints were made with 0.16 cm thick aluminum bars; the overlap was 1.27 cm. The Γ was, for instance, at $-30°$, $0°$, and $+115°$, about 1200, about 700, and about 170 kilodynes/cm. The ratio F_m/wL (F_m, breaking load; w, width of the bar; L, length of the overlap) for the lap joints was, at these temperatures, 140, 120, and 20 bars. Thus, the ratio of Γ to F_m/wL was almost independent of temperature and equal to 0.007 cm. The ratio of the tensile strength f_M to F_m/wL was a little below 3 at all temperatures.

Two different external stresses were applied to identical specimens.[7] These consisted of two short vertical steel cylinders (diameter $2r = 2.9$ cm) glued together over the bases with a flexible epoxy adhesive. They were broken either by shearing (i.e., by a horizontal force applied to the cylindrical faces) or by twisting (i.e., by a horizontal force acting on the circumference). The shear stress in the adhesive layer was assumed to be in both instances $F_m/\pi r^2$. The stresses causing rupture were found to be different for the two methods of attack, and it was concluded that torque caused less intense stress concentrations than did the direct push. When r was varied between 0.8 and 6.2 cm, F_m was, as expected, practically proportional to r^2.

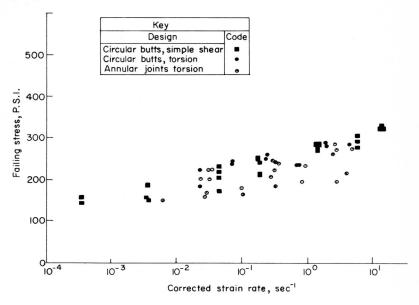

FIG. 118. Breaking stress of adhints of different types. Abscissa: strain rate (sec^{-1}). Ordinate: breaking stress (psi) (multiply by 0.0689 to obtain it in bars).

The above cylinders were joined also with a silicon rubber and an identical rubber was employed to join two annular faces of thin-walled steel tubes.[7] The thickness of the adhesive in all specimens was 0.025 cm. The solid cylinder adhints were broken, in separate experiments, by shear and by torsion, and the annular joint was ruptured by torsion only. Thus, three sets of values were obtained on three chemically identical systems. Figure 118 represents the results. The breaking stress is plotted as a function of the strain rate. No definite effect of the adhint type can be detected in the graph.

Three methods of attack were compared[8] also for pine wood glued with a phenol-resorcinol or a urea-formaldehyde adhesive.

The adhints were of the block shear type (§81), or the cross-lap type (the long axes of the two adherends being perpendicular to each other); or they were cleaved by a wedge as indicated in Fig. 119: a metal wedge with an angle of 90° was gradually forced into the adhesive layer between two wood blocks. The breaking stress, i.e., the ratio of the breaking force to the area of the adhesive film, was 100 to 130 bars for block shear, 16 to 18 bars for cross-lap, and 16 to 21 bars for cleavage. Evidently, stress concentrations were more severe in the second and third than in the first arrangement. For additional comparisons see §§86, 89, and 118.

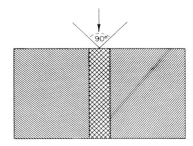

FIG. 119. Cleavage test. The thickness of the adhesive film (cross-shaded) is exaggerated.

It may be mentioned that also during the rupture of butt joints, oscillations (§97) were observed[9]; however, it is not known how much these were influenced by the rigidity of the instrument employed.

Strength and Dimensions of an Adhint

103   The cement in every adhint has a thickness or a range of thicknesses; it also has a radius, or a width and a length, and so on. Also the adherends have linear dimensions. What is known about the correlation between the dimensions of the adhesive film and the adherends on one hand and the final strength of adhints on the other hand, is reviewed in this and the five following sections. The thickness h_0 of the cement film is discussed first.

The rule that "a joint is stronger the thinner the adhesive layer in it" has been established long ago by nonsystematic observations and mentioned many times in trade literature. Apparently the first scientific publication in which this rule was tested was a paper by Crow.[10] Copper cylinders, 0.63 cm in diameter, were soldered (basis to basis) with the tin–lead eutectic alloy and broken in tension. Figure 120 shows the results. Its ordinate represents the breaking stress at which each joint failed, and the abscissa is the thickness of the solder film. In spite of the poor precision of the experimental values, common to all measurements of the final strength of adhints, the tendency of f_m to increase when h_0 decreases is unmistakable. The discontinuous line at the right indicates the tensile strength of the solder (633 bars).

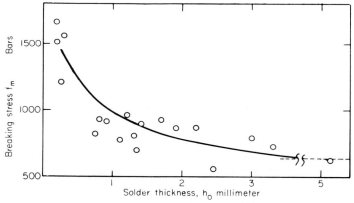

FIG. 120.   Rupture stress and adhesive film thickness in soldered joints. Abscissa: film thickness (mm). Ordinate: breaking stress (bars). Data of reference 10.

A similar tendency has been observed many times since. Thus, the strength of a commercial shellac adhesive between two nickel adherends[11] was 213–254 bars when the cement film was "extremely thin," 138–143 bars when h_0 was 0.30 mm, and 69–76 bars at $h_0 = 1.2$ mm. When two quartz cylinders were joined (basis to basis) with paraffin wax whose tensile strength was 7.31 bars, the f_m was 14.6, 14.5, 7.6, and 3.3 bars at h_0 equal to 0.003, 0.04, 0.07, and 2.5 mm, respectively.[12] One hundred paraffin wax joints between a brass cylinder and a steel plate were broken in tension[13]; the maximum value of f_m was 34.3, the minimum was 14.2, and the arithmetic mean 24.1 bars when the thickness h_0 was approximately 0.057 mm, while the mean f_m of 40 joints having $h_0 = 0.54$ mm was 14.6 bars.

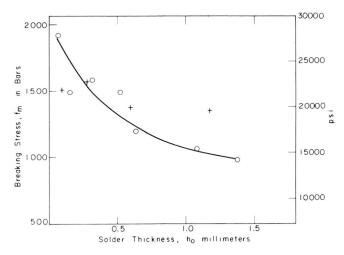

FIG. 121. Rupture stress and adhesive film thickness in soldered joints. Abscissa: film thickness (mm). Ordinate: breaking stress (bars). Circles: narrow cylinders. Crosses: thick cylinders. Data of reference 14.

Some of the more recent results, still for butt joints, are reproduced in Figs. 121, 122, and 123. Figure 121 is drawn according to the tables given in the original thesis.[14] Brass cylinders were soldered together by means of the tin–lead eutectic alloy. Only the sound joints containing no visible bubbles were considered in constructing the figure. The values of f_m for narrow cylinders (diameter 1.17 ± 0.02 cm) were combined by the present author into seven groups, of which only one represented a single measurement while the others contained three to five individual values. The average breaking stress and the average thickness for each group are shown by circles in the figure. An analogous procedure was applied to thicker cylinders (diameter 2.445 ± 0.045 cm), except that only four groups were possible; the averages for these groups are represented by crosses. When Fig. 121 is compared with Fig. 120, it is clear that the reproducibility of rupture stress measurements did not markedly change from 1924 to 1949; and the properties of the eutectic solder, naturally, did not change either.

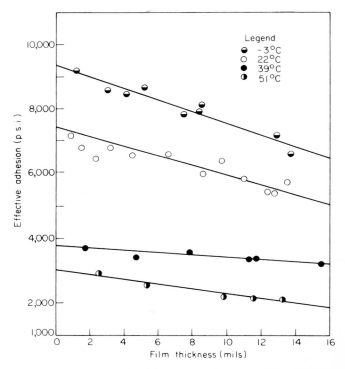

FIG. 122. Rupture stress and adhesive film thickness in poly(vinyl acetate) joints. Abscissa: film thickness (thousandths of an inch). Ordinate: breaking stress (psi), for test temperatures of −3°, 22°, 39°, and 51°C.

Figure 122 is for poly(vinyl acetate) joints between two steel cylinders.[15] Breaking stress (the ordinate) is expressed in pounds per square inch; multiply by 0.06895 to obtain f_m in bars. The thickness h_0 (the abscissa) is given in 0.001 inch; multiply by 25.4 to obtain h_0 in microns. The lines are, from top to bottom, for test temperatures of $-3°$, $22°$, $39°$, and $51°C$, respectively. The average molecular weight of the polymer was 225,000.

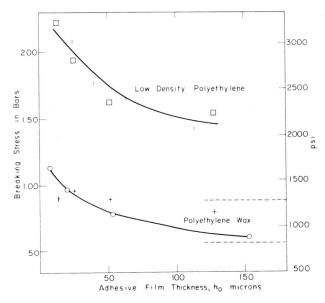

FIG. 123. Rupture stress and adhesive film thickness in polyethylene joints. Abscissa: film thickness, in microns. Ordinate: breaking stress, in bars. Discontinuous lines indicate the tensile strength of the polyethylenes. From reference 1.

Figure 123 combines data[1] for a low-molecular-weight polyethylene (molecular weight between 2500 and 3000, lower curve) and a high-molecular-weight polyethylene (high-pressure, low-density type, upper curve). The adherends were: steel-to-glass for vertical lines, glass-to-glass for squares and crosses, and steel-to-steel for circles. All adhints were designed to minimize stress concentrations at the adherend–adhesive boundary. The discontinuous lines near the right-hand edge of the sketch indicate the tensile strength of the two polyethylenes, namely about 88 bars for the high and 56 bars for the low-molecular-weight material. Later measurements[16] indicated a higher value for the tensile strength of the wax so that the effect of h_0 on f_m was less pronounced than shown in Fig. 123.

§104   Although the graphs in Figs. 120 to 123 (and several analogous graphs in the literature) make decrease of f_m with increasing h_0 in butt joints certain, almost nothing can be said about the shape of the function $f_m = f(h_0)$. In several instances, the values of f_m at the lowest h_0 were smaller than at slightly higher h_0 values so that f_m seemed to have a maximum; see, for instance, the crosses in Fig. 123 and reference 17. However, it is generally believed that this decrease of f_m at extremely small cement thicknesses is due to the trivial circumstance that these adhesive films are likely to contain voids; when, in an attempt to produce a particularly thin joint, the experimenter applies a very small amount of the cement, this amount may be insufficient to fill the clearance between the two adherends; thus a *starved joint* may result.

If starved joints are disregarded, f_m monotonously _ically_ decreases when h_0 increases. The curves of f_m versus h_0 are similar in Figs. 120, 121, and 123, but in Fig. 122 f_m appears to be a linear function of h_0; see also reference 18. Unfortunately, the cause of this discrepancy is not known. The results are too sketchy to decide whether and how the shape of the f_m-versus-h_0 curve depends on the adhesive, the adherends, the geometry of the joint, and so on. If we knew this shape for various adhints, the theory of the relation between thinness and strength would be more explicit than it is now.

The first question to answer is whether or not this relation is real. As reported in §116, the breaking stress depends on the velocity of rupture. Suppose that the two adherends of a butt joint are moved apart (along their common axis) at a rate u cm/sec. Then the rate of strain, i.e., $dh/h_0\ dt$, h being the thickness of the adhesive "pancake" at time t, is inversely proportional to the initial thickness h_0 since $dh/dt = u$ is constant. The velocity dh/dt has no molecular meaning; what molecules "feel" is $dh/h_0\ dt$. Thus the effect of stretching an adhesive film is greater the smaller h_0. This was believed to be the (or at least a) cause of the observed dependence of f_m on h_0.

At present it appears that the influence of rate is not decisive. Experimental data for butt joints could not be found but are presented in §106 for block shear adhints. The main reason for doubting the great importance of the rate of strain is that, usually, measurements are not performed at a constant u. In many instances, dead loads were used and the increase of the thickness h in time was not controlled.

If it is admitted that the major part of the influence of h_0 on f_m is real, this may be due to a change in ξ, α, β, s, or several of these quantities together. Consider the cohesion first.

It is argued that the vicinity of a solid hinders[19] the free mobility of polymer chains (see §109); hence, a polymer region next to the adherend has mechanical properties differing from those in bulk; as these regions are relatively more important the thinner the adhesive film, a relation is established between h_0 and the mechanical behavior of the adhesive. Butt joints of a poly(vinyl acetate) of molecular weight 10,000 between two glass blocks were made at one temperature and then broken at temperatures varying from $-10°$ to $+40°$. When h_0 was 30 μ, f_m had a maximum at 11°, and when h_0 was 3 μ, the greatest f_m was observed at 20°. The absolute values of the maxima were almost identical; thus, f_m of the thicker adhints was greater than that of the thinner between 0° and 16°, while at higher temperatures the thin adhints were stronger. As expounded in §119, a maximum of f_m is sometimes observed near the glass transition temperature T_g of the polymer; it is believed that restriction of the chain mobility raises T_g and thus shifts the maximum f_m to a higher temperature.

An effect of h_0 on β would be expected because the weakest spot in a sample is weaker the larger the sample (§62). Thus, adhints with a thicker cement film are more likely to contain a particularly bad flaw than adhints in which there is less adhesive material. This theory has been tested by the method outlined in the last paragraph of §62. Ten groups of adhints, each of 10 samples 57 μ thick, were broken and the lowest breaking stresses for each group recorded.[13] In between, 40 samples of 540 μ each were measured. The average for the lowest rupture stresses of the thin joints (in groups of ten) would be approximately equal to the average of all rupture stresses of the thick joints, if the probability of flaws were the only factor influencing the relationship between f_m and h_0. As mentioned in §103, the latter average was 14.6 bars, and the former was 17.8 bars; and statistical analysis of the data proved that the difference between 17.8 and 14.6 was too great to be attributable to chance; thus, another factor (or factors) must also have contributed to the decrease of f_m with increasing h_0.

Factor β of Eqs. (68) and (149) can be influenced by the thickness of the adhesive film also in virtue of another mechanism. The texture (e.g., the crystal size) of a solid depends on its rate of solidification. A thin film of molten adhesive between two metal adherends, as a rule, will solidify on cooling in a shorter time than a thick film of an identical material. Thus, the texture of the cement often will be different in a thin and in a thick joint; consequently, the strength of the adhesive also may be different in the two instances. This is true also when the adhesive sets because of the loss of solvent or because of a chemical reaction (see §48). For instance, polymerization of low-molecular-weight unsaturated compounds usually is associated with evolution of heat; removal of heat is relatively more rapid when the volume in which reaction proceeds is smaller; thus, a thin film of polymer may form at a lower internal temperature than a thick one; and if the strength of the polymer depends on the formation temperature, the strength of this polymer in adhints will depend on h_0. This explanation was advanced for the above-mentioned difference between 17.8 and 14.6 bars,[13] but no experimental proof of the hypothesis exists.

Differences in the rate of setting between thin and thick adhints will, generally, cause differences in the intensity of the residual stresses s. These stresses may facilitate rupture (§75), but may also oppose it (as in hardened glass) and it is difficult to predict their effect on the function $f_m = f(h_0)$. Apparently, no experimental data of value for this discussion are available.

The effect of h_0 on the stress concentration factor α can approximately be deduced from the theories of §80. In particular Eq. (114) predicts that f_m should be inversely proportional to h_0 for rigid-plastic adhesives. None of the curves of Fig. 120 to 123 agrees with this prediction; for instance, for a substance as ductile as tin–

lead eutectic alloy, the product $f_m h_0$, instead of being independent of h_0, increases from about 20–30 at the smallest h_0 to over 300 bars × cm at the greatest thicknesses tested. Evidently, the assumptions on which Eq. (114) rests are not in accord with the experimental conditions employed.

An additional reason for the effect of h_0 on f_m exists when the adhesive is a rubberlike material. Not by chance, typical rubbers are similar to gases and liquids in the sense that they are easily deformed but are resistant to volume changes; it is easy to stretch a rubber filament but the extension produced is not associated with any significant increase in volume because the Poisson ratio ν is very near to 0.5. (The values of ν for common solids are near 0.3, and stretching a rod entails a decrease in density.) When a layer of rubber between two rigid cylinders of radius a is relatively thick (or the ratio h_0/a is not too small), the circumferential depression illustrated in Fig. 69 can be so deep that the volume of the adhesive can remain almost constant when the two adherends are pulled apart. However, when h_0/a is very small, the groove along the circumference of the adhesive "pancake" can have only a slight effect on the total volume; at a first approximation, the rubber volume increases in the ratio $h:h_0$ when the distance between the adherends rises from h_0 to h in the tensile test. Thus the deformation of thick rubber films proceeds at a nearly constant volume and, consequently, is easy, while an identical deformation of a thin film means an expansion and, hence, is difficult.

It is implied in the preceding discussion that before the stretch, h_0 is constant over the whole adhesive film. This assumption is not always correct. A uniform sheet of a vinyl-phenolic adhesive was[20] heat-pressed between two aluminum panels, 0.13 cm thick; the aluminum was dissolved away, and the central parts of the liberated film were compared with the peripheral parts. The mass and the thickness of 1 cm² of the film near its center were greater than those at the edge, e.g., in the ratio 109:100.

Equation (114) includes another dimension of the adhint in addition to the thickness h_0. If the equation is applicable, f_m should be proportional to a/h_0 (i.e., radius/thickness). Unfortunately, the variation of f_m with h_0 is so small and the unavoidable scatter of the values of f_m so large that it is unsafe to decide whether f_m depends on a/h_0 or on h_0 alone. Preference for $f_m = f(a/h_0)$ was expressed, for instance, in references 14 and 21. In Fig. 121, crosses refer to adhints whose a was 2.1 times that of the adhints represented by circles. Consequently, to make f_m a function of h_0/a, the abscissa of the crosses should be reduced in the ratio 1:2.1. This translation would place the cross at the extreme right of the figure almost exactly on the curve for the thin joints, but the position of the other three crosses would not be improved. If f_m is plotted versus h_0/a, a rectangular hyperbola should result, but the experimental data for silver as the cement between two steel cylinders[21] afforded linear dependence between f_m and h_0/a. New experiments would be welcome.

Whatever the exact shape of the function $f_m = f(h_0)$, f_m seems to increase indefinitely when h_0 gets smaller and if starved joints are avoided; thus the strength of a butt joint should reach the strength of the adherend if the cement film is extremely thin. This state was almost achieved when two steel bars were joined by means of pure silver[21] or some other metals.[18]

§105   In *lap joints*, rupture stress should often be approximately proportional to $\sqrt{h_0}$ [see Eqs. (123) and (126)]. The predicted increase of f_m with h_0 is visible in Fig. 100. If the two joints for which Fig. 100a and 100b are drawn were identical in all respects except the adhesive thickness h_0, then h_0 in Fig. 100b is 25 times as great as in Fig. 100a. The ordinates of these figures are proportional to breaking stress. It is seen that, for instance, at the ratio of overlap to cement thickness equal to 10, the ordinate for the *G-R* curve in Fig. 100b is about four times as great as in Fig. 100a; thus f_m in this example increased fourfold when h_0 increased 25 times.

Those few publications, in which the experimental dependence of f_m on h_0 in single lap joints is treated, do not confirm the prediction of the theory. Breaking force F_m and breaking stress f_m seem to decrease when adhesive thickness h_0 increases, and with a gradient similar to that obtaining in butt joints (§103).

Thus, for aluminum and a Neoprene–phenolic adhesive the rupture stress was 3000 psi ($\approx$207 bars) at h_0 of about 50 μ and 1200 psi ($\approx$83 bars) at $h_0 = 508$ μ, and the decrease was similar for a "Buna N-phenolic resin."[17] It is true that a filled epoxy resin adhesive (consisting of 45 parts resin and 55 parts alumina + asbestos) showed breaking stresses independent of h_0 when this varied from 250 to about 750 μ, for both butt and single lap joints,[22] but the range of thicknesses perhaps was too narrow to detect the effect of h_0.

Decrease of f_m on increasing h_0 in single lap joints can be seen in Fig. 117, §102. The ribbons (1 mm thick, 20 mm wide) were of an Al-Cu-Mg alloy, a commercial epoxy resin (Araldite I) was the adhesive, and the overlap was 10 mm long. The lower band refers to lap joints.

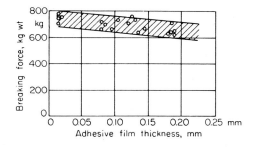

FIG. 124. Rupture stress and adhesive film thickness in lap joints. Abscissa: film thickness (mm). Ordinate: breaking force (kg wt.). From reference 23.

A similar behavior is exhibited in Fig. 124, whose ordinate is force F_m (kg wt.) required to break single lap joints of thickness h_0 (mm) plotted along the abscissa.[23] The adherends were 1 mm thick and 25 mm wide ribbons of an Al-Cu-Mg alloy, and the adhesive was an epoxy resin apparently similar to, or identical with, that used in the tests of Fig. 117. The absolute values of F_m are in good agreement with the f_m values of Fig. 117 as these have to be multiplied by 200 mm² (i.e., 20 mm × 10 mm) to obtain F_m.

It is not known whether the discrepancy between these experimental results and the theory is caused by (a) the inexactitude of the calculation of the stress concentration factor α, Eq. (149), §100 or (b) by the influence of factor β which almost always tends to be greater in thicker cement films, or (c) the difference in the magnitude of s stresses in thin and thick joints.

A very peculiar observation has been made[23] on the dependence of the "fatigue" of a lap joint on its thickness. Single lap joints, similar to those whose behavior is summarized in Fig. 124 and thus having resistances to fracture of 600 to 800 kg wt., were loaded with 100 kg each and left in air at 20° and 35–45% relative humidity. The adhint in which the adhesive was about 20 μ thick broke after about 20 hr, the adhints whose h_0 was between 40 and 120 μ lasted 300 to 500 hr, and those having h_0 near 180 μ yielded after less than an hour. No explanation is available for the short endurance times of very thin and relatively thick adhesive films.

The effect of the adherend thickness δ on the breaking force was mentioned in §86. Another example[24] deals with plates of an Al-Mg-Mn alloy glued with a phenol-vinyl-formaldehyde adhesive. When, at a constant overlap of 10 mm, δ increased from 0.5 to 2 mm, the force increased in the ratio 1.4:1.

§106   Block shear specimens are similar to lap joints; but the adherends are thick and short instead of being long and thin. The effect of h_0 on F_m was measured in specimens described in §102: two short cylinders glued basis to basis were[7] sheared apart. The adhesive was a silicon rubber whose apparent modulus of elasticity was as low as 30 bars. A valuable feature of these determinations was that the strain rate was kept constant when h_0 was varied (see §104); in all tests the shear strain increased by 0.0001 every second. The results are summarized in Table XIV.

It is seen that the force needed for shearing increases, e.g., threefold when h_0 decreases in the ratio 12:1. This is a steeper change than those shown in the graphs of this Chapter. It is difficult to assess the meaning of this conclusion as the stress pattern of block shear tests is imperfectly known. As stated in §81, the adhesive film is disregarded in the only theory available. If the adhesive film is included in the model, Fig. 125 results. Forces F_m give rise to a bending moment which is greater the thicker the film. Thus, at present the possibility cannot be excluded that the decrease of F_m on an increase in h_0 was partially caused by a simultaneous rise

TABLE XIV
BLOCK SHEAR FORCE F_m AND ADHESIVE THICKNESS h_0

Adherends	h_0 (cm)	F_m (dynes)
Aluminum alloy	0.010	133×10^6
	0.025	81×10^6
	0.119	44×10^6
Mild steel	0.010	81×10^6
	0.051	62×10^6
	0.119	35×10^6
Glass	0.010	87×10^6
	0.051	41×10^6
	0.119	31×10^6

of the moment. In the twist experiments whose results are sum-marized in Fig. 117, §102, the dependence of f_m on h_0 evidently was quite small; no explanation for this exists.

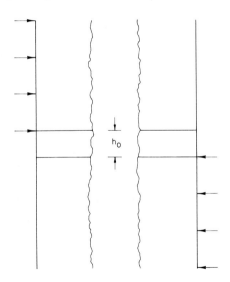

FIG. 125. Bending moment acting in a block shear test. h_0: the thickness of the adhesive.

§107   The force required to peel an adhint would be proportional to $h_0^{0.25}$ [see Eq. (133)] if all members of the joints were Hookean solids, if the rupture occurred in the plane of the force, if the angle of peel were 90°, and if the stress concentrations reported in §§95–96 were absent.

Experiments, which are in a semiquantitative agreement with this expectation, have been made with a Thiokol adhesive between cotton duck and rigid aluminum plates.[17] The angle of peel, however, was 180°. Peeling tension was about 800 kilodynes/cm at $h_0 = 40 \mu$, about 3400 kilodynes/cm at $h_0 = 750 \mu$, and 5300 kilodynes/cm at $h_0 = 1600 \mu$ (i.e., 1.6 mm). Unfortunately, determination of the thickness of an adhesive film on a crudely porous material, such as cotton duck, is not always convincing. This remark applies also to some experiments on rubber adhesives.[25]

When a synthetic rubber was vulcanized in contact with poly-(caprolactam) (Nylon 6), the peeling tension Γ was greater the thinner the film but the increase was moderate.[26] At the best vulcanization conditions, Γ was 640 and 780 kilodynes/cm when h_0 was 800 and 150 μ, respectively.

In another set of experiments[23] stripping force decreased when the cement thickness increased, i.e., the behavior was similar to that of butt joints (§103). The adherends were made of a weak Al-Mg-Si alloy whose yield stress at 0.2% strain was approximately 600 bars; the ribbons were 0.8 mm thick and 25 mm wide. An epoxy cement, the same as used for the experiments of Fig. 124, was the adhesive. The peeling angle apparently was not kept constant. When h_0 increased from about 0.02 to 0.19 mm, peeling tension Γ (kilodynes/cm) decreased from about 8000 to about 6800. At a peel angle of 180°, Γ was independent of thickness[27] in the range between 152 and 557 μ but its absolute value was so small (about 100 kilodynes/cm) that the presence of a weak boundary layer may be suspected; the system consisted of chrome-tanned gelatin, a butadiene-acrylonitrile polymer (as the adhesive) and a percale fabric.

An extensive series of measurements[28] was performed on double peeling adhints (see Fig. 106 in §97). Two strips of plasticized cellophane were coated with a polyacrylate latex and pressed together; the adhesive was cured at 150°, and the adhint was cooled and delaminated. Figure 126 presents the main results, slightly idealized; two curves (for $h_0 = 9.8$ and $14.6\ \mu$) are omitted as they cross the neighboring curves. At every rate u of separation (plotted along the abscissa) the Γ (plotted along the ordinate) was greater the greater the h_0 (marked at each curve). For instance, at $u = 0.1$ cm/sec, Γ was 97, 396, and 600 kilodynes/cm at h_0 equal to 1.2, 58, and 258 μ.

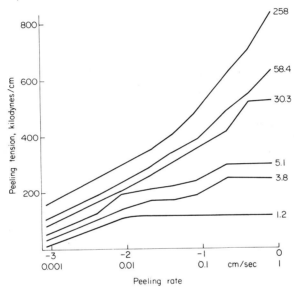

FIG. 126. Dependence of peeling tension on peeling rate at different thicknesses h_0 of the adhesive. Abscissa: peeling rate (cm/sec) (logarithmic). Ordinate: peeling tension (kilodynes/cm). The numbers at the curves mean h_0 in microns. Data of reference 28.

The effect of h_0 on the work "γ" of splitting two thick bars glued together (§99) was moderate.[29] When the bars were each 1.27 cm wide, the "γ" was high (3×10^5 ergs/cm^2) for thin (0.0025 cm) and thick (0.5 cm) adhesive films but had a minimum value (1.6×10^5 ergs/cm^2) at $h_0 = 0.05$ cm.

§108   The effect of the diameter of the adhesive film on the final strength of a butt joint was mentioned in §104.

The importance of the width of a lap joint apparently has not been systematically studied. Because many lap joints fail in peel and because peeling tension of ductile adhesives may depend on this width w (§95), some dependence of f_m on w in lap joints may be expected.

For the dependence of f_m on the length of the cement film (i.e., on the length of overlap) see §86.

The length of the adhesive film which is still attached to the plate in stripping tests must influence the peeling strength, if this length is very short, but no effect was noticed when it was, say, 200 times the combined thickness of ribbon and adhesive, or greater.

Those dimensions of the adherends, which are independent of the dimensions of the cement film, have been but little investigated in their relation to the mechanical strength of adhints. In butt joints, the extension of the adherends in the direction normal to the adherend–adhesive interface (such as the length of the cylinders in Fig. 70) should be irrelevant as long as the cylinders are long enough. In lap joints, the effect of thickness δ of the adherends is exemplified in Fig. 83, §86. Its abscissa represents $(L/\delta)^2$; if the overlap is constant, it is proportional to δ^{-2}. When L/δ is small, that is, δ is great, $F_m/w\delta$ is an almost linear function of log δ, i.e.,

$$\frac{F_m}{w\delta} = k_1 - k_2 \log \delta \text{ or } F_m = (k_1 - k_2 \log \delta)w\delta, \qquad (152)$$

k_1 and k_2 being constants. Thus, F_m increases with δ but less than linearly. This behavior was noticed several times. For instance,[30] the F_m of a lap joint between two magnesium panels increased in the ratio 2:1 when the thickness of the panels increased from 0.25 cm to 1.4 cm; and an equal increase in the δ of aluminum panels raised F_m in the ratio 2.2:1.

In peeling, the thickness δ of the ribbon should influence F_m/w according to Eq. (133). In some experiments[2] the effect was smaller than predicted. When aluminum ribbons were attached to rigid glass with a polyethylene and then stripped off, the ratio of F_m (or F_m/w) values for a ribbon of 0.0076 cm to that of a ribbon having $\delta = 0.0025$ cm was about 1.8 for a brittle and about 0.9 for a ductile adhesive. The theoretical ratio is 2.3. As Eq. (133) is less correct the stiffer the ribbon, i.e., the greater δ, the disagreement is not unexpected. The difference between 1.8 and 0.9 may be caused not only by the different lengths of the moment arm ζ (§94), but also by the fact that the most dangerous stress concentrations occur in different regions when the brittleness of the polymer varies (§§95–96). See also §43.

Adhesives in Bulk and *In Situ*

§109   Several properties of the adhesive *in situ* are mentioned in the preceding sections and appear in equations which are supposed to predict the mechanical properties of the adhint. Thus, cohesion ξ and stress concentration factor β are referred to in Eq. (68), the modulus of elasticity E_1 is present in Eq. (133), shear modulus G_1 in Eq. (123), and so on. The question is, whether the values of ξ, E_1, etc., determined on bulk specimens may be inserted in these formulas; in other words, whether the material in the adhesive "pancake" is identical with that of large samples. The main difficulty in answering it is due to the thinness of the adhesive *in situ*. If, for instance, the cement film in a butt joint cracks when its total relative elongation is 2%, and the initial thickness of the film is 0.002 cm, the total elongation is 0.00004 cm and the measuring instrument should be sensitive to 0.0000004 cm if we want the elongation to be measured to 1%.

One way of overcoming this difficulty is to prepare a pile of adhints (see Fig. 127), and to measure the extension of the whole pile when tensile forces are applied to it as shown; the adherend discs are shaded and the adhesive films are white. The extension of the adherends usually can be determined fairly accurately, and the extension of the adhesive is the difference between the total extension of the pile and that of the adherends in it. If the pile contains n adhesive films, the effect looked for is magnified n times.

Adhints containing just one, and those containing up to 10 adhesive films, were used[31] to determine the main mechanical constants of the adhesives in them. Each specimen consisted of two aluminum alloy tubings, 5.1 cm outside and 3.8 cm inside diameter, glued to-

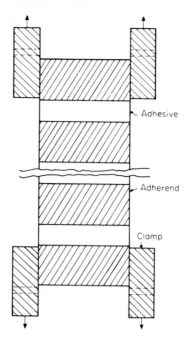

FIG. 127. A pile of adhints for the determination of the stress–strain curves of the adhesive.

gether over the annular areas, when n was 1, or of these tubings and several washers, each 0.3 cm thick, when n was >1. A torque (force F) was applied to the circumference of one of the cylinders to turn it about its axis relatively to the other cylinder. The shear stress in the adhesive was $2Fr_o/\pi(r_o^4 - r_i^4)$, r_o and r_i being the outside and the inside radius. From the deflection of the second cylinder the shear strain in the adhesive was calculated. Calculation of the tension modulus and the compression modulus were performed in an analogous manner. The values of E_1 ranged from 3.5×10^9 for an epoxy adhesive and for a mixture of a phenol resin solution and a vinyl polymer powder to 3.7×10^7 baryes for a mixture of Neoprene, nylon, and a phenolic resin. Usually, G_1 was approximately $E_1/3$; Poisson's ratio ν was 0.3–0.5; tensile strength σ_m was between 90 and 600 bars, and shear strength between 200 and 600 bars. The adhesive films usually were between 0.005 and 0.1 cm thick. Thus, the properties of the adhesives *in situ* were not significantly different from those of the bulk polymers. It has been stated in §99 that also the "γ" of the adhesives was quite similar *in situ* and in bulk.

A highly extensible mixture (AF-6) of an acrylonitrile-butadiene rubber and a phenolic resin demonstrated[31] a pronounced hysteresis. For instance, a shear stress of 5×10^7 baryes corresponded at the first loading to a strain ϵ of 0.33, at the first unloading to the strain 0.85, at the second loading to $\epsilon = 0.43$, and so on.

Another device is to use thicker adhesive layers although in these instances the doubt may linger whether the properties of a "pancake," say, 0.1 cm thick, really are identical with those of a film of, say, 0.0005 cm. The shear modulus G_1 of relatively thick adhesive layers (e.g., 0.05 cm) was determined[32] by painting microscopic marks on the side of the film (e.g., 0.5×0.05 cm) in the mutual distance of, say, 0.02 cm, applying a shear stress to the adherends, and measuring the tilt φ (in radians) of the marks at each magnitude of the stress τ. As an approximation, $G_1 = \tau/\varphi$. The G_1 of a commercial epoxy adhesive after a 7-day cure at 29° was about 550 bars and of a mixture of this material with a polysulfide rubber, about 42 bars.

Stress–strain curves of a single adhesive film *in situ* can be obtained[33] if butt joints are used as electrostatic capacitors. At a first approximation, the capacity *(C)* of a butt joint is inversely proportional to the thickness h of the cement (assumed to be an electrical insulator). Thus, when the adhint is axially strained and the adhesive thickness increases, C decreases. As very sensitive devices for measuring electrostatic capacity exist, this method would be very suitable. Unfortunately, capacity is proportional also to the dielectric constant *(D)* of the adhesive, and D varies when the adhesive is stretched. Thus, C depends on the ratio D/h rather than on h alone, and the effect of h on D has to be ascertained before changes in h can be computed from the experimental changes in C.

Figure 128 is an example of stress–strain curves obtained by the capacity method. They are similar to those recorded for the AF-6 rubber (see above). Tensile force in pounds-weight (multiply by 4.45×10^5 to obtain it in dynes) is plotted along the ordinate,

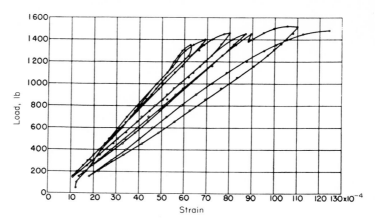

FIG. 128. Stress–strain curves of an adhesive, calculated from electrostatic capacity. Abscissa: relative elongation. Ordinate: tensile force (lb wt.). A methacrylate resin between steel cylinders. From reference 33.

and the relative elongation of the adhesive is the abscissa. Short steel cylinders (1.27 cm in diameter) glued with a methacrylate cement made up the adhint; the initial film thickness was approximately 0.004 cm. The load was gradually raised to almost 1200 lb, then lowered to about 100 lb, raised again, and so on. Apparently the methacrylate resin was elastically deformed by loads smaller than 1000 lb but flowed at higher loads. The apparent modulus of elasticity of a fresh sample at small stresses was about 5×10^{10} gm/cm sec^2.

The elastic modulus E_1 and the viscous modulus E_v of the adhesive can be calculated from an experimental comparison of a butt joint with an unbroken piece of the adherend.[34] When electric waves pass from one adherend cylinder (of length $0.5l$ cm) through the adhesive film (of thickness h cm) into the other adherend (of length $0.5l$ cm), the resonant frequency ν_1 and the width Δ_1 of the resonance band (that is, the range of frequencies in which the vibration amplitude is >0.707 maximum amplitude) are different from those (ν_0 and Δ_0, respectively) of a cylinder, l cm long and otherwise identical with the adherends. For hard adhesives

$$E_1 = \frac{4\rho}{g_0} \, hlv_0{}^2 \, \frac{v_1}{v_0 - v_1} \qquad (153)$$

and

$$E_v = \frac{E}{2} \, \frac{\Delta_1 - \Delta_0}{v_0 - v_1} \qquad (154)$$

if ρ is the density of the adherend material and g_0 a consistency factor.

In the evaluation of the above measurements it was consistently implied that the adhesive was uniform across the film. There are indications, however, that the vicinity of a foreign solid (such as an adherend) may affect the properties of a polymer. As mentioned in §104, the obstacle presented by the walls to the free mobility of polymer chains is supposed to be serious. Experimentally, the glass transition temperature T_g is raised by solid inclusions.[35] Thus, T_g of unfilled polystyrene was 84°; of 100 parts polystyrene filled with 10 parts short glass fibers (about 0.02 cm long), 86°; with 50 parts glass fibers, 94°; and so on. The poly(methyl methacrylate) employed had two transition temperatures, at 85.5° and 113.2°. Addition of 50 parts glass to 100 parts polymer raised these temperatures to 110° and 131.8°. At the same time, the "equilibrium" degree of swelling of these plastics also increased. This was, for instance, for unfilled polystyrene, polystyrene 100 + glass 23, and polystyrene 100 + glass 50 parts, 80%, 190%, and 290%. Shrinkage stresses in the polymer must be affected by the presence of glass filaments but it is not known what effect on T_g they have.

Strength of Adhints and of Adhesives

§110   The relation between the breaking stress f_m of an adhint and the tensile strength f_M of the adhesive depends first of all on whether the adhint is of the proper or the improper type. A similarity between f_m and f_M can be expected only if no weak boundary layer is present; otherwise, f_m is determined by the properties of this layer and is much smaller than f_M. If f_M is varied by gradually changing the composition of the adhesive, the change of f_m usually is similar as long as no weak boundary layer forms; and if it does form, f_m decreases without a corresponding decrease in f_M.

Clear instances of both behaviors were noticed[16] in butt joints in which the stress concentrations represented by the factor α (§61) were avoided as much as possible. The adherends were stainless steel cylinders and the adhesive was purified polyethylene (§69), either alone or mixed with varying amounts of oleic acid, ethyl palmitate, stearone, or 4-methyl-2,6-di-*tert*-butylphenol. Ethyl palmitate is an impurity which, in small concentrations, has little effect on either f_M or f_m and lowers both when the concentration is high; only when the final mixture contained about equal amounts of polyethylene and palmitate did f_m and f_M become too weak for measurements; ethyl palmitate was a liquid at the temperature of the experiments.

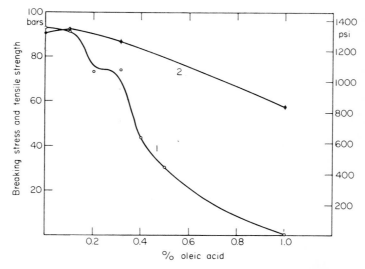

FIG. 129. Effect of oleic acid on the tensile strength of polyethylene in bulk (upper curve) and on the breaking stress of steel–polyethylene–steel butt joints (lower curve). Abscissa: concentration of the impurity, %. Ordinate: stress to failure (bars). From reference 16.

On the contrary, oleic acid markedly lowered f_m at concentrations as low as 0.1% (see §69), while its effect on f_M was small. Figure 129 shows how different are the responses of f_m (curve 1) and f_M (curve 2). Figure 130 illustrates the difference between an addition which does, and one which does not, give rise to weak boundary layers. The ratio $f_m:f_M$ is a little above 1.0 for purified polyethylene alone (see §103). Addition of ethyl palmitate raises it to 1.5–2.0, presumably since it is difficult to prepare uniform specimens of the mixture for tensile tests; but contamination with oleic acid reduces $f_m:f_M$ to practically zero at concentrations at which ethyl palmitate has still almost no effect on either f_m or f_M.

Apparently, analogous effects were observed[36] when various amounts of dibutyl phthalate or a chlorinated diphenyl were added to a chlorinated poly(vinyl chloride) and f_M of the materials obtained was compared with the Γ of adhints; unfortunately, the description

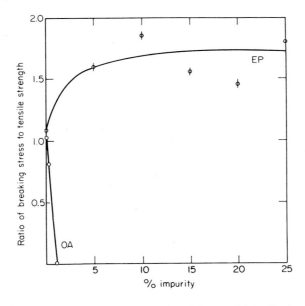

FIG. 130. Ratio of the breaking stress of butt joints to the tensile strength of the adhesive in the systems polyethylene—ethyl palmitate (upper curve) and polyethylene—oleic acid (lower curve). Abscissa: concentration of the impurity, %. Ordinate: f_m/f_M. From reference 16.

of the experiments is too superficial to permit a more definite judgement.

§111   As long as attention is restricted to proper adhints, the ratio of f_m to f_M is given by Eq. (151), §100. As the quantities appearing in this equation have never been all determined for an adhint and its adhesive in bulk, only semiquantitative or frankly qualitative correlations between f_m and f_M can be hoped for from experimental data.

A clear correlation is demonstrated in Fig. 123. If the curves of f_m versus h_0 are extrapolated to great values of h_0, the values of f_m will approach those of f_M marked as discontinuous lines. The graph combines data for two polyethylene samples. A third type also was used; it had (allegedly) a molecular weight near 100,000 and was of a high-density kind. Also for this material, extrapolation of the f_m-h_0 curve leads to values almost identical with the experimental tensile strength of the bulk polyethylene.[1]

In the adhints of Fig. 123, $\alpha - 1$ apparently was very small (see §101). Since the bulk specimens of the polyethylenes were prepared under conditions similar to those used for the preparation of the adhints, the shrinkage stresses s and s_0 presumably had similar magnitudes. Thus the difference between f_m and f_M probably was caused chiefly by the difference between β and β_0; as these two quantities are likely to be nearly identical when h_0 is large, an accord between f_M on one hand and f_m extrapolated to $h_0 = \infty$ on the other hand may be expected.

Similarity between f_m and f_M exists also when no attempt is made to reduce α to unity. Two examples, for the eutectic solder and for paraffin wax, are mentioned in §103, and a third, for "Metallon 130," in §102. The tensile strength of ice a few degrees below the melting point usually lies between 10 and 18 bars; and the strength of adhints in which copper, steel, or glass were joined together with ice proved to be near 19 bars.[37] The strength of soldered joints is similar to the bulk strength of the solder whatever the ratio of tin to lead in the latter.[38]

Four mixtures of an epoxy resin with diethylenetriamine were cured[39] under different conditions so that the tensile strength f_M of the cast polymers varied from 670 to 910 bars. Then aluminum butt joints were prepared with identical materials cured in the identical manner. The ratios of f_m to f_M in the four systems were confined to the range 0.62 to 0.70.

In reinforced plastics (§74) the "finishes" are supposed to avoid formation of weak boundary layers. At least in some instances they seem to enhance the strength of the composites also by augmenting the tensile strength of the polymer matrix. Thus[40] glass fibers were embedded in, and then pulled out of, a polymer film which in one series consisted of a poly(vinyl butyral) 85 and phenol-formaldehyde 15 parts and in the other series, of the same mixture plus 2 parts of, apparently, γ-aminopropyltriethoxysilane $H_2N(CH_2)_3Si$ $(OC_2H_5)_3$; this compound is one of the popular "finishes." The stress needed to extract the fiber was 188 and 255 bars without and with the silicon compound, but the f_M also was raised from 540 to 610 bars.

112 If the magnitudes of f_m and f_M are similar, all adhints made with a definite cement should have comparable breaking stresses independent of the nature of the adherend. This obviously is true for many commercial adhesives because their manufacturers claim (in technical leaflets, not only in advertisements) relatively narrow ranges of strength, e.g., between 2000 and 2500 psi, for their products without specifying the adherends, the geometry of the joints, and so on. Some examples of f_m being almost independent of the adherends in controlled experiments are mentioned in the earlier sections of this monograph, for instance in §§103 and 111. In general, of course, f_m must depend on the mechanical properties of the adherends since these affect the stress distribution in the cement film. See also §44.

An unexpected effect of the adherend is recorded.[41] As in §111, single glass fibers were pulled out of a polymer film. When the glass was "alkali-free" (actually it contained 1.8% sodium oxide), the breaking stress f_m was 172 bars; and when glass containing 15% Na_2O was used instead, this stress was only 112 bars. Strangely enough, this difference persisted also after the fibers were treated with γ-aminopropyltriethoxysilane: the former fibers were extracted by 206 and the latter by 119 bars. The fibers themselves were stronger when the alkali content was smaller.

As long as f_m and f_M are similar, the strength of adhints made with various adhesives should fall in an order independent of the adherends. Thus, joints made with the strongest polyethylene were stronger than those made with the second best, which in their turn were stronger than those made with the weakest polymer, whatever the adherends (stainless steel or glass) (§111). A more extensive comparison is reproduced in Table XV, from reference 42.

A is a poly(vinyl acetate), B a cellulose nitrate, C a resorcinol-formaldehyde resin, D casein, E gum arabic, F smoked sheet rubber, and G Neoprene. The order of strengths is not identical for all adherends but the discrepancies apparently can be accounted for by special circumstances. For instance, casein glue and gum arabic set because of loss of water; this loss is more rapid with

TABLE XV
ORDER OF STRENGTH OF BUTT JOINTS WITH DIFFERENT
ADHERENDS AND ADHESIVES

Adherend	Adhesives
Stainless steel	$A > B > D > F > G > E > C$
Aluminum alloy	$A > B > F > G > D > E > C$
Paper–phenolic laminate	$A > B > C > D > E > G > F$
Glass	$A > B > E > G > F > C > D$
Birch wood	$C > B > D > A > E > G > F$
Hard rubber	$C > B > A > E > G > D > F$

TABLE XVI
EFFECT OF ADHESIVES AND ADHERENDS ON THE BREAKING STRESS

Adhesive	f_m (bars)				f_M (bars)
	Butt adhints			Lap adhints	
	Steel	Copper	Aluminum	Aluminum	
Nylon 6	720	730	660	280	830
66	680	750	670	260	720
48	300	350	280	165	300 (?)
610	530	620	570	210	480
11	390	260	410	180	590
Polyethylene	170	110	170	75	300

porous adherends such as paper–phenolic laminate and birch wood; hence, these two solids gave rise to higher strengths with D and E than some nonporous adherends; in other words, in these systems the order of adhesives was not constant because the adhesive substances were different in contact with different adherends. Also, some adherends were weakened by some adhesives (e.g., paper–phenolic laminate by casein glue). Finally, weak boundary layers evidently were not always avoided; thus adhesive C gave zero strengths with glass and metals both in butt and in double lap joints.

Table XVI records[4] breaking stress data for six adhesives and three adherends. Invariably, Nylon 6 and Nylon 66 were the strongest, either in bulk or *in situ;* Nylons 610 and 11 were in the middle, and polyethylene was weaker than any of the nylons. The effect of the adherend, generally, was not conspicuous.

Effect of the Adhesive Composition

§**113**   When a new adhesive is being formulated in industry, the composition is varied until the desired (or a compromise) strength is attained. Thus, the relation between the composition of a cement and the strength of adhints made with this cement has been and is being studied in numerous laboratories on numberless systems. Some of the results thus obtained are deposited in patents, and a small percentage finds its way into scientific and technical literature. Unfortunately, even this selected minority of abundant research reports too often has no value for the science of adhesive joints. This is so because the materials used for the formulation in too many instances are poorly characterized and, perhaps, do not exist anymore since their manufacture was discontinued; and because the tests were conducted without any theory or with the guidance by a wrong theory, which means that the experimenter did not know what parameters should be controlled to obtain results of general validity.

A logical way of studying the relation between composition and strength would be

(a) to map the regions of composition in which proper and improper adhints are obtained (§110);

(b) in proper adhints—to investigate the relation between the composition of a material and its tensile or shear strength f_M; to compare this f_M with the strength f_m of adhints; to find out what combination of the parameters α, β, and s, Eq. (149), caused the difference between f_M and f_m (see §111); and

(c) in improper adhints—to study the relation between the nature of an adhesive and its tendency to form a weak boundary layer of class 1, class 2, class 4, class 6, or class 7 (§67).

§114   Only a few of the attempts to establish empirical relations between glue composition and adhint strength, without any regard to either f_M or weak boundary layers, can be outlined here.

In butt joints, rupture stress of poly(vinyl acetate) fractions between steel cylinders increased[15] with the molecular weight (M.W.) of the fraction as long as this was 150,000 or less, but there was no significant difference between the strengths of adhints made with polymers of M.W. = 147,000 and M.W. = 225,000; at the thickness of the cement film equal to 25 μ, breaking stress was about 228, 393, and 490 bars (3300, 5700, and 7100 psi) for the average molecular weights of 54,000, 77,000, and above 140,000.[43] This presumably was the effect of the tensile strength of the adhesive since this also in many instances increases with M.W. to a limiting value.

Other examples of butt joints are more complicated. The basis faces of two aluminum cylinders[43] were coated with a 10% solution of a copolymer of polystyrene ($100 - x$ parts) with acrylic acid (x parts) in a solvent, dried at 80°C so that coatings approximately 50 μ thick remained on each face, pressed together, and heated for 15 to 20 min at 180°C. Then the breaking stress f_m of the adhints was measured. When benzene was the solvent, f_m was about 80 bars for polystyrene alone, 320 bars at $x = 1$, and 210 bars at $x = 3$. Thus, the conclusion could be reached that in the copolymer series studied the maximum of "adhesiveness" is achieved near $x = 1$. But the results were strikingly different when 2,4-pentadione was used as the solvent. In this instance, f_m remained between 290 and

320 bars at all values of x between 2 and 24. Methyl ethyl ketone, pyridine, and ethyl acetate, as solvents, took up intermediate positions between 2,4-pentadione and benzene. The reason for this solvent effect is not known but it may have been trivial. Suppose that, as often happens, the tensile strength of the copolymer increases with x; then, for proper joints, f_m also is likely to increase with x. This, of course, presupposes a healthy joint. If the consistency of the copolymer at 180°C also increases with x (a very reasonable assumption), the constant duration of heating may be sufficient to eliminate air bubbles at low values of x but insufficient at $x > 1$; this would account for the maximum of f_m at $x = 1$ in the instance of benzene solutions. When a higher boiling solvent (or one which more slowly evaporates from the copolymer) is employed, the adhesive film after drying at 80° may still contain enough solvent to act as a plasticizer; thus the consistency of the cement at 180° is lower and elimination of gas bubbles is achieved also at $x > 1$. As long as this or a similar possibility is not shown to be absent, the meaning of the experiments is doubtful.

Another example[44] concerns lap joints between clad aluminum strips, the adhesives being a series of epoxy resins cured with phthalic anhydride. The exact structure of the cured adhesive naturally was not known, but the series contained, for one epoxy group, 0.85 molecule of anhydride and $n[-O \cdot C_6H_4 \cdot C(CH_3)_2 \cdot C_6H_4 \cdot O \cdot CH_2 \cdot CHOH \cdot CH_2-]$ groups, and n covered the range between 0.05 and 5. Rupture stress of the adhints was 151 to 159 bars (2191 to 2313 psi) as long as n was greater than, say, 1.5, but at $n < 0.5$ it was 118 to 124 bars (1708 to 1794 psi). As shear strength of cured epoxy resins usually increases with n, the above observation can simply be accounted for as another example of the common parallelism between f_m and f_M (see §111). If we wish to emphasize the effect of composition, we may state that f_m increases with the molecular weight of the resin, or with the number of hydroxyl groups in it, or with the number of isopropylidene groups $[:C(CH_3)_2]$, or decreases on an increase in the number of benzene rings; many such correlations are possible. Hence, the correlation between f_m and the volume density of OH groups, preferred by the experimenter, does not appear convincing.

§115   Three examples may be mentioned for peeling.

Two polymers, one containing 85% vinyl chloride and 15% vinyl acetate, and the other consisting of 85% vinyl chloride, 9.3% vinyl acetate, and 5.7% maleic acid, were mixed in various proportions, plasticized with a nonspecified mixture of plasticizers and used to coat sheets of regenerated cellulose containing 16% glycerol; then two coated strips were heat sealed together, kept at 35% relative humidity for 24 hr, and peeled apart.[45] As long as the ratio of the two polymers was greater than 96:4 (i.e., the concentration of maleic acid was less than 0.342%), peeling force increased with the percentage of maleic acid; e.g., at 10°, peeling tension Γ was approximately 18, 49, and 78 kilodynes/cm when this percentage was 0.03%, 0.09%, and 0.34%, respectively. It was concluded that "adhesion" increased with the concentration of free acid according to a kind of Freundlich's adsorption isotherm. Regrettably, the acidity of the film was not measured. Maleic anhydride would react, for instance, with glycerol and form esters; in this case, vinyl acetate would be supplanted by maleic acid esters rather than by free acid, i.e., the comparison would be between two different esters. As none of the quantities needed to calculate Γ was ascertained (see §§92–95), it is impossible to decide where the rupture occurred. However, the low values of the peeling tension would better agree with the existence of a weak boundary layer.

That chemical activity, contrary to the authors' view, was not important, can be concluded from some later measurements.[46] When, in copolymers, the mole fraction of methyl vinyl ketone was increased at the expense of either styrene or vinyl acetate, the improvement in peeling resistance was very similar; from the viewpoint of the chemical theory of adhesion (§60.2), substitution of a ketone for a hydrocarbon should greatly enhance the adhesion to cellulose but substitution of a ketone for an ester is more likely to lower this adhesion.

A system in which stripping force, again with Cellophane, was smaller the greater the percentage of "chemically active" groups was found in copolymers of butadiene and acrylonitrile.[47] The Cellophane was not plasticized. It was coated with a copolymer solution in which a percale fabric was embedded (see §107), and the fabric was stripped off after the evaporation of the solvent. The peeling tension (kilodynes per centimeter width) was about 1600, 1400, and 130 when the percentage of acrylonitrile was 18.4%, 28.6%, and 37.7%, respectively. The visible character of rupture also varied with the nitrile content. The first adhesive (i.e., that containing 18.4% CH_2:CHCN) broke clearly in cohesion, the second was severed partly in the middle and partly near a boundary of the cement film, and the third ruptured only near a boundary. The difference could have been accounted for by a shift of the dangerous stress concentration from the center to the boundary, as happened, for instance, when the brittleness of the adhesive increased (§§95 and 96). However, the value of 130 kilodynes/cm seems to be too small to be explained by stress concentrations; presumably, a weak boundary layer was present. The presence of such a layer is even more probable in the system of Cellophane and a copolymer of butadiene 1 + styrene 1 which broke near the interface at the peeling tension of 14 kilodynes/cm, while another copolymer containing 2.3 parts butadiene for 1 part of styrene required over 1300 kilodynes/cm.

Finally, a study may be mentioned in which a weak boundary layer was deliberately although unwittingly produced.[48] Polymer films were cast on, and then peeled off, glass plates previously equilibrated with saturated water vapor; thus, a water-rich zone initially existed between the glass and the polymer. However, the polymer was applied as a solution (in an organic solvent) and solvent was removed by evaporation before the peeling test; thus it is not known how much, if any, water was still present on the glass surface during the stripping. The experimental values for peeling tension were, for instance, benzyl cellulose 72, cellulose nitrate 59, ethyl cellulose 24, and cellulose acetate 13 kilodynes/cm. The significance of this series, even assuming that it is reproducible, is obscure.

Rate of Loading and of Rupture

§116   The effect of rate of loading on the strength of adhints would be expected to be determined above all by the influence of this rate on the tensile or shear strength or plasticity of the adhesive (or, in improper joints, of the weak boundary layer). Apparently, no systematic comparison between the adhint strength f_m and the adhesive strength f_M at different rates of loading has ever been carried out. An analogous remark may be made concerning the length of time during which a given adhint or a given bulk specimen can support a definite load; or the rate of stripping (in an adhint or in a bulk adhesive) in its dependence on stripping force.

Probably the rate of loading, i.e., dF/dt, F being the external force and t being time, is less important than the strain rate, i.e., $dh/h_0 \, dt$ (h_0 is the initial, and h the variable thickness of the adhesive film); this problem has been considered in §104.

Both dF/dt and $dh/h_0 \, dt$ were measured[9] for butt joints "steel cylinder–guttapercha–copper cylinder." The h_0 of the gum interlayer was 200 to 300 μ. The adherends were moved apart along their common axis at a constant rate, and the dynamometer reading and the distance h were photographed 3000 to 8000 times a second. The force acting on the dynamometer increased rapidly during the first 0.002 sec, rose very little from 0.002 to 0.005 sec, and dropped to zero within 0.003 sec. The increase of h was almost linear between 0.0015 and 0.004 sec. Unfortunately, the maximum stress observed in these experiments (about 600 bars) was not compared with f_m valid for slower rupture.

Such a comparison was performed in two later and simultaneous studies, still on butt joints. Two steel rods were glued together with an epoxy resin hardened by aromatic amines, and then ruptured in tension.[49] At $-54°$, f_m was near 1450 bars when the fracture was accomplished in 0.01 sec and remained almost constant (about 1000 bars) when the time (t_m) was above 0.2 sec. At $23°$, f_m was 1100 bars at $t_m = 0.01$ sec and approximately 760 bars at all $t_m > 0.2$ sec. At $94°$, f_m was 690 bars and 520 bars at $t_m = 0.01$ sec and $t_m > 0.2$ sec, respectively. Thus f_m for a rapid rupture was about 1.4 times the f_m at a slow separation, whatever the temperature.

The behavior was more complex when "copper–epoxy–copper" adhints were investigated.[50] They were cured at $110°$ and cooled slowly to dissipate frozen stresses as far as possible. Then they were loaded to achieve a stress f_m, and kept under a constant load until fracture (t_m sec after the load application). At 25°, f_m was 253 bars at $t_m = 20{,}000$ sec and 299 bars at $t_m = 50$ sec; and at 75°, the pairs $f_m = 155$ bars, $t_m = 2800$ sec and $f_m = 176$ bars, $t_m = 15$ sec were recorded. Thus, the time of rupture was affected by the external load also at times at which practically no effect was noticeable in the data of the preceding paragraph. It was possible to express t_m as

$$t_m = t_0 \, e^{-\alpha F_m} \tag{155}$$

t_0 and α being two constants. See also §119.

With the value of α derived from the measurements of reference 50 an increase of the rate of separation at 25° in the ratio 80:1 would raise f_m by about 6%. An increase of 15% was observed[15] in the rupture of butt joints of poly(vinyl acetate) between two steel cylinders.

When rate of loading cross-lap joints was doubled,[51] breaking stress of a rubbery cement was little affected but that of two brittle adhesives increased in ratios ranging from 1.06 to 1.14. For single lap joints of a vinyl-phenolic adhesive the time before failure increased, for instance, in the ratio 250:1 when stress in the adhesive decreased from 240 to 180 bars.[52]

§117   The effect of peeling tension on the rate of peeling is easy to determine. A few of the many published examples are reproduced here.

Figure 131 refers[53] to peeling of a 38-μ thick aluminum ribbon attached to a glass reinforced laminate with an epoxy resin cross-linked with diethylenetriamine. The ordinate shows peeling tension in gram-weight per inch (multiply with 0.386 to obtain it in kilodynes per centimeter) on the logarithmic scale, and rate of stripping (in inches per minute, multiply with 0.042 to express it in centimeters per second) is plotted, again logarithmically, along the abscissa. The curves show the slight effect of surface treatment (solvent cleaned and chemically cleaned) and also the effect of the angle of peel (see §98). As far as the rate is concerned, it is clear

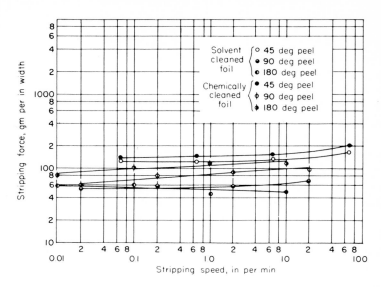

FIG. 131. Peeling force and peeling rate. Abscissa: log of rate of stripping, in inches per minute. Ordinate: log of peeling tension (gm wt./in.). From reference 53.

that its influence was small; when rate u increased in the ratio 1000:1, peeling tension rose only in a ratio 1.2:1 or a similar ratio.

Another example of peeling tension being almost independent of rate u is shown in Fig. 132 which presumably refers to splitting a weak boundary layer[48] (see §115). The ordinate is log (F_m/w) (i.e., of peeling tension in dynes per centimeter) and the abscissa is log u in centimeters per second. A cellulose acetate film was peeled off glass. Numbers 1, 2, and 3 indicate three sections of the curve which are said to correspond to different stripping mechanisms. It is seen that increase of u in the enormous ratio of $10^8:1$ caused an increase of F_m/w in a ratio of about 5:1.

Results of clearly cohesive failures in the cement film are summarized[25] in Fig. 133. Two pieces of a fabric, 1.5 in. wide, were impregnated with a rubber cement, pressed together, and then pulled apart at a peel angle of 180°. Peeling force in lb wt (multiply with 117 to obtain peeling tension in kilodynes per centimeter) is plotted along the abscissa, while the speed of stripping in inches per minute (multiply with 0.042 to have it in centimeters per second) is shown

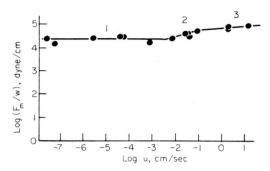

FIG. 132. Peeling force and peeling rate. Abscissa: log of rate of stripping, in centimeters per second. Ordinate: log of peeling tension (dynes/cm). From reference 48.

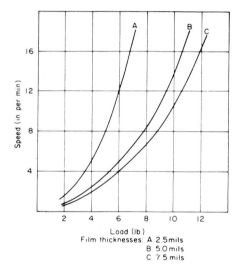

FIG. 133. Peeling force and peeling rate. Abscissa: peeling force (lb wt.), for three different film thicknesses. Ordinate: rate of stripping (in./min).

on the ordinate. Curves A, B, and C are for film thicknesses of 0.0063, 0.013, and 0.019 cm, respectively. For additional data on the rate of peeling see §§43 and 98.

In splitting (see Fig. 111 of §99), the "γ" was[54] a definite function of the crack velocity dl/dt, independent of the exact composition of the epoxy system used and the conditions of cure. It was also almost independent (and equal to $5.3-7.0 \times 10^4$ ergs/cm²) of dl/dt as long as this varied between 0.3 and about 150 cm/sec but increased with dl/dt at higher speeds when dl/dt was overtaking the advance of the cross-head; thus "γ" was 9.5×10^4, 13×10^4, and 24×10^4 ergs/cm² at dl/dt equal to 450, 1050, and 1800 cm/sec. The rate dependence of "γ" is another argument against its identification with the surface energy of the solid adhesive.

In several instances, rate of stripping affected not only peeling tension but also the type of rupture. Thus[25] some rubber-based adhesives broke clearly in the cement film when u was small (e.g., 0.1 cm/sec) but parting occurred near the interface when u was great (e.g., 2 cm/sec); and the magnitude of u at which the transition from clearly cohesive to apparently adhesive failure took place, was less the greater the degree of vulcanization of the rubber.

Also when adhints of "percale fabric — a copolymer of butadiene and acrylonitrile — chrome tanned gelatin"[27] were peeled apart, ruptures far from the interface occurred only at the smallest rate tested (0.083 cm/sec) while at all higher rates (0.17 to 0.30 cm/sec) separation at the interface was observed.

The dependence of the type of rupture on stripping rate might be caused by the maximum strain effect outlined in §96. The curvature of the ribbon at the "knee" as a rule will be greater (i.e., the radius of curvature will be smaller) on increasing rate u. Thus the strain in the ribbon at the boundary with adhesive also will increase with u; as soon as this strain exceeds the total relative elongation of the adhesive, this will crack near the boundary thus simulating an interfacial failure.

§118   An adhint can be broken by repeated application of a load too weak to cause instantaneous rupture. Only one example of this effect can be described here. Two strips, 1.5 mm thick, of an Al-Cu-Mg alloy were used to make either single lap or scarf joints with, apparently, an epoxy adhesive. Then tension was applied to them about 2000 times a minute, the stress varying each time between zero and a maximum value f. The magnitude of f (in kg wt./mm², multiply

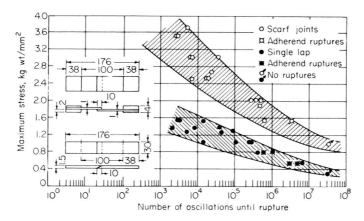

FIG. 134. Fatigue of an adhint. Abscissa: number of pulls before rupture. Ordinate: maximum value of pull (kg wt./mm²). Upper range: scarf joints. Lower range: single lap joints. From reference 3.

with 98.1 to express it in bars) is shown on the ordinate of Fig. 134; its abscissa means the number of pulls before the cement or a metal strip broke down; the metal failures are marked with four-ray stars, and circles with arrows mean that the test was stopped before any fracture took place. The upper range of values refers to scarf joints, and it is seen that they are much stronger than single lap joints (the lower range) for all stresses tested. The highest stress applied to scarf joints was about one-half the tensile strength of the adhesive.[3] For reports on analogous experiments see references 23 and 51.

Effect of Temperature

119   The effect of the test temperature T on the breaking stress f_m may be expected to be determined above all by a transformation proper ⇋ improper adhint (see §110). Suppose, for instance, that the adhesive contains an impurity which is insoluble in the bulk of the adhesive material at lower, and soluble at higher temperatures. A weak boundary layer will be present and f_m will be small below some temperature T_w and f_m will be high above T_w; at much higher temperatures f_m will be smaller again as the tensile strength of polymers generally decreases when T increases above the glass transition range T_g. Consequently, a maximum of f_m would be noticed in these adhints.

An instance of the above-indicated behavior was, perhaps, observed in peeling films of poly(n-butyl methacrylate) from a steel plate, at an indefinite angle of peel.[55] The film was deposited from a solution. When the solvent was removed by baking at 100° for 1 hr, the peeling tension Γ had a shallow maximum near 60°. When the temperature of the baking was 150°, still for 1 hr, then Γ monotonously decreased between about 45° (2700 kilodynes/cm) and 100° (350 kilodynes/cm). The low-molecular-weight compounds not removed at 100° may have formed partial weak boundary layers at temperatures below 60°.

When the adhints remain proper in the whole temperature range explored, a maximum of f_m may result because of the opposite effect of temperature on ξ/β and s in Eq. (149), §100. The ratio ξ/β is approximately equal to the tensile strength f_M of the adhesive and usually decreases when T increases. On the other hand, the shrinkage stress is lowered by a higher T whenever the thermal expansion coefficient of the adhesive is greater than that of the adherend; e.g., the "frozen" stress of a cellulose nitrate film on a metal (?) strip decreased[56] from 100 bars at 20° to 40 bars at 100° and was reversible with T. As f_m is proportional to $(\xi/\beta) - s$, it ought to increase in the temperature range in which ξ/β is still almost constant but s decreases on a temperature increase, and to decrease when s is small and ξ/β is less the higher the temperature.

Experimentally, curves of $f_m = f(T)$ with a maximum and a minimum have been obtained. Thus, a surgical tape was peeled at a 180° angle from various metal surfaces at various temperatures.[57] The peeling tension Γ decreased, for instance, from 350 kilodynes/cm at 20° to 150 kilodynes/cm at 45°, rose to 300 at 52° and was 20 kilodynes/cm at 75°. Similar curves were presented[58] for Γ of polybutadiene deposited from a solvent on copper or aluminum. The effect seems to be specific for a few systems; for instance, polyisobutylene, deposited and peeled in the same manner as the polybutadiene, exhibited only a shallow maximum of Γ at about 20°. Of two butadiene–acrylonitrile copolymers, one had a shallow maximum of Γ and the other manifested a maximum and a minimum. It is not clear how much these phenomena were influenced by formation and dissolution of weak boundary layers.

In proper adhints, a maximum of f_m sometimes is seen in the neighborhood of T_g. Thus,[19] adhints (apparently, butt joints) of "glass–BF–glass," in which BF was a mixture of phenol–formaldehyde and poly(vinyl butyral), had highest f_m at about 60° while the adhesive material alone had a T_g near 69°. The f_m of lap joints "aluminum–an alkyd + epoxy polymer–aluminum" was,[59] e.g., 100 bars at −40°, 200 bars at 20–25°, and 80 bars at 60°. The T_g of this polymer was near 0°–5°, i.e., about 20° below the temperature of the highest f_m. Another polymer of the same type had T_g near 30°. When it was used as an adhesive, the f_m was 180, 330, and 190 bars at −40°, +20° to 25°, and 60°, respectively; here f_m passed through a maximum at a temperature about 10° below T_g. It is not known whether these changes are examples of the temperature sensitivity of the term $[(\xi/\beta) - s]$.

In many other studies only a decrease of f_m with rising temperature was recorded. For instance, the time t_m needed to rupture a "steel–polyethylene–steel" adhint by a tensile stress of 118 bars was[60] over 1000 sec at 24° and only 2 sec at 77°. In this temperature range it was possible to express t_m as

$$t_m = t^* \, e^{U/RT} \qquad (156)$$

t^* and U being empirical constants, R the gas constant, and T the absolute temperature. Without much justification, U was termed the "activation energy per gram-molecule"; it was, for instance, 36 kcal; that is, the temperature coefficient of t_m was similar to those observed in breaking unattached plastic specimens. In a later work[50] on an epoxy adhesive two different values of U were obtained, namely 40 kcal between 20° and 40° and 60 kcal between 70° and 80°. It was suggested that this higher value was caused by the fact that the glass transition range of the polymer included the interval 70°–80°.

The equation

$$f_m = f_0 e^{E/RT} \tag{157}$$

was repeatedly proposed for the effect of temperature on f_m; f_0 and E are constants. For an epoxy adhesive, E was 0.81 kcal for rapid, and 1.1 kcal for a slow supture.[49] Obviously, Eqs. (156) and (157) can have only narrow validity ranges: mathematically, t^* and f_0 are the time and the stress required for rupture at very high temperatures; and these time and stress, physically, are zero.

As in the measurements on unattached polymer samples, it is more instructive to treat temperature effects together with those of the rate of testing (see §116).

§120   A few of the random observations reported in the literature are recorded here.

Butt and lap joints between copper adherends were made with a mixture of an epoxy-amine adhesive (9 parts) and alumina and asbestos filler (11 parts). The strength of the butt joints was about 500 bars between 20°K ($= -253$°C) and 300°K ($= 27$°C) but the lap joints broke at about 70 bars at 20° and 70°K and at about 250 bars at 300°K.[22]

Single lap joints between 1-mm thick strips of an Al-Cu-Mg alloy; a commercial adhesive apparently of the epoxy type. Strength was constant (220–260 bars) between -40° and 70°C but decreased to about 100 bars at 100° and 20 bars at 150°.[3]

Again single lap joints between aluminum alloy (7178-T6 clad) strips; ratio of overlap length to bar thickness 30, a vinyl-phenolic adhesive. Breaking stress was highest between 40° and 60°C; at -75° it was 0.5 to 0.9 of the maximum value; and at 200° it sank to about 0.1 of it.[52]

Single lap joints, aluminum alloy 24T-3 clad, a phenol-epoxy adhesive. Shear strength at 27° was about 120 bars and at 260° only about 40 bars, although at least one modification of the cement improved its heat resistance.[61]

There are conflicting data on the temperature coefficient of the strength of adhints in which ice is the adhesive.[37,62,63]

Some adhints broke clearly in cohesion when temperature was high and near the interface when it was low (see §117). This was noticed, for instance, in peeling leather attached to another leather strip with a rubber cement[64]; in this system the "low" temperature was $-20°$ and the "high," $+50°C$.

It is possible by special experiments to determine whether ξ or s determines the temperature dependence of adhint strength. An adhesive containing phenol-formaldehyde and vinyl butyral was employed in these tests.[65] When aluminum–aluminum and steel–steel joints were heated and then broken at room temperature, the loss in strength was less for the former than for the latter systems; this presumably was caused by the difference in thermal stresses because the difference between the coefficients of heat expansion of adhesive and aluminum was less than that between adhesive and steel. When the joints were strongly cooled for a while and then broken at room temperature, the decrease in their rupture stress was smaller than after a temperature increase of a comparable magnitude; apparently, the deleterious effect of temporary heating included also a chemical change resulting in a lower value of ξ (see §73), while cooling was not associated with a chemical reaction.

Effect of Environment

121   Environment can cause formation or disappearance of weak boundary layers. With reference to Eq. (149), §100, it can affect the ratio ξ/β of the adherend or the adhesive, or change the stress concentration factor α, or enhance or reduce the internal stress s.

An example of the growth of a weak boundary layer in an unfavorable atmosphere was outlined in §73. Water seems to be able to form such layers in many systems. Plates of "alkali-free" glass were coated with an epoxy resin and, after curing, exposed[66] to hot water in three different manners. (a) A column of water was placed on the central part of the coating only. (b) Only the edge of the coating was in contact with water. (c) The coated plate was completely submerged. In the arrangement (a), there was no effect for about 2 months. In both arrangements (b) and (c), the coating became loose in 3 hr or less. Also in some unpublished work of the present author on polymer coatings on copper and brass it was observed that protection of the edges greatly lengthened the life of the coating in boiling water. It appears, consequently, that water migrates along the adhesive–adherend interface starting from the boundary of the latter with liquid water.

Probably, this migration is facilitated by the swelling of the two solids in contact, such as glass and cured epoxy resin. Swelling pressure would act as a wedge opening the crack. Without this mechanical effect, the ordinary diffusion of water molecules along the interface probably would be too slow. Volume changes associated with a chemical reaction may have accelerated also the advance of oxygen along the metal–adhesive interface mentioned in §73. When the adherends are electric conductors, weakening of adhints in water or humid air may be caused by electric currents between different points on the adherend surface, §9. As no investigation of the actual mechanism of this weakening seems to have been published, only a selection of bare facts can be presented here.

When lap joints between plates of aluminum alloys, cured epoxy resin being the adhesive, were immersed in distilled water for about a year, the final strength was 10–25% of the initial if the alloy contained copper (and magnesium) but about 40% of the initial strength was retained if magnesium and silicon were the main alloying elements.[23] In some instances corrosion of the copper alloy was discernible under the adhesive film. The gradual formation of a weak boundary layer was noticeable also in that fresh adhints failed clearly in cohesion while aged specimens broke near an interface.

Presumably, weak boundary layers formed also when steel coated with a fluorine-containing polymer was exposed to a humid atmosphere.[67] The coating was 150 μ thick, and its edges were protected. Nevertheless, the effect of 95% relative humidity (RH) was striking. When the film was peeled off by a tension $\Gamma = 128$ kilodynes/cm, the rate of peeling in dry air was less than 0.001 cm/sec and slightly decreased on aging, while it was over 1 cm/sec after 200 hr at the high RH. The conditions of coating were not varied in these experiments. In the author's unpublished tests, it was possible to attach a copolymer of tetrafluoroethylene and hexafluoropropylene to copper by heating so well that no loosening occurred in a very humid environment.

When an adhint after conditioning at 95% RH was kept in dry air, its Γ did not increase.[67] A recovery of adherence after humidifying and drying at room temperature was noticed for another polymer containing fluorine; the glass transition range of this substance was below, and that of the former coating was above, room temperature. Complete healing took place when adhints "granite plate–asphalt–aluminum foil" were prepared under water and then kept in laboratory air at 25°. The peeling rate at $\Gamma = 123$ kilodynes/ cm was immeasurably high after 1 hr of aging, about 0.05 cm/sec after 5 hr, and about 0.008 cm/sec after 25 hr.[68] The drying of marble appeared to take more time than drying of granite.

Formation of weak boundary layers may be facilitated by prestressing the adhint; this effect, it is true, has been studied[69] on systems which cannot qualify as adhesive joints. When a fabric of glass fibers is embedded in a polymeric substance (a polyester or a cured epoxy resin) and then stretched, the stress–strain curve exhibits a "knee"; at stresses below the kink the modulus of elasticity is greater than at higher stresses. Apparently the system (called a laminate) behaves as one material in the first and as two materials in the second region, and the matrix ceases to follow the deformation of the fabric when stresses increase beyond the "knee." The cracks thus produced near the glass–polymer interface cause a kink also in the curve representing water uptake as a function of prestressing. When, for instance, the direction change in the stress–strain curve occurred between 0.5 and 0.6 f_M, f_M being the ultimate tensile strength of the laminate, then laminates prestressed to 0.4f_M and then immersed in water (in the unstressed state) for several weeks took up as little water as the specimens never subjected to a deliberate stress; but when the stress before immersion amounted to 0.7f_M, water uptake was almost twice that of never stressed samples.

Moisture often affects the magnitude of the residual stress s. When wood swells at 80% RH and then shrinks at 30% RH, the stresses thus produced weaken the block shear and other specimens, and it is advisable to use flexible, almost rubbery, adhesives to prevent cracking.[70] Shrinkage stresses in a surface of a glass plate on which a triethyleneglycol ester of methacrylic acid was polymerized at 80° increased[71] for several hours after cooling and then slowly decreased for several weeks. However, no decrease was noticed when aging took place in a desiccator loaded with sulfuric acid; apparently, water vapor or rather occluded water acted as a plasticizer.

The effect of water on ξ/β can be spectacular. No adhint in which sugar cubes are the adherends and no adhint in which sucrose is the adhesive is likely to survive a protracted immersion in water.

REFERENCES

1. Bikerman, J. J., and Huang, C.-R., *Trans. Soc. Rheol.* **3**, 5 (1959).
2. Bikerman, J. J., *J. Appl. Polymer Sci.* **2**, 216 (1959).
3. Winter, H., and Krause, G., *Aluminium* **33**, 669 (1957).
4. Lewis, A. F., and Tanner, G. A., *J. Appl. Polymer Sci.* **6**, S 35 (1962).
5. Shiryaeva, G. V., Gorbatkina, Yu. A., and Andreevskaya, G. D., *Zh. Fiz. Khim.* **37**, 237 (1963).
6. Rieke, J. K., Hart, G. M., and Saunders, F. L., *J. Polymer Sci.* **C4**, 589 (1964).
7. Bryant, R. W., and Dukes, W. A., *Appl. Polymer Symp. No.* **3**, 81 (1966).
8. Stanger, A. G., and Blomquist, R. F., *Forest Prod. J.* **15**, 468 (1965).
9. Krotova, N. A., Morozova, L. P., and Sokolina, G. A., *Dokl. Akad. Nauk SSSR* **127**, 302 (1959).
10. Crow, T. B., *J. Soc. Chem. Ind. (London)* **43**, 65 T (1924).
11. McBain, J. W., and Lee, W. B., *J. Phys. Chem.* **31**, 1674 (1927).
12. Konstantinova, W. P., *Acta Physicochim. URSS* **1**, 286 (1934).
13. Bikerman, J. J., *J. Soc. Chem. Ind. (London)* **60**, 23 (1941).
14. Baldauf, G. H., Thesis, M. I. T. (1949); Meissner, H. P., and Baldauf, G. H., *Trans. ASME* **73**, 697 (1951).
15. Lasoski, S. W., and Kraus, G., *J. Polymer Sci.* **18**, 359 (1955).
16. Bikerman, J. J., and Marshall, D. W., *J. Appl. Polymer Sci.* **7**, 1031 (1963).
17. Koehn, G. W., *in* "Adhesion and Adhesives. Fundamentals and Practice," p. 120. Wiley, New York, 1954.
18. Bredzs, N., *Welding J.* **33**, 545-s (1954).
19. Malinskii, Yu. M., Prokopenko, V. V., and Kargin, V. A., *Vysokomolekul. Soedin.* **6**, 1832 (1964).
20. Tarkow, H., *J. Appl. Polymer Sci.* **4**, 343 (1960).
21. Moffatt, W. G., and Wulff, J., *J. Metals* **1957**, 442.
22. McClintock, R. M., and Hiza, M. J., *Mod. Plastics* **35**, No. 10, 172 (1958).
23. Wellinger, K., and Rembold, U., *VDI Zeitschrift* **100**, 41 (1958).

24. Winter, H., *Z. Flugwiss.* **3,** 87 (1955).
25. Hammond, G. L., and Moakes, R. C. W., *Trans. Inst. Rubber Ind.* **25,** 172 (1949).
26. Raevskii, V. G., Voyutskii, S. S., Livanova, I. V., and Shteinberg, Z. D., *Rubber Chem. Technol.* **35,** 1041 (1962).
27. Shapovalova, A. I., Voyutskii, S. S., and Pisarenko, A. P., *Kolloid. Zh.* **18,** 485 (1956).
28. Gardon, J. L., *J. Appl. Polymer Sci.* **7,** 625 (1963).
29. Ripling, E. J., Mostovoy, S., and Patrick, R. L., *Am. Soc. Testing Mater., Spec. Tech. Publ.* No. **360,** 5 (1964).
30. Muchnik, S. N., *Mech. Eng.* **78,** 19 (1956).
31. Kuenzi, E. W., and Stevens, G. H., *U.S. Dept. Agr., Forest Serv., Forest Prod. Lab.* No. **011** (1963).
32. Krueger, G. P., *Mater. Res. & Std.* **2,** 479 (1962).
33. Norris, C. B., James, W. L., and Drow, J. T., *ASTM Bull.* **218,** 40 (1956).
34. Dietz, A. G. H., Closmann, P. J., Kavanagh, G. M., and Rossen, J. N., *Am. Soc. Testing Mater., Proc.* **50,** 1414 (1950).
35. Lipatov, Yu. S., *Vysokomolekul. Soedin.* **5,** 290 (1963); *Plastics Inst. (London), Trans. J.* **1966,** 83.
36. Gribkova, N. Ya., Kozlov, P. V., and Yakubovich, S. V., *Polymer Sci. (USSR) (English Transl.)* **7,** 831 (1964).
37. Kobeko, P. P., and Marei, F. I., *Zh. Tekhn. Fiz.* **16,** 277 (1946).
38. Nightingale, S. J., "Tin Solders." Brit. Non-Ferrous Metals Res. Assoc., London, 1932.
39. Lewis, A. F., and Ramsey, W. B., *Adhesives Age* **9,** No. 2, 20 (1966).
40. Gorbatkina, Yu. A., Guseva, N. B., Andreevskaya, G. D., and Galakhova, G. S., *Polymer Sci. (USSR) (English Transl.)* **6,** 2118 (1964).
41. Andreevskaya, G. D., and Shiryaeva, G. V., *Polymer Sci. (USSR) (English Transl.)* **8,** 854 (1963).
42. DeLollis, N. J., Rucker, N., and Wier, J. E., *Trans. ASME* **73,** 183 (1951).
43. Jenckel, E., and Huhn, H., *Kolloid-Z.* **159,** 118 (1958).
44. DeBruyne, N. A., *J. Appl. Chem.* **6,** 303 (1956).
45. Hofrichter, C. H., and McLaren, A. D., *Ind. Eng. Chem.* **40,** 329 (1948).
46. McLaren, A. D., and Seiler, C. J., *J. Polymer Sci.* **4,** 63 (1949).
47. Voyutskii, S. S., Shapovalova, A. I., and Pisarenko, A. P., *Kolloid. Zh.* **19,** 274 (1957).
48. Krotova, N. A., Kirillova, Yu. M., and Deryagin, B. V., *Zh. Fiz. Khim.* **30,** 1921 (1956).
49. Wegman, R. F., and O'Brien, E. L., *J. Appl. Polymer Sci.* **10,** 291 (1966).
50. Sanzharovskii, A. T., Dyl'kov, M. S., and Evminov, S. S., *Dokl. Akad. Nauk SSSR* **170,** 629 (1966).
51. Moser, F., and Knoell, S. S., *ASTM Bull.* **227,** 60 (1958).
52. Sheridan, M. L., and Merriman, H. R., *Am. Soc. Testing Mater., Spec. Tech. Publ.* No. **201,** 33 (1957).

53. Snoddon, W. J., *Am. Soc. Testing Mater., Spec. Tech. Publ.* No. **201,** 73 (1957).
54. Mostovoy, S., and Ripling, E. J., *J. Appl. Polymer Sci.* **10,** 1351 (1966).
55. Huntsberger, J. R., *J. Polymer Sci.* **A1,** 2241 (1963).
56. Grozinskaya, Z. P., Sanzharovskii, A. T., and Zubov, P. I., *Vysokomolekul. Soedin., Adgeziya Polimerov, Sb. Statei* **1963,** 35.
57. Bright, W. M., *in* "Adhesion and Adhesives. Fundamentals and Practice," p. 13υ. Wiley, New York, 1954.
58. Voyutskii, S. S., Markin, Yu. I., Gorchakova, V. M., and Gul, V. E., *Zh. Fiz. Khim.* **37,** 2027 (1963); *Adhesives Age* **8,** No. 11, 24 (1965).
59. Ward, R. J., and Bobalek, E. G., *Ind. Eng. Chem., Prod. Res. Develop.* **2,** 85 (1963).
60. Dyl'kov, M. S., Sanzharovskii, A. T., and Zubov, P. I., *Dokl. Akad. Nauk SSSR* **155,** 389 (1964).
61. Black, J. M., and Blomquist, R. F., *Adhesives Age* **2,** No. 6, 27 (1959).
62. Raraty, L. E., and Tabor, D., *Proc. Roy. Soc. (London)* **A245,** 184 (1958).
63. Lachs, H., Quatinetz, M., and Freiberger, A., *ASTM Bull.* **224,** 48 (1957).
64. Krotova, N. A., *Kauchuk i Rezina* **1940,** No. 8, 28.
65. Dietz, A. G. H., Bockstruck, H. N., and Epstein, G., *Am. Soc. Testing Mater., Spec. Tech. Publ.* No. **138,** 40 (1952).
66. Laird, J. A., and Nelson, F. W., *SPE Trans.* **4,** 120 (1964).
67. Lobanov, Yu. E., *Vysokomolekul. Soedin., Adgeziya Polimerov, Sb. Statei* **1963,** 79.
68. Bikerman, J. J., *J. Mater.* **1,** 34 (1966).
69. Desai, M. B., and McGarry, F. J., *ASTM Bull.* **239,** 76 (1959).
70. Krueger, G. P., and Blomquist, R. F., *U.S. Dept. Agr., Forest Serv. Res. Note* FPL-076 (1964).
71. Zubov, P. I., Sukhareva, L. A., and Smirnova, Yu. P., *Vysokomolekul. Soedin., Adgeziya Polimerov, Sb. Statei* **1963,** 83.

CHAPTER X / **TESTS**

§122   The number of tests suggested and adopted for adjudging adhints is so great that a book longer than "The Science of Adhesive Joints" would be needed to describe them adequately. Unfortunately, hardly any of these tests affords results having general significance. If a definite treatment is applied to several supposedly identical joints and a range of values is obtained, we may conclude that also other joints made in the same manner and subjected to an identical treatment will give values of a similar magnitude. This, of course, is an important piece of information whenever joints are used. But such tests do not enable us to make any prediction as to the behavior of slightly different adhints or of identical adhints treated in a slightly different way (see §100). Prediction is predicated on understanding.

Because of the frankly empirical nature of the usual tests and because they are easily found in the publications of the American Society for Testing and Materials, as British Standard Specifications, and so on, they are not described in this book. In this chapter, a few examples of less common methods of testing are outlined. See also §§19 and 47.

§123   A method often used in the rubber industry is the "pull-through" test. A straight length of a string (or cord, or rope) is embedded in a rubber mixture, the mixture is vulcanized, and the string is pulled out by a longitudinal force as indicated in Fig. 135. The external cylindrical surface of the rubber plug is firmly clamped. Obviously, the system is analogous to a cylindrical lap joint (§91).

319

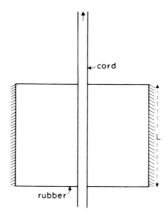

FIG. 135. A "pull-through" test.

To derive an approximate theory of the test,[1] we refer to §82.2. If the reasoning leading to Eq. (119) is repeated for the present instance, in which h_0 is indefinite because the whole block of rubber corresponds to the adhesive in §82.2, we obtain the equation

$$\frac{\partial^2 l_1}{\partial z^2} = \frac{2cl_1}{Er} ; \qquad (158)$$

E is the modulus of elasticity of the cord (assumed to be a Hookean solid), r is the radius of the cord [corresponding to δ in Eq. (119)], and c is the ratio of shear stress to displacement in the system; thus, shear stress acting in the cord–rubber interface is cl_1; the dimension of c is gm/sec^2.

Integration of Eq. (158) affords

$$l_1 = 2 A \cosh \lambda z = A(e^{\lambda z} + e^{-\lambda z}), \qquad (159)$$

A being an arbitrary constant and $\lambda = (2c/Er)^{0.5}$. Since $f = E(\partial l_1/\partial z)$ [see Eq. (116)]

$$f = AE\lambda(e^{\lambda z} - e^{-\lambda z}) = 2AE\lambda \sinh \lambda z. \qquad (160)$$

Thus,

$$f = E\lambda l_1 \tanh \lambda z. \tag{161}$$

Assume now that rupture starts when l_1 anywhere reaches the maximum possible value which we shall denote l_m. Let the corresponding stress be f_m. The greatest value of l_1 is reached first, naturally, at $z = L$, L being the length of the embedded part of the cord. Hence,

$$f_m = E\lambda l_m \tanh \lambda L. \tag{162}$$

The paradoxical consequence of Eq. (159), namely that $l_1 = 2A$ at $z = 0$ where no force exists to cause any deformation, was mentioned in §82.2

Equation (162) predicts that the force needed to pull a cord out of a rubber block is proportional to tanh of the embedded length. Figure 136 reproduces some experimental results.[1] Its ordinate is the above force (in pounds weight, multiply with 445 to obtain it in kilodynes) and the abscissa is L in inches (multiply by 2.54 to have it in centimeters). The curves really are similar to those of tanh. The material of the cord (brass-plated steel, cotton, a polyester of terephthalic acid, nylon, and a rayon) is marked at the curves.

Because the maximum shear stress (at which still no failure occurs) is cl_1, it can be calculated from the data presented in Fig. 136. It proves to be little dependent on the nature of the cord and apparently does not contradict the idea that usually rubber gives way first.

§**124**   A similar test[2] is illustrated in Fig. 137. A glass rod is embedded in a polymer disc. The rod is firmly clamped at both ends, and the disc is pushed up as indicated in the sketch. In these experiments, force F_m needed to achieve irreversible displacement of the disc was a linear function of the embedded length L when this varied from about 0.2 cm to about 1.5 cm, for a rod 0.2 cm in diameter. Extrapolation of F_m to $L = 0$ led to a considerable value of force; this was traced to the fact that the thickness of the disc was greater adjacent to the rod than further away because the resin wetted the

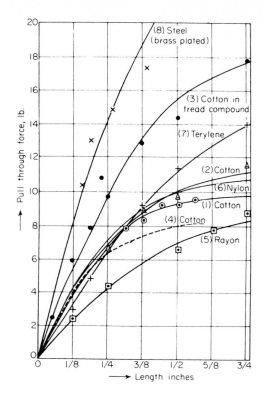

FIG. 136. Experimental results of a "pull-through" test. Abscissa: length of embedded cord, in inches. Ordinate: maximum pulling force, in lb. wt. From reference 1.

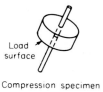

Compression specimen

FIG. 137. A "push-along" test. From reference 2.

glass and formed a meniscus which persisted also after curing. The above values of L (0.2–1.5 cm) have been corrected for this effect.

If again [see Eq. (115)], it is assumed that dF_m/dL is proportional to the maximum possible shear stress at the rod–disc boundary, this stress can readily be calculated. It is similar to the shear strength of the polymer in bulk for the instance of a cured epoxy resin but is unexpectedly small in the instance of a copolymer of styrene and esters of dibasic acids; thus we may conclude that a weak boundary layer exists along the glass–polyester interface.

Instead of being pulled out of a thick polymer disc, the fiber can be extracted from a thin polymer film solidified between two other fibers.[3] These methods have been repeatedly used but, apparently, not critically examined.

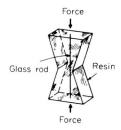

FIG. 138. An adhesion test based on Poisson's contraction. From reference 4.

A method which permits rupturing a glass–matrix bond by a force perpendicular to the glass–matrix interface is indicated in Fig. 138. The plastic body has[4] approximately the shape of an hourglass, and the glass filament is wholly embedded along its axis of cylindrical symmetry. When pressure is applied to the top and bottom surfaces of the composite body, the height of the latter decreases. Since stress is greater the smaller the horizontal cross section of the plastic body, the main part of this decrease occurs along the waist of the hourglass. The theory of this method is given in §58.

25   Discussion of tests for the adherence of coatings does not belong in this monograph but four of the many suggested procedures for such tests are outlined here to show that the difficulty of measuring the true adhesion in the instance of coatings is just as great as in the case of adhints.

Two of these procedures manifest some analogy with the tensile breaking of butt joints. In one,[5] the coating is removed by centrifugal force. For instance, the cylindrical surface of a bar can be coated and the bar rotated around its axis of cylindrical symmetry; when the rate of rotation is very great, the coating may fly off. In this arrangement, the so-called hoop stresses are operative; see, e.g., reference 6. Their nature may be explained as follows. Let the radius of the cylinder at rest be r_0; when the cylinder rotates, its radius increases because of centrifugal forces to, say, r_1. Consequently the circumference of the cylinder, that is the length of the coating–bar boundary increases from $2\pi r_0$ to $2\pi r_1$. Thus, the coating is elongated, and this elongation produces stresses resisting further elongation; they are the hoop stresses.

To simplify the system, assume that we rotate the cylinder around an axis perpendicular to its generatrix (see Fig. 139), and that the basis faces are coated. Obviously, no hoop stresses can appear in this arrangement but the stress pattern still is anything but simple. The centrifugal force on a slice, dl cm thick, of the cylinder (cut normally to its axis and parallel to the axis of revolution) is $A\rho\omega^2 l\,dl$, if A is the area of the cross-section, ρ the density of the material, ω the angular velocity (in radians/sec., the dimension of ω is sec.$^{-1}$), and l is the distance from the axis of revolution. Thus in the region near the bar–coating boundary where, because of surface roughness the planes characterized by $l = $ const. pass partly through the adherend and partly through the coating, centrifugal stress $\rho\omega^2 l\,dl$ is greater in the denser material (usually in the bar) than in the less dense substance. Apparently, no calculation of this differential effect ever has been made.

When the bar depicted in Fig. 139 rotates, it elongates parallel to the cylinder axis; this elongation must be accompanied by Poisson's contraction of the radius. An identical effect must occur in the coating. Since the moduli of elasticity and the Poisson ratios of the two materials are different, stresses analogous to those considered in §80 must exist near the interface. Thus, as far as simplicity of interpretation is concerned, centrifugal force offers no advantage compared to tensile force on butt joints.

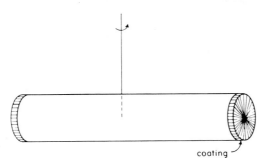

FIG. 139. Test of adhesion by centrifuging.

Analogous remarks apply to the "bullet method."[7] In this, the central part of a basis of a cylinder is coated, and the cylinder is shot in the direction of its axis at a target which essentially is a ring normal to the direction of the movement. The internal diameter of the ring is greater than that of the coated patch but smaller than that of the cylinder. Thus the cylinder is stopped by the ring but the coating, because of inertia, tends to continue its flight. If the thickness of the coating is h, the pressure tending to remove the coating, at a first approximation, is $\rho h j_{max}$, if j_{max} is the maximum deceleration (cm./sec.^{2}) achieved during impact and ρ is the density of the coating. However, this approximation presumably is a crude one. When the periphery of the bullet basis is stopped by the ring, the center (which is coated) continues to advance and then must vibrate about the equilibrium position; it is not known what stresses exist during these vibrations but evidently they are different from $\rho h j_{max}$.

The third method uses bursting. In a rigid plate a hole is drilled (see Fig. 140). The hole is plugged with an easily removable material such as an amalgam or a water-soluble plastic, so that the surface of the plug and the surface of the plate form one plane. Then plate + plug is coated (the thickness of the coating is exaggerated in the figure), the plug is removed (for instance, by dissolving it in water) without hurting the film, and the underside of the film is connected with a reservoir of compressed air (or mercury). Air pressure P at which the coating is torn off is supposed to be a measure of

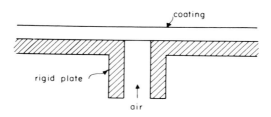

FIG. 140. Test of adhesion by bursting.

adhesion between coating and plate. In a more elaborate arrangement,[8] only a rectangular strip of the coating is permitted to bulge out and to rupture.

The actual stress causing failure seems to be a function of P and of several mechanical and geometrical properties of the coating membrane and, in all probability, has no connection with the molecular attraction between plate and coating. If, at a first approximation, the membrane before bursting may be treated as a part of a spherical surface, it has a constant radius of curvature, say R, and the tension in the membrane then is $0.5PR$ gm/sec². Real membranes do not have a constant curvature and their R varies from center to periphery according to a law which depends on the stiffness of the membrane. If, for instance, the membrane is so flexible that the energy associated with its bending is small compared with that associated with stretching, then the tensile stress at the boundary of the hole is[9] $f = 0.328\ (EP^2a^2/h^2)^{1/3}$; E is modulus of elasticity, a radius, and h thickness of the membrane. Equation (148), §99, gives the work spent in this test.

As is apparent from Fig. 141, stress f causes peeling and, thus, should be treated according to the pattern of §92. Peeling of a circular membrane is, in one respect, simpler than that of a long ribbon because the edge stresses depicted in Fig. 104 do not exist; on the other hand, it is less predictable because the effective angle of peeling depends on the stiffness and the diameter of the membrane; thus an additional variable is introduced.

The fourth method uses scraping: a knife is pushed along the substrate to remove the coating. The mechanics of this test has been studied by Asbeck.[10]

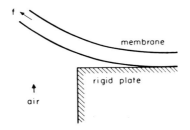

f

membrane

rigid plate

air

FIG. 141. Peeling effect in the bursting test.

§**126** All tests so far described in this chapter involve destruction of the specimen. It is clear that nondestructive tests would be very valuable; we would like to be able, by examining a completed ad-hint, to predict whether it will stand up to the use intended for it.

The majority of the nondestructive tests so far suggested, and so far as they are known to the present author, are based on the resonance properties of the adhint. The simplest test consists in hitting a metal–adhesive–metal joint with "a large coin" [11] or another solid; a sound adhint gives forth a sonorous, and a faulty one, a dull sound. Evidently, the difference corresponds to that between a whole and a slightly cracked glass vessel.

More ambitious tests utilize supersonic vibrations. In §109, equations are given for calculating the modulus of elasticity E of adhesive films in butt joints. If these films are incomplete, that is, contain voids, their overall E may be expected to be smaller than that of a sound film. On the other hand, voids would depress the strength of adhints. Thus we may expect, in a series of supposedly identical adhints, breaking stress to increase with the value of $E;$ hence, by measuring E it would be possible to predict the value of the rupture stress. This method was successfully used in some systems [12] but was not always sufficiently sensitive. [13]

An ultrasonic resonance instrument which detects porosity, mismatch of adherends, and similar coarse defects is being routinely used in industry. [14]

The above procedures involve comparing an adhint with the adherend. In another method, production adhints are compared with a perfect adhint of the same type. [15,16] A vibrating barium titanate plate is placed on a perfect joint and the mode of its vibration is observed on the screen of an oscilloscope. Then the plate is brought in contact with an adhint of unknown quality; if a marked change occurs in the oscillogram, the joint under test is not perfect. If a series of adhints of different degrees of perfection is available, the instrument (in which a galvanometer is substituted for the oscilloscope) can be calibrated with their help. For a review of these and the following methods see reference 17.

In another modification[18] one piezoelectric plate is pressed against one side of an adhint and another, identical, plate against the opposite side. The first plate vibrates, and the second picks up the vibrations and transforms them into electric pulses. If the regions of bad bonding are large in comparison with the wavelength of the vibrations, the second plate (i.e., "the receiver") emits weak signals only. If these regions are small, the transmission of vibrations is almost as good as when there are no defective areas; in these instances another effect can be utilized to detect flaws, namely the retardation of the arrival of the signals (sent out by the first plate) at the receiver. The procedure was not sufficiently sensitive; even voids of 1 cm in diameter could not be safely detected unless the adhint was strained so that the adhesive film was extended by, for instance, 10%.

REFERENCES

1. Wood, J. O., *Trans. Inst. Rubber Ind.* **32**, 1 (1956).
2. McGarry, F. J., *ASTM Bull.* **235**, 63 (1959).
3. Shiryaeva, G. V., Gorbatkina, Yu. A., and Andreevskaya, G. D., *Zh. Fiz. Khim.* **37**, 237 (1963).
4. Mooney, R. D., and McGarry, F. J., *14th Ann. Conf., Reinforced Plastics Div., Soc. Plastics Ind.* 12-E-1 (1959).
5. Alter, H., and Soller, W., *Ind. Eng. Chem.* **50**, 922 (1958).
6. Beams, J. W., Breazeale, J. B., and Bart, W. L., *Phys. Rev.* **100**, 1657 (1955).
7. May, W. D., Smith, N. D. P., and Snow, C. I., *Trans. Inst. Metal Finishing* **34**, No. 9 (1957); *Nature* **179**, 494 (1957).
8. Dannenberg, H., *J. Polymer Sci.* **33**, 509 (1958).
9. Timoshenko, S., and Woinowsky-Krieger, S. "Theory of Plates and Shells," p. 404. McGraw-Hill, New York, 1959.
10. Asbeck, W. K., *in* "Adhesion and Cohesion" (P. Weiss, ed.), p. 101. Elsevier, Amsterdam, 1962.
11. Noton, R. B., *Aluminium* **35**, 266 (1959).

12. Dietz, A. G. H., Bockstruck, H. N., and Epstein, G., *Am. Soc. Testing Mater., Spec. Tech. Publ.* No. **138,** 40 (1952).
13. Tapp, P. F., Broodo, A., Horn, C. E., and Castner, S. V., *Aircraft Eng.* **29,** 350 (1957).
14. Smith, D. F., and Cagle, C. V., *Appl. Polymer Symp.* No. **3,** 411 (1966).
15. Arnold, J. S., *Am. Soc. Testing Mater., Spec. Tech. Publ.* No. **201,** 83 (1957).
16. Schijve, J., *Aircraft Eng.* **30,** 269 (1958).
17. Barr, H. E., *Appl. Polymer Symp.* No. **3,** 405 (1966).
18. Heughan, D. M., and Sproule, D. O., *Trans. Inst. Rubber Ind.* **29,** 255 (1953).

CHAPTER XI / **SUMMARY FOR THE PRACTICAL MAN**

§127   If a series of joints has satisfactory strength, no study of the materials or processes used is indicated for the practical man. If, however, joints do not perform satisfactorily, the cause of the weakness must be found and removed. In this search, the first question to be answered is that of the location of the failure. Rupture can occur in an adherend, the adhesive, or in a weak boundary layer. In many instances simple visual inspection of the fracture faces permits a decision as to where the adhint fractured. When this inspection proves inconclusive, the following remarks may be of help.

I. A weak boundary layer should always be suspected if (a) joint strength appears to be too small to be accounted for by Eq. (163), §128, and (b) the fracture surface is situated very near to the surface of the adherend. Both (a) and (b) are needed.

II. If a material used as adhesive gives rise to poor joints with very different adherends (such as glass, aluminum, stainless steel, galenite), we may assume that weak boundary layers form and that the substances finally present in these layers originally were a part of the adhesive.

III. If an adherend gives rise to poor joints with very different adhesives (low-melting alloys, adhesionable polyethylene, polyesters, and so on) which can be successfully used with other solids, we may assume that the surface of the adherend carries an inherent weak boundary layer.

If adherend A_1 affords weak joints with adhesive a_1 while it can be glued well with other adhesives and while a_1 can be used for other

330

adherends, then only the above rule No. I can be helpful in estimating the probability of a weak zone at the interface of A_1 and a_1.

Suppose that the presence of a weak boundary layer has been made probable. According to the classification of §67, weakness can have seven different origins, and the remedy will vary with the diagnosis.

1. The material of the weak zone comes from the surroundings. For the customary joints made in air, this means that air remains trapped along the adherend–adhesive interface (see §68). The degree of wetting should be determined, and it should be possible to achieve an improvement in the joint strength by using an adhesive which perfectly wets the solid or by assembling joints in a vacuum.

2. The material of the weak zone comes from the adhesive. This usually can be recognized as described in II above. The remedy is to remove the deleterious ingredients by fractional precipitation, extraction, or another suitable procedure. For an example see §69.

3. The material of the weak zone comes from the adherend. This is the case outlined in III above. Cleaning of the adherend surface or extraction of the adherend with solvents may be attempted (see §70).

4. The weak boundary layer forms in an interaction between the adhesive and the environment: thus, if the adhesive is subjected to an excessive temperature during its application, oxidation by atmospheric oxygen may occur and may, because of special circumstances, be more pronounced near the adherend–adhesive interface. The effects of this kind would be eliminated by producing the adhint in different surroundings (e.g., nitrogen gas) and, if a change in the environment really improves the strength, it is proved that the weak zone has the origin defined in this paragraph.

5. The weak boundary layer forms in an interaction between the adherend and the environment: thus a brittle oxide of copper is sometimes produced by heating the metal during the formation of the joint. Detection and prevention of this ill would be performed as outlined in the preceding paragraph.

6. The weak boundary layer forms in a reaction between the adherend and the adhesive. For examples see §72. The number of reactions which may create a zone of weakness is great and, at

present, no general instruction can be formulated as to how to find the culprit.

7. All three phases (i.e., air, adherend, and adhesive) participate in the formation of a zone of weakness (see §73). This type is detected by proving that change of only one of the components is sufficient to avoid weak joints; thus substitution of aluminum for copper, or of another adhesive for that showing the effect, or of nitrogen for air prevented deterioration of the interfacial layer in the above instance. The remedy is to alter one of the three components.

§128   If no weak boundary is present, the adhint breaks in the adherend or in the adhesive. In the first case, the science of adhesive joints is not involved. If the adhesive breaks, we wish to utilize as much as possible of its inherent strength, that is, we aspire to have rupture stresses of adhints about as great as or greater than those of the adhesive in bulk. Our success depends on the equation

$$\frac{f_m}{f_M} = \frac{\beta_0}{\alpha\beta}\frac{\xi - \beta s}{\xi - \beta_0 s_0} \tag{163}$$

already given in §100. The greater the ratio f_m/f_M, the better the utilization of the adhesive.

To reduce the macroscopical stress concentration factor α to a value not much greater than its minimum magnitude (i.e., unity) the rheological properties of adherend and adhesive should be as similar as feasible. If neither the adhesive nor the adherend can be changed, we may sometimes lower the value of α by inserting an intermediate layer (a primer) between the two; the material of this layer should have a modulus of elasticity intermediate between those of the adherend and the cement. Another possibility is to alter the design of the adhint; the magnitude of α in adhints of various types is treated in Chapter VIII.

The ratio f_m/f_M is greater the smaller the shrinkage stress s. This can be reduced by using adhesives which have almost identical densities before and after setting (assuming, as usually is the case, that the density of the adherends remains practically constant during setting). When this cannot be done, again a primer coat which shrinks more than the adherends and less than the adhesive would be helpful. By a skillful design it should be possible in some instances to buttress f_m by shrinkage stresses; if, for instance, the adhint is made in such a manner that it is strained in compression during use, the sign of s would be reversed and f_m would be greater the greater s. As a rule, s is less the thinner the cement film; thus, the effect of shrinkage stress on f_m can be influenced by the thinness of the joint.

To make β small, we should try to avoid formation of air bubbles and analogous flaws during setting and to remove (for instance, by squeezing the excess cement out) those bubbles, etc., which are bound to appear during the application of the adhesive. Since β is greater the thicker the "glue line," the adherends should be brought together as closely as feasible.

Finally, ξ itself may be smaller in the adhint than in the bulk, if, for instance, polymerization or cross-linking of the adhesive *in situ* resulted in a degree of polymerization or type of cross-linking less favorable than those in the bulk sample.

§129   A survey of the two preceding paragraphs in the form of a table may be welcome. The low strength of an adhint may be due to

I. A weak boundary layer originating from	II. Low breaking stress of the adhesive because of
(1) the surroundings	(1) deterioration of the adhesive material
(2) the adhesive	(2) stress concentrations
(3) the adherend	(3) shrinkage stresses
(4) the adhesive and the surroundings	(4) bad flaws in the adhesive.
(5) the adherend and the surroundings	
(6) the adherend and the adhesive	
(7) the adherend, the adhesive, and the surroundings.	

§130   In §§127 to 129 the diagnosis and the therapeutics of unsatisfactory adhints were described. A related problem consists in selecting the best adhesive for a given pair of adherends. It also comprises two parts, one dealing with the avoidance of weak boundary layers and the other, with minimizing stress concentrations.

The procedure to adopt in avoiding improper joints depends on how much effort can be spent on purifying the materials employed. It is clear that a household cement will be applied to relatively dirty solids; therefore, an adhesive sensitive to impurities cannot be chosen. Thus, polyethylenes are practically insoluble in all common solvents and, correspondingly, are (in the solid state) very poor solvents themselves; in other words, almost any fluid which comes in contact with polyethylene remains on its surface and thus may constitute a weak boundary layer. Hence, polyethylenes are not suitable as household cements. An identical remark applies to other substances which have a low degree of miscibility with matter (such as finger grease) which is likely to be present on the solids to be glued.

The usual household cements are solutions of several ingredients in a powerful solvent. When they are placed on a solid whose surface is contaminated with finger grease and similar common impurities, these impurities are dissolved by the solvent and thus distributed among the other components. The miscibility of these components with each other and with finger grease is so good that no separation in distinct phases occurs and, consequently, no weak boundary layer can form.

At the opposite extreme are the adhesives designed for a specific application of great responsibility. The adherends in these instances can be thoroughly prepared for the application, and the first column of the table in §129 may be used as a guide to systematic removal of the possible sources of a weak zone.

As far as stress concentrations are concerned, an adhesive very similar to the adherends in its rheological behavior would be the ideal choice; the magnitude of the α factor (§128) would not be much greater than unity in such a combination. When also the heat expansions of adherends and cement are comparable, the shrinkage stresses of thermal origin also will be small. A third favorable similarity would be that in the chemical resistance of the two materials; if, for instance, one of these does, and the other does not, swell in humid atmosphere, every change of relative humidity of the atmosphere will cause stresses near the adherend–adhesive boundary. Thus the adhesive should be as like the adherends in all respects as can be achieved under the circumstances.

The rule formulated in the preceding sentence is valueless when the two adherends are different, such as a metal and a rubber. Probably, adhesives having mechanical properties halfway between those of the two adherends would be most suitable in these combinations. Thus, if the two adherends have moduli of elasticity E_1 and E_2, total relative elongations $(\Delta l/l)_1$ and $(\Delta l/l)_2$, etc., then an adhesive whose modulus is near $0.5(E_1 + E_2)$ and the total relative elongation is near $0.5[(\Delta l/l)_1 + (\Delta l/l)_2]$ would be indicated (if all its other properties fit the case). Unfortunately, no experimental check of this deduction is known to the author.

The reasoning of this section, so far, implies that the final strength of the adhint (§56) is the only, or at least the main, property the user is interested in. This implication is incorrect in numberless instances. Often any final strength above a modest minimum is satisfactory but some other properties are critical. Thus a "quick grab" or tack is the first consideration in manufacturing cardboard boxes (see Chapter IV). In other applications, none of the mechanical or rheological properties is of primary importance: the cement may be weak but must be transparent, or may be weak but must not evolve gases or vapors. Selection of the best cement for the two last-named systems presumably will be better helped by a book on adhesives than by a monograph on adhints.

Author Index

Numbers in parentheses are reference numbers and indicate that an author's work is referred to, although his name is not cited in the text. Numbers in italics show the page on which the complete reference is listed.

A

Abbey, W. F., 45(5), *89*
Abraham, H., 121(3), *136*
Adams, R. J., 27(26), *28*
Afanas'ev, I. I., 1(2), *27*
Alfrey, T., 129(15), *136*
Altenpohl, D., 19(20), 20(20), *28*
Aleck, B. J., 193(3), *260*
Alter, H., 324(5), *328*
Anderko, K., 137(1), *162*
Anderson, J. S., 24(25), 25(25), *28*
Anderson, O. L., 31(5), 32(8), *42*
Andreevskaya, G. D., 271(5), 297(40, 41), *316, 317,* 323(3), *328*
Arkharov, V. I., 182(43), *190*
Armand, G., 8(6), *27*
Arnold, J. S., 327(15), *329*
Asbeck, W. K., 326(10), *328*

B

Bachetta, V. L., 183(47), *190*
Baldauf, G. H., 275(14), 282(14), *316*
Banks, W. H., 97(10), *118*
Barr, H. E., 328(17), *329*
Bart, W. L., 324(6), *328*
Bartell, F. E., 53(23), 54(23), *89*
Bateman, S. K., 167(5), *189*
Beams, J. W., 324(6), *328*
Beattie, J. A., 141(4), *163*
Beaven, E. W., 75(35), *90*
Becher, J. J., 168(8), *189*
Bek, V. L., 166(2), *189*

Belyi, V. A., 46(11), *89*
Belykh, I. N., 133(23), *136*
Bernstein, L., 138(2), *163*
Bikerman, J. J., 1(1), 7(3), 8(5), 10(7), 24(3), 27(27), *27, 28,* 31(7), 37(15), 39(17), *42,* 51(19, 20, 21), 52(22), 57(24), 60(28), 74(32), 82(44), 86(50), 87(50), *89, 90,* 95(8), 97(8), 98(8), 98(15), 104(19), 105(19), 106(19, 21), 109(8), 110(29), 111(30), 113(34), 115(34), 116(37, 34), 117(34), *118, 119,* 124(9, 10), *136,* 143(8), 150(18), 151(19, 20), 156(28, 29), *163,* 170(10), 171(11), 172(11, 12), 173(12, 13), *189,* 243(53), 245(54), 249(54), 250 (54), 252(63), 253(54), 258(73), 259(73), *262, 263,* 266(1), 267(1), 269(1,2), 275(13), 277(1,16), 279(13), 280(13), 288(2), 296(1), 315(68), *316, 318*
Black, J. M., 185(52), *191,* 312(61), *318*
Blaisdell, B. E., 57(25), *89*
Blech, I. A., 182(44), *190*
Blet, G., 13(12), *27*
Blin, J., 182(42), *190*
Blomquist, R. F., 185(52), *191,* 272(8), 312(61), 316(70), *316, 318*
Bobalek, E. G., 311(59), *318*

Bockstruck, H. N., 313(65), *318*, 327(12), *329*
Bodnar, M. J., 174(15), *189*
Boenig, H. V., 122(7), *136*
Bortz, S. A., 157(31), *163*
Bosworth, P., 37(14), *42*
Breazeale, J. B., 324(6), *328*
Bredzs, N., 87(51), *90*, 182(41), *190*, 278(18), 282(18), *316*
Brenner, A., 195(7), 196(7), *261*
Breslau, A. J., 129(16), *136*
Breu, H., 47(16), *89*
Bright, W. M., 145(15), *163*, 310(57), *318*
Brinza, V. N., 33(10), *42*
Bristol, K. E., 53(23), 54(23), *89*
Broodo, A., 327(13), *329*
Bruenner, R. S., 97(12), *118*
Bryant, R. W., 271(7), 272(7), 284(7), *316*
Buchan, S., 177(30), 184(30), *190*
Bueckle, H., 182(42), *190*
Buiko, G. N., 176(25), *190*
Bullett, T. R., 19(19), *28*, 45(8), 46(8), *89*, 179(34), *190*
Busse, W. F., 113(32), 116(32), *119*
Butler, L. H., 83(46), *90*

C

Cagle, C. V., 327(14), *329*
Castner, S. V., 327(13), *329*
Chadwick, R., 182(45), *190*
Chang, F. S. C., 112(31), *119*
Chaplin, T. K., 213(35), *261*
Chessin, N., 46(12), *89*
Chistyakov, A. M., 198(15), *261*
Chzhan, In-si, 146(11), 148(11), *163*
Clark, G. L., 36(11), *42*
Clash, R. F., 129(12), *136*
Closmann, P. J., 292(34), *317*
Cole, S. S., 40(19), 41(19), *42*
Coleman, B., 197(14), *261*
Cornell, R. W., 232(48), 233(48), 234(48), *262*
Croft-White, P. G., 75(35), *90*

Crolius, V. G., 176(23), *190*
Crow, T. B., 274(10), *316*
Curran, V., 46(12), *89*

D

Dahlquist, C. A., 104(18), 105(18), 108(24), *118, 119*
Dannenberg, H., 326(8), *328*
Davydov, P. V., 180(36), *190*
deBoer, J. H., 154(24), *163*
DeBruyne, N. A., 72(31), *89*, 165(1), 166(3), 167(3), *189*, 301(44), *317*
DeLollis, N. J., 298(42), *317*
Deryagin, B. V., 117(39), *119*, 152(22), 153(23), *163*, 255(67), *262*, 303(48), 306(48), 307(48), *317*
Desai, M. B., 315(69), *318*
Dietz, A. G. H., 198(19), *261*, 292(34), 313(65), *317, 318,* 327(12), *329*
Doede, C. M., 146(9), *163*
Doi, Y., 257(70), *263*
Dolzhenkov, F. E., 33(9), *42*
Draugelates, U., 225(42), 227(42), *262*
Drobek, J., 47(18), 51(18), *89*
Drow, J. T., 291(33), 292(33), *317*
Dukes, W. A., 271(7), 272(7), 284(7), *316*
Dupré, A., 258(71), *263*
Dyl'kov, M. S., 305(50), 311(60, 50), *317, 318*

E

Ebeling, W. E., 176(23), *190*
Egan, F., 108(25), *119*
Ehlers, J. F., 186(53), *191*
England, A. H., 143(6), *163*
Epifanov, G. I., 197(13), 198(13), *261*
Epshtein, V. G., 108(28), 109(28), *119*
Epstein, G., 313(65), *318,* 327(12), *329*
Erb, R. A., 99(16), *118*
Evminov, S. S., 305(50), 311(50), *317*

F

Firestone, R. F., 157(31), *163*
Fiske, R. L., 45(6), *89*

Fletcher, D. A., 129(14), *136*
Floyd, J. R., 183(49), *190*
Forbes, W. G., 76(39), 79(39), *90,* 92(2), 95(2), *118*
Forrestal, L. J., 168(7), *189*
Foster, R. E., 176(26), *190*
Fouser, D. F., 216(39), *262*
Francke, K. P., 183(46), *190*
Frederick, K. W., 183(47), *190*
Freiberger, A., 312(63), *318*
Friese, K., 167(6), *189*
Froment, M., 12(11), *27*
Fuks, G. I., 84(47), *90*

G

Galakhova, G. S., 297(40), *317*
Galilei, G., 94(4), *118*
Gamo, M., 257(70), *263*
Gardon, J. L., 246(57), 248(57), 249(61), 253(61), *262,* 286(28), 287(28), *317*
Garner, P. J., 75(35), *90*
Geffken, C. F., 117(40), *119*
Goland, M., 216(38), 221(38), 223(38), 225(38), *262*
Goldfinger, G., 129(15), *136*
Gorbatkina, Yu. A., 271(5), 297(40), *316, 317,* 323(3), *328*
Gorchakova, V. M., 181(39), *190,* 310(58), *318*
Gottschalk, A., 77(41), *90*
Green, H., 95(7), 114(7), *118*
Greene, C. H., 157(30), *163*
Gribkova, N. Ya., 295(36), *317*
Griffith, A. A., 258(72), *263*
Grinsfelder, H., 198(19), *261*
Grishin, N. A., 166(2), *189*
Gromov, V. K., 148(14), 149(14), *163*
Grozinskaya, Z. P., 174(17), *189,* 310(56), *318*
Gul, V. E., 146(11), 148(11), *163,* 177(28a), 181(39), *190,* 310(58), *318*
Guseva, N. B., 297(40), *317*

H

Haas, E. G., 130(18), *136*
Hahn, F. C., 129(14), *136*
Hahn, K. F., 216(39), *262*
Hammond, F. H., 114(35), *119*
Hammond, G. L., 251(62), *262,* 286(25), 306(25), 308(25), *317*
Hammond, R. A. F., 47(17), *89*
Hansen, M., 137(1), *162*
Hansen, R. H., 174(14), *189*
Hanson, R. S., 99(16), *118*
Harrison, L. G., 21(24), *28*
Harrison, W. N., 40(18), *42,* 183(48), *190*
Hart, G. M., 271(6), *316*
Hartman, A., 237(50), *262*
Hata, T., 257(70), *263*
Healey, A., 86(49), *90*
Heidebroek, E., 98(14), *118*
Henning, G., 225(43), 226(43), 227(43), 231(43), *262*
Herczeg, A., 168(9), *189*
Hetenyi, M., 200(26), 243(26), *261*
Heughan, D. M., 328(18), *329*
Hill, A. E., 195(8), 196(8), *261*
Hill, R., 212(33), *261*
Hinken, E., 131(21), *136*
Hiza, M. J., 283(22), 312(22), *316*
Hoefling, E., 47(16), *89*
Hoffman, G. R., 195(8), 196(8), *261*
Hoffman, L. C., 183(47), *190*
Hofrichter, C. H., 302(45), *317*
Holland, L., 167(5), *189*
Holm, R., 30(1), *42*
Horn, C. E., 327(13), *329*
Hothersall, A. W., 47(17), *89*
Huang, C. R., 266(1), *316*
Huhn, H., 300(43), *317*
Hull, H. H., 10(8), *27*
Hunter, E., 129(13), *136*
Hunter, M. S., 16(16), *28*
Hunter, R. J. E., 177(29), *190*
Huntsberger, J. R., 146(12), *163,* 310(55), *318*

I

Inoue, Y., 193(4), 196(4, 11), 208(31), 256(68), *261, 262*

J

James, W. L., 291(33), 292(33), *317*
Jenckel, E., 300(43), *317*
Jellinek, H. H. G., 130(19), *136, 176 (24), 190*
Johnson, W. T. M., 19(18), *28,* 146(10), 148(10), *163*
Josefowitz, D., 91(1), 95(1), *118*
Jouversma, C., 246(56), 248(56), *262*

K

Kabanov, V. Ya., 174(17), *189*
Kaelble, D. H., 248(58, 59), 254(66), 257(59), *262*
Kainer, H., 122(8), *136*
Kaliske, G., 230(45), 231(45), *262*
Kamenskii, A. N., 177(28a), *190*
Kamenskii, B. Z., 71(30), 74(30), 75(30), 78(42), *89, 90,* 177(28), 185(51), *190, 191*
Kanamaru, K., 69(29), 70(29), 77(29), *89,* 193(1,2), *260*
Kapitsa, P. L., 118(41), *119*
Karasev, V. V., 153(23), *163*
Kargin, V. A., 77(40), *90,* 279(19), 311(19), *316*
Kavanagh, G. M., 292(34), *317*
Keller, F., 16(16), *28*
Kirillova, Yu. M., 303(48), 306(48), 307(48), *317*
Kirschstein, B., 30(1), *42*
Kiselev, M. R., 198(15), *261*
Kleinert, H., 45(9), 46(9), *89*
Knoell, S. S., 305(51), 309(51), *317*
Kobatake, Y., 193(4), 196(4, 11), 208 (31), 256(68), *261, 262*
Kobeko, P. P., 167(4), *189,* 296(37), 312(37), *317*
Koehler, W. F., 11(9), *27*

Koehn, G. W., 230(46), *262,* 278(17), 283(17), 286(17), *316*
Konstantinova, W. P., 275(12), *316*
Kopylov, E. P., 108(28), 109(28), *119*
Korolev, A. Ya., 166(2), 180(36), *189, 190*
Kotova, L. I., 118(42), *119*
Kozlov, P. V., 295(36), *317*
Kraus, G., 178(33), *190,* 276(15), 300 (15), 305(15), *316*
Krause, G., 268(3), 269(3), 270(3), 309(3), 312(3), *316*
Kreidl, W. H., 174(18), *189*
Krieger, G. L., 31(3), *42*
Krimmling, W., 45(9), 46(9), *89*
Krivonosov, Y. I., 33(9), *42*
Krotova, N. A., 47(15), *89,* 138(3), 152(22), *163,* 255(67), *262,* 272 (9), 303(48), 304(9), 306(48), 307(48), 313(64), *316, 317, 318*
Krueger, G. P., 291(32), 316(70), *317, 318*
Kuchenkova, R. V., 180(36), *190*
Kuenzi, E. W., 289(31), 291(31), *317*
Kuznetsov, A. Ya., 21(23), *28*

L

Lachs, H., 312(63), *318*
Laird, J. A., 313(66), *318*
Lambert, J. M., 113(32), 116(32), *119*
Lapujoulade, J., 8(6), *27*
Lasoski, S. W., 178(33), *190,* 276(15), 300(15), 305(15), *316*
Lazaryanz, E. G., 108(28), 109(28), *119*
Lee, W. B., 120(1), *136,* 274(11), *316*
Leeds, S., 175(22), *190*
Lestrade, J. C., 12(11), *27*
Lewis, A. F., 168(7), *189,* 271(4), 296(39), 299(4), *316, 317*
Lipatov, Yu. S., 293(35), *317*
Livanova, I. V., 287(26), *317*
Lobanov, Yu. E., 314(67), 315(67), *318*
Loughborough, D. L., 130(18), *136*
Lubkin, J. L., 234(49), 235(49), 236(49), 237(49), 240(52), 241(52), *262*

M

McBain, J. W., 120(1), *136,* 274(11), *316*
Macaulay, J. M., 31(4), *42*
McClintock, R. M., 283(22), 312(22), *316*
McDonald, W. J., 27(26), *28*
McEwan, A. D., 97(13), 105(20), *118*
McGarry, F. J., 315(69), *318,* 321(2), 322(2), 323(4), *328*
Macht, M. L., 129(14), *136*
McInnes, I., 237(51), *262*
McLaren, A. D., 302(45, 46), *317*
McLaren, A. S., 237(51), *262*
McLeod, L. A., 76(39), 79(39), *90,* 92(2), 95(2), *118*
Malden, J. W., 177(31), *190*
Malinskii, Yu. M., 279(19), 311(19), *316*
Malyshev, B. M., 143(7), *163,* 258(74), 259(74), 260(74), *263*
Mardeshev, S., 182(43), *190*
Marei, F. I., 167(4), *189,* 296(37), 312(37), *317*
Marian, J. E., 37(13), *42*
Mark, H., 91(1), 95(1), *118,* 129(15), *136,* 154(25), *163*
Markin, Yu. I., 181(39), *190,* 310(58), *318*
Marra, A. A., 131(21), *136*
Marshall, D. W., 173(13), *189,* 277(16), *316*
Mason, M. A., 183(48), *190*
Matting, A., 225(42), 227(42), 230(42, 47), *262*
May, W. D., 325(7), *328*
Medvedeva, A. M., 153(23), *163*
Merriman, H. R., 228(44), 229(44), *262,* 305(52), 312(52), *317*
Meyerhof, G. G., 213(35), *261*
Mill, C. C., 97(10), *118*
Mittrop, F., 46(13), *89*
Moakes, R. C. W., 251(62), *262,* 286 (25), 306(25), 308(25), *317*
Moffatt, W. G., 282(21), *316*
Mokievskii, V. A., 1(2), *27*
Moneva, I., 177(28a), *190*

Mooney, R. D., 323(4), *328*
Moore, D. G., 40(18), *42,* 183(48), *190*
Morgan, P., 122(6), *136*
Morozova, L. P., 47(15), *89,* 138(3), *163,* 273(9), 304(9), *316*
Morrison, J. A., 21(24), *28*
Moser, F., 199(20), *261,* 305(51), 309 (51), *317*
Mostovoy, S., 253(64), 259(64, 75), 260(64, 76), *262, 263,* 287(29), 307(54), *317, 318*
Muchnik, S. N., 288(30), *317*
Muller, R. H., 7(4), *27*
Mylonas, C., 208(32), 209(32), 248(60), *261, 262*

N

Nakao, K., 174(19), *189*
Nearn, W. T., 17(17), *28,* 36(12), *42*
Needs, S. J., 85(48), *90*
Neiman, M. B., 148(14), 149(14), *163*
Nelson, F. W., 313(66), *318*
Nightingale, S. J., 121(2), *136,* 296(38), *317*
Nishiuchi, M., 174(19), *189*
Niskanen, E., 214(36), *261*
Nonaka, Y., 254(65), *262*
Norris, C. B., 291(33), 292(33), *317*
Noton, R. B., 327(11), *328*

O

Oakes, W. G., 129(13), *136*
Oberth, A. E., 97(12), *118*
O'Brien, E. L., 304(49), 312(49), *317*
Oel, H. J., 77(41), *90*
Orlov, A. I., 114(36), 115(36), *119*
Ormandy, E., 95(6), *118*

P

Paigne, J., 8(6), *27*
Palmov, V. A., 202(27), *261*
Parker, D. H., 122(5), *136,* 176(27), *190*
Parsons, R. C., 176(23), *190*

Partington, J. R., 129(17), *136*
Partridge, J. H., 199(21), *261*
Passmore, G. H., 156(29), *163*
Patrick, R. L., 146(9), *163,* 253(64),
    259(64, 75), 260(64), *262, 263,*
    287(29), *317*
Pavlov, I. M., 33(10), *42*
Peirce, F. T., 156(27), *163*
Peukert, H., 175(20), *189*
Pickup, B., 74(34), *90,* 113(33), 114(33),
    119
Pisarenko, A. P., 286(27), 302(47),
    308(27), *317*
Pitts, J. W., 40(18), *42*
Plateau, J., 156(26), *163*
Popereka, M. Ya., 193(5), 195(5), 196
    (9), *261*
Popilov, L. Ya., 20(22), *28*
Poritsky, H., 203(28), *261*
Prokopenko, V. V., 279(19), 311(19),
    316
Prosser, J. L., 19(19), *28,* 45(8), 46(8),
    89, 179(34), *190*
Prostakov, M. E., 44(1), 46(10), 51(10),
    89

Q

Quatinetz, M., 312(63), *318*

R

Raevskii, V. G., 177(28a), *190,* 286(26),
    317
Ramsey, W. B., 296(39), *317*
Raraty, L. E., 180(35), *190,* 312(62),
    318
Rawson, H., 199(22), *261*
Redston, G. D., 203(29), *261*
Reegen, S. L., 149(16), *163*
Reissner, E., 198(19), 216(38), 220(38),
    223(38), 225(38), 240(52), 241
    (52), *261, 262*
Rembold, U., 283(23), 284(23), 286(23),
    309(23), 314(23), *316*
Renfrew, A., 122(6), *136*
Reynolds, O., 83(45), *90*

Reznikovskii, M. M., 71(30), 74(30),
    75(30), 78(42), *89, 90,* 177(28),
    185(51), *190, 191*
Richmond, J. C., 40(18), *42*
Rieke, J. K., 271(6), *316*
Ripling, E. J., 253(64), 259(64, 75), 260
    (64, 76), *262, 263,* 287(29),
    307(54), *317, 318*
Roark, R. J., 157(32), *163*
Robinson, D. L., 16(16), *28*
Rogers, N. L., 45(4), *89*
Rooney, G., 75(35), *90*
Rose, G. S., 21(24), *28*
Rossen, J. N., 292(34), *317*
Rossmann, K., 174(16), *189*
Roydhouse, R. H., 97(9), *118*
Rucker, N., 298(42), *317*
Rutto, R. A., 46(11), *89*
Rutzler, J. E., 152(21), *163*
Ryan, J. A., 30(2), *42*
Rynkiewicz, L. M., 129(12), *136*

S

Salganik, R. L., 143(5, 7), *163,* 258(74),
    259(74), 260(74), *263*
Sanzharovskii, A. T., 196(10), 197(13),
    198(13), *261,* 305(50), 310(56),
    311(50, 60), *317, 318*
Satas, D., 108(25), *119*
Saunders, F. L., 271(6), *316*
Savin, G. N., 157(33), 159(33), 160(33),
    163
Schijve, J., 327(16), *329*
Schonhorn, H., 174(14), *189*
Schrader, W. H., 174(15), *189*
Schwartzbart, H., 182(41), *190*
Scott, J. R., 100(17), *118*
Seiler, C. J., 302(46), *317*
Sello, H., 182(44), *190*
Senderoff, S. J., 195(7), 196(7), *261*
Shafrin, E. G., 59(27), *89*
Shapovalova, A. I., 286(27), 302(47),
    308(27), *317*
Sheridan, M. L., 228(44), 229(44), *262,*
    305(52), 312(52), *317*

Sherrer, R. E., 222(40), 223(40), *262*
Shield, R. T., 213(34), *261*
Shiryaeva, G. V., 271(5), 297(41), *316,*
    317, 323(3), 328
Shreiner, S. A., 196(12), 197(12), 198
    (12, 17), *261*
Shtarkh, B. V., 108(26), *119*
Shtarkman, B. P., 77(40), *90*
Shteinberg, Z. D., 287(26), *317*
Sikorski, M. E., 31(6), *42*
Sinegub-Lavrenko, A. A., 175(21), *189*
Skeist, I., 122(4), *136*
Skewis, J. D., 76(38), *90*
Smirnov, N. S., 44(1), 46(10), 51(10),
    89
Smirnova, Yu. P., 198(18), *261,* 316(71),
    318
Smirnova, Z. A., 1(2), *27*
Smith, D. F., 327(14), *329*
Smith, N. D. P., 325(7), *328*
Snoddon, W. J., 257(69), *262,* 305(53),
    306(53), *318*
Snow, C. I., 325(7), *328*
Sokolina, G. A., 47(15), *89,* 273(9),
    304(9), *316*
Soller, W., 324(5), *328*
Sommer, G., 40(19), 41(19), *42*
Sorg, E. H., 129(16), *136*
Sorokin, S. M., 117(39), *119*
Spies, J., 246(55), 248(55), *262*
Spitsyn, V. I., 174(17), *189*
Spooner, R. C., 16(15), *28*
Sproule, D. O., 328(18), *329*
Stanger, A. G., 272(8), *316*
Stanworth, J. E., 203(29), *261*
Stefan, J., 82(43), *90,* 94(5), 95(5), *118*
Stevens, G. H., 289(31), 291(31), *317*
Stoney, G. G., 195(6), *261*
Strasburger, H., 97(11), *118*
Stuart, N., 47(14), *89,* 184(50), *191*
Stumbo, D. A., 37(13), *42*
Sugg, R. E., 11(10), *27*
Sukhareva, L. A., 198(15, 18), *261,*
    316(71), *318*
Svenson, N. L., 199(23), *261*

Swanson, J. W., 168(8), *189*
Sweerman, A. J. W., 39(16), *42*

T

Tabor, D., 180(35), *190,* 312(62), *318*
Talmud, S. L., 75(36), *90*
Tanner, G. A., 271(4), 299(4), *316*
Tapp, P. F., 327(13), *329*
Tarkow, H., 197(14), *261,* 281(20), *316*
Taylor, D., 152(21), *163*
Taylor, G. I., 105(20), *118*
Timoshenko, S., 200(25), 208(30), *261,*
    326(9), *328*
Tombach, H., 225(41), *262*
Truax, T. R., 133(22), *136*
Truman, A. B., 107(22), *119*
Tsareva, Yu. S., 178(32), *190*
Turnbull, J. C., 198(16), *261*
Tylecote, R. F., 181(38), *190*

U

Ulmer, K., 230(47), *262*

V

Vagramyan, A. T., 178(32), *190*
Vakula, V. L., 108(27), *119,* 146(11),
    148(11, 14), 149(14), *163*
van Eltern, J. F., 59(26), *89*
Vaughan, W. A., 146(9), *163*
Verdery, R. B., 113(32), 116(32), *119*
Vickers, H. H., 92(3), 96(3), *118*
Vinogradova, L. M., 180(36), *190*
Vodopivec, F., 181(40), *190*
Voet, A., 59(26), *89,* 117(38, 40), *119*
Volkersen, O., 216(37), *262*
Volkova, T. A., 198(17), *261*
Vostroknutov, E. G., 71(30), 74(30),
    75(30), *89,* 177(28), 185(51), *190,*
    191
Voyutskii, S. S., 74(33), 76(37), 77(33,
    40), *90,* 108(26, 27), *119,* 125(11),
    136, 146(11), 148(11, 14), 149
    (14), *163,* 177(28a), 181(39), *190,*
    286(26, 27), 302(47), 308(27),
    310(58), *317, 318*

Vratny, F., 19(21), *28*

W

Ward, R. J., 311(59), *318*
Weatherwax, R. C., 197(14), *261*
Wegman, R. F., 45(7), *89,* 180(37), *190,*
  304(49), 312(49), *317*
Weidner, C. L., 107(23), *119,* 146(13),
  163
Weil, N. A., 157(31), *163*
Wellinger, K., 283(23), 284(23), 286(23),
  309(23), 314(23), *316*
Weisbecker, H. L., 27(26), *28*
Weiss, L., 150(17), *163*
White, M. L., 47(18), 51(18), *89*
White, W. C., 11(9), *27*
Whitney, W., 37(15), 39(17), *42,* 116
  (37), *119,* 124(10), *136*
Wier, J. E., 298(42), *317*
Wilson, G. J., 31(3), *42*
Winn, E. B., 176(26), *190*

Winter, H., 268(3), 269(3), 270(3),
  284(24), 309(3), 312(3), *316, 317*
Woinowsky-Krieger, S., 326(9), *328*
Wood, J. O., 320(1), 321(1), 322(1), *328*
Wulff, J., 282(21), *316*

Y

Yakubovich, S. V., 295(36), *317*

Z

Zaid, M., 199(24), *261*
Zaitseva, L. P., 20(22), *28*
Zamazii, V. M., 76(37), *90*
Zherebkov, S. K., 44(3), 45(3), *89,*
  153(23), *163*
Zhukov, I. I., 75(36), *90*
Zinchenko, N. P., 176(25), *190*
Zisman, W. A., 59(27), *89*
Zubov, P. I., 174(17), *189,* 196(12),
  197(12), 198(15, 17, 18), *261,*
  310(56), 311(60), 316(71), *318*

Subject Index

A

Abrasion, 47, 146, 180
Absorption and adsorption, 22
Addition reactions, 127, 129
Adherends
  definition, 2
  dimensions and strength, 105, 108, 281, 284
  porous and nonporous, 36, 121, 124, 126
  pretreatment, 43
  stratified, 38
  tack and, 108
  weakening by adhesive, 185
Adhesion
  of cells, 150
  molecular, 1
  specific, 133
  in vacuum, 30
Adhesional failures, 137
Adhesives
  classification, 120
  composition and adhint strength, 108, 299
  flaws in, 128, 133
  household, 123
  mechanical properties, 289
  need for, 1
  permanently tacky, 35
  pressure-sensitive, 35
  residue on adherend, 74, 145, 171
  selection of, 334
  strength of, and adhint strength, 293
Adhesive tapes, 35, 107, 147

Adhints
  classification, 34
  definition, 1
  of different types, 265
  dimensions, 273, 281
  history, 35
Adsorption
  of gases, 2, 3, 22
  from solutions, 26
Air pockets, 2, 165
Alkyd resins, 123, 146
Aluminum, 16, 19, 20, 32, 33, 43, 46, 149, 166, 171, 174, 180, 182, 183, 225–230, 248, 269, 314
Animal glue, 124
Approach of parallel plates, 80
Asphalt, 7, 74, 99, 121, 166
Asymmetry of adhints, 109
Attraction
  between solid and liquid, 53
  of two solids, 1, 92, 150
Autohesion, 75, 113

B

Bingham body, 100
Block shear test, 213, 273, 284
Boundary layers, 1
  weak, *see* Weak boundary layers
Brass, 21, 33, 46–48, 177, 182–184, 186
Breaking stress of adhints, 153, 192
  adherend and, 38
  adhesive composition and, 299
  adhesive thickness and, 273

345

cohesion and, 153
environment and, 313
experimental, 265
final, 137
geometry and, 38
penetration and, 37, 74
sample dimensions and, 273
during setting, 74
shrinkage stresses and, 192, 310
strength of adhesives and, 76, 293
surface treatment and, 45, 305
wetting and, 164, 167
Brittleness of adhesives, 152, 182, 253, 305
Bubbles in adhesive films, 78, 79, 87, 97, 131
Butt joints, 45, 74, 173, 178
adhesive thickness and, 274, 283
elimination of stress concentrations, 266, 277
lap joints and, 269, 298
peeling and, 267
scarf joints and, 143, 235
stresses in, 199, 204
tack in, 74
torsion and, 269–272

C

Capillary pressure, 63, 66, 93, 96, 176
Cartons, 135
Centrifugation test, 324
Chromic acid treatment, 46, 48, 174, 177
Cleanness of solids, 18–21, 43–49, 58
Cleavage, 273
Coatings
adherence, 33, 176, 323
porosity, 16
shrinkage stresses, 193
Cohesion, 141, 152–154, 279
Condensation reactions, 126, 129
Consistency, 63, 76, 112
Contact angle, 49, 145, 147
advancing and receding, 60, 73
equilibrium, 50, 73

hysteresis, 60
measurement, 54
strength of adhints and, 167, 170, 175
Contact
between adherend and adhesive, 39, 140
between two solids, 2, 31
Copper, 32, 46, 137, 166, 181, 182, 185
Corrosion, 183
Coupling agents, 187, 297
Crystal growth, 123, 133

D

Dentures, 97
Diffusion bonding, 138
Displacement of bubbles, 79
Drop dimensions and wetting, 56
Drops between parallel plates, 85
Dust, 18

E

Electrochemical effects, 18, 20, 21, 183, 314
Electrodeposits, 177, 193, 196
Electron microscope, 13, 146
Electrostatic attraction, 93, 152
Electrostatic capacity, 6, 291
Enamel, 40, 183
Epoxy resins, 127, 166, 174, 179, 185, 198, 260, 296, 301, 304, 305, 311

F

Fastening, 29
Fatigue of adhints, 284, 308
Fibrous materials, 36
Fillers, 131
Final strength, 137
Finishes, 187, 297
Flaws, 133
Formation of adhints, 39, 43
Fracture
side effects, 1, 2, 14
theory, 153
Friction, 9, 31, 145

Frozen stresses, 153, 192

G

Gelatin
  crystallization and, 134
  shrinkage, 196
Glass, 17, 21, 147, 149, 167, 199
  fibers, 186, 271, 297
  safety, 122
Glue line, 34
Gold, 182, 183
Gummed tape, 114

H

Hills on solid surfaces, *see* Surface
  roughness
Holes, stresses at, 157
Hooking adhints, 34
Hot-melt adhesives, 120
Household cements, 123

I

Ice, 130, 176, 180, 296
Improper adhints, 34, 45, 164
Inkometer, 116
Interface thickness, 142
Interfacial forces, 150
Intermixing of adherend and adhesive,
  32, 33, 36–41, 48, 138, 153
Iron, 181, 183

L

Laminates, *see* Reinforced plastics
Lap joints
  bending, 220, 232
  butt joints and, 269, 298
  double and single, 216, 229
  fortified, 229
  incomplete, 230
  peeling and, 221, 271
  without peeling, 216, 229, 238
  strength, 46, 225, 308
  stresses, 215
  thickness and, 228, 233, 282

torsion and, 269–272
  tubular, 239
Location of rupture, 37, 139, 308, 313

M

Maxwell body, 70, 107
Microhardness, 19
Migration of impurities, 175
Mixing, *see* Intermixing
Modulus of elasticity of adhesives, 289
Mold shrinkage, 129
Molecular forces across interface, 1, 50,
  141, 150–152

N

Nondestructive testing, 327

O

Optical properties of surfaces, 7, 10–13,
  19, 21, 146
Oscillations, 100, 253, 260, 273
Oscillating loads, 284, 308
Oxides on metals, 18, 19, 43

P

Paper, 36–39, 124, 125
Paperboard, 36, 38
Parting agents, 180
Peeling, 153
  butt joints and, 267
  double, 253, 286
  experimental data, 171, 249, 302, 310
  of hooking adhints, 37
  lap joints and, 271
  in lap joints, 221
  in liquids, 104
  rate, 107, 287, 305
  ribbon dimensions and, 249, 288
  stresses, 242, 248, 253
  tack and, 104
  theory, 107, 242
  thickness of adhesive film and, 286
  time of contact and, 76, 182
  work of, 256

Peeling angle, 106, 114, 255, 286
Penetration into pores, 39
Permanently tacky adhesives, 35
Phenol-formaldehyde resins, 127
Photoelasticity, 159, 196, 197, 208, 237
Plasticity, 32, 209
Poisson's ratio, 144, 323
Polarity, 152
Polyesters, 126, 197, 198, 271
Polyethylene, 77, 121, 122, 152, 167–
    176, 249–252, 277, 294, 311
Polymerization, 126
Poly(vinyl acetate), 122, 178, 193, 250,
    257, 276, 279, 300
Porous adherends, 36
Pressure during adhint formation, 68,
    74, 83, 199
Pressure-sensitive adhesives, 35
Probability of interfacial failure, 139
Probability theory of strength, 142, 155,
    279
Profilometers, 4
Proper adhints, 34, 47
Pull-through test, 297, 319
Push-along test, 322

R

Radioactivity, 6, 21, 145, 148
Rate of formation, 39
Rate of loading, 278, 284, 303
Rate of separation, 94, 99
Rate of setting, 135, 280
Rate of wetting, 63
Reinforced plastics, 40, 186, 297, 305,
    315
Removal of air, 63, 73, 87
Replica method, 13, 14
Residue on adherend after rupture, 74,
    145–150, 171, 252
Rosin, 99
Rubber, 40, 44, 45, 47, 74, 79, 92, 95,
    113, 176, 177, 183–185, 281, 310
Rugosity, 3
Rupture

location, 37, 139, 308, 313
probability theory, 142, 155

S

Sandblasting, 13, 45, 46, 48
Scarf joints, 143, 234, 308
Scraping test, 326
Sealers, 129
Sedimentation in adhesives, 133
Set, time of, 135
Setting, 72, 120
Shear by compression, 214, 271
Shear modulus of adhesives, 290
Shrinkage during setting, 128, 192, 280
Shrinkage stresses, 192, 310, 315
Sliding of drops, 10, 32, 62
Slip lines, 211
Snap fastener, 32, 130
Solders, 87, 121, 131, 137, 181–183,
    274–276
Solidification, location of, 132
Solids, heterogeneity, 155–162
Solid surfaces, 3
    pretreatment, 43
    as transition layers, 3
    variability across, 18
    variability along, 17
Solid-to-solid adhesion, 29–34, 92–94
Solvent cements, 123
Solvent effect on adhint strength, 300
Stagnant boundary layers, 7
Starved joints, 278
Steel, 5, 15, 19, 33, 45, 46, 130, 145,
    173, 178, 179, 182, 183, 185,
    193, 228, 271, 314
Strength, see Breaking stress
Stress concentration
    elimination, 266
    factors, 154
    geometrical, 205
    near phase boundary, 202, 206, 216,
        280
    at voids, 157
Stress relaxation, 1, 193, 198, 205

Stress-strain curves of adhesives, 289
Surface area, 5, 25, 27
Surface conductance, 21, 172
Surface contamination, 18, 19, 43–49
Surface energy, 150
Surface porosity, 16
Surface profile, 4, 5
Surface roughness, 1–17, 30, 32, 208
  adhesional failure and, 143
  air displacement and, 73, 83
  measurement, 4
  numerical data, 15
  shrinkage and, 202
  strength of adhints and, 45, 49, 149, 183
  tack and, 78, 93, 98
  wetting and, 61, 73
Surface tension, 52, 63
Surface treatment, 43, 305
Swelling, 53, 73, 188, 293, 314
Syneresis, 170

T

Tack, 74, 91
  adhesive composition and, 108
  at high velocity, 99
  measurement, 112
  of non-Newtonian liquids, 100
  in peeling, 104
Tackiness, 91
Temperature
  final strength and, 276, 309
  rate of formation and, 74, 77
  tack and, 95
  work of peeling and, 77
Tensile strength and adhint strength, 76, 293

Theories of adhesion, 150
Thickness of adhesive film, 49, 197, 274
Time of contact, 39, 72, 74
Torsion rupture, 269–272
Tubular lap joints, 202

V

Vacuum, 30, 166, 167
Vibrations, *see* Oscillations
Viscosity, 63–69, 73, 78–86, 92–99, 105, 112, 123
  non-Newtonian, 69–72, 76, 100

W

Water
  breaking stress and, 46, 181, 183, 198, 313
  contact angle and, 53
  uptake by laminates, 186, 313, 315
  in weak boundary layers, 165–167, 189
Waviness, 3, 10
Weak boundary layers, 1, 2, 14, 29, 33, 47, 139, 164, 302, 313
  of fifth class, 180
  of first class, 2, 148, 164, 303, 306
  of fourth class, 180
  of second class, 168, 310
  of seventh class, 185
  of sixth class, 48, 181
  of third class, 43, 177
Wetting, 24, 37, 49, 121, 151, 175
  hysteresis, 59
  rate, 63
Wood, 17, 36, 185
Work of breaking adhints, 77, 114, 118, 151, 258, 287, 307